FRESHWATER
FISHERY BIOLOGY

by

KARL F. LAGLER
Professor of Fisheries and of Zoology,
and Chairman, Department of Fisheries,
University of Michigan

Second Edition

WM. C. BROWN COMPANY PUBLISHERS
Dubuque, Iowa

Preface

My chief aim in writing this book was to provide a documented text and reference for informed fishermen, students, teachers, and professional workers in the field of freshwater fisheries in North America. The extent to which I have accomplished my objective is only moderate; the inadequacies and errors which exist, however, should in no way reflect upon the many colleagues who have given me encouragement, material, and constructive criticism.

Inspiration for this undertaking came from the late George C. Embody, Professor of Aquiculture at Cornell University. Greatest direct help was given by A. S. Hazzard, Director of the Institute for Fisheries Research of the Michigan Department of Conservation. Most encouragement accrued from Carl L. Hubbs of the University of California, who provided facilities for my work on the manuscript in the spring of 1951 at Scripps Institution of Oceanography.

Principal counsel was generously given to me on certain chapters, as follows: II, C. L. Hubbs, R. M. Bailey, and R. R. Miller; III, C. L. Hubbs, and R. R. Miller; VI, N. E. Kemp and E. C. Pierson; VII, C. L. Hubbs; IX, X, XI, R. Hile; XIV, L. N. Allison; XV, C. M. Tarzwell; XVIII, XIX, XXI, A. S. Hazzard, C. J. D. Brown, G. P. Cooper, and F. F. Hooper; XXIV, R. Hile.

Suggestions for the improvement of presentation or content were made by many individuals. Chief among these were W. F. Carbine, K. D. Carlander, G. C. deRoth, W. H. Everhart, F. T. Knapp, R. Lagueux, V. Legendre, G. Orton, C. D. Riggs, and L. L. Smith.

Much of the value of this book lies in its illustrations, many of which were loaned by colleagues and fishery agencies. Sources of illustrative material not my own, and figures provided follow: American Fisheries Society, 4, 47-50; American Society of Ichthyologists and Herpetologists, 35; Appleton-Century, 61; R. M. Bailey, 1; H. I. Battle, 12-26, 28, 29 (from her original drawings); W. C. Beckman, 47-50; W. Crowe, 109; Holt and Company, 27; F. F. Hooper, 35; G. W. Hunter III, 59, 60; Institute for Fisheries Research of the Michigan Department of Conservation, 3-7, 33, 38, 39, 43, 53, 64, 76, 81, 93, 100, 105, 112, 113, 116, 121, 173-184; R. McEwen, 27; Michigan Department of Conservation, 66, 72, 103, 111; New York State Conservation Department, 59, 60; Oregon Department of Fish and Game, 122; Oregon Fish Commission, 125; D. S. Rawson, 85, 127; Pennsylvania Board of Fish Commissioners, 114, 115; J. Rayner, 122; H. Schultz, 69; U. S. Fish and Wildlife Service, 30; U. S. Soil Conservation Service, 118; C. Verduin and Marine Publishing Company, 120, 123.

Original figures were prepared by: J. Roemhild, 11; G. Byers, 9; and Q. Carlson, 10, 31, 128, 134. W. Cristanelli made many of the figures and prints borrowed from the Institute for Fisheries Research.

The Sport Fishing Institute, through its Trust Fund for Fishery Research, provided for some of the clerical and research assistance required.

My patient wife, Mary Jane Lagler, helped immeasurably in the onerous tasks of reading proof and verifying literature citations.

I am very grateful to all of the persons and organizations here named and to many others for their kindnesses. The task could not have been undertaken without the opportunities for uninterrupted effort provided by former Dean S. T. Dana and present Dean S. G. Fontanna of the School of Natural Resources.

KARL F. LAGLER

University of Michigan
September, 1952

PREFACE TO SECOND EDITION

More than ever, this book is a work of synthesis and is the result of important help from many individuals. I continue to be grateful to all those who gave aid in the preparation of the first edition and to many others, including the following for assistance in revision as indicated for particular chapters: I, W. J. Koster; II, R. M. Bailey; III, R. R. Miller and R. G. Bjorklund; IV, L. W. Scattergood; V, V. D. Vladykov; VI, Fr. R. Legault; VII, G. Orton; VIII, S. D. Gerking; IX and X, R. Hile; XI, K. D. Carlander; XII, G. P. Cooper; XIII, K. E. Christensen; XIV, S. F. Snieszko; XV, C. M. Tarzwell; XVI, N. Olds; XVII, A. V. Tunison; XVIII and XIX, J. B. Moyle, G. H. Lauff, and R. G. Bjorklund; XX and XXII, O. H. Clark and W. Tody; XXI, L. L. Smith; XXIII, H. S. Swingle; XXIV, J. W. Moffett and S. H. Smith; XXV, H. Circle; Appendix F, R. M. Bailey and P. R. Needham. Needless to say, none of the foregoing are responsible for my interpretation or treatment of their many suggestions.

Credits for replacement figures that are not original are as follows: fish illustrations in Chapter II, James Heddons Sons; opercle in Fig. 35, J. E. Bardach; Fig. 44, S. H. Smith and U. S. Fish and Wildlife Service; Figs. 49 and 50 and text-fig. on p. 170, G. P. Cooper, Michigan Institute for Fisheries Research, and Wildlife Management Institute.

F. D. Wieck made an editorial reading of the entire revised manuscript. M. J. Lagler, my wife, and J. H. Johnson helped with the proofs. R. G. Bjorklund and J. H. Johnson did most of the work on the index.

The experience in revising and enlarging this book for its second edition was in many ways disheartening. I was unable to escape the pressure of time sufficiently to attain many desired and desirable ends —and, reviewers to the contrary notwithstanding, no one knows the limitations of the present achievement better than I do.

KARL F. LAGLER

Ann Arbor, Michigan
August 16, 1956

Table of Contents

Chapter I

Natural History and Ecology

Greatest among the many lures and rewards in the life of a fishery biologist are the days spent afield. On these days, his primary objective is most often to secure information on the life history or environmental relationships of a fish. Perhaps he is trying to discover how and why a certain kind of fish is distributed in an area; perhaps he is concerned with the presence or absence of a species in a single lake or stream; perhaps it is his job to analyze environmental limitations or advantages for key organisms; or perhaps he is securing living specimens for corroborative or analytical laboratory testing of some form of fish behavior observed in the field. Almost certainly, these days are among the happiest of his professional life; and if he is schooled in planning his activities rightly, and in sound techniques of observation, recording, interpretation, and report writing, they may also be his most fruitful days.

The importance of some knowledge of the natural history and ecology of the many organisms affecting fishery management cannot be overestimated. Such knowledge is largely the basis for the legal restrictions on fishing to protect spawners. It helps greatly in determining if there is a need to improve a given environment, and what direction the improvement should take. The fundamental principles of artificial propagation rest upon a prior understanding of life ways in natural surroundings. Furthermore, the information available on some species enhances the worker's understanding of what he observes regarding both these and other organisms in the field. For these reasons, a scholar must continually strive to keep abreast of pertinent literature.

PLANNING

More often than not, the success of a field study or an experiment depends on the care with which the work to be done is planned beforehand. Any investigation of the kind we are here considering should first be designed to satisfy a modern interpretation of the principles of the scientific method: search for the truth; maintain an open mind; collect fullest information possible on the pros and cons of each question; verify the data obtained by repetition of observations or by experiments; analyze the findings; test quantitative data statistically when possible; make justifiable deductions; publish the results, including a description of any new methods you developed.

1

Essentially, planning means to isolate and formulate succinctly the problem that is to be attacked, to coordinate the investigation with all the available pertinent information, to break the entire operation up into manageable units of investigation, and finally, to schedule with care each of the steps that will lead to the desired information. For the sake of reliability, it is wise to set up procedures that will lend themselves to the application of significance tests whenever possible. Such organization will also help to guarantee efficiency in the collection of information. Too often investigators gather their material in a haphazard fashion and thereby seriously weaken the conclusions that may be drawn from the data obtained.

RECORDING

The most common difficulties of research workers are caused by their failure to keep adequate records. To guard against this blunder, it is good procedure to draw up blank forms which will help to insure the systematic recording of basic information. Many of the blanks in an appendix to this book illustrate this practice. Although such forms are undeniable investigational assets, they may also be serious liabilities. If they are poorly conceived, or if they set up a mental block which keeps the user from seeing and noting things for which no spaces are provided, they do more harm than good. The investigator employing such records must be sure to avoid these pitfalls. For journalizing in natural history and ecology, a safe method is to record everything that comes to mind on the chance that much of it may in the end prove valuable.

In so far as possible, notes should be developed while operations are in progress, not afterwards. The fallibility of the human memory has been so thoroughly attested that if notes are written up at a time other than while the observations are made, this should be stated in the record.

Abbreviations

In keeping notes on changing phenomena, such as in experiments or observations on behavior, the investigator is sometimes faced with the problem of making a record of many different things that occur simultaneously. In exceptional circumstances, he may resort to various mechanical aids such as tape recorders, motion picture cameras, or other instruments. Often, however, he will be tempted to develop some personal form of shorthand in order to keep up with events. Wherever possible, such a development, even one including standard abbreviations, should be avoided. Any shortened form of writing leads to error and loss of information, since it may become incomprehensible not only to others, but in time even to the author. There are certain common abbreviations which have been used to record observations which otherwise would have gone unrecorded for lack of time. A list of these "emergency" abbreviations follows.

LIST OF SOME ABBREVIATIONS AND SYMBOLS IN COMMON USE IN FISHERY BIOLOGY

Chemistry
M, molar strength solution
M.O., methyl orange
N, normal strength solution
Phth., phenolphthalein

Mathematics
av., average
M, mean
N, number
Σ, sum

Writing
e. g., exempli grata (for example)
et al., et alii (and others)
ibid., ibidem (in the same place)
op. cit., opere citato (in the work
    cited)
q.v., quod vide (which see)

Relative Abundance
abdt, abundant
com, common
r, rare

Relative Density
D, dense
M, medium density
S, sparse

Sex
δ , male
$\delta\ \delta$, males
$\female$, female
$\female\ \female$, females

Fish Parts and Measurements
A, anal fin
D_1, first dorsal fin
D_2, second dorsal fin
P_1, pectoral fin
P_2, pelvic or ventral fin
SL, standard length
FL, fork length
TL, total length

Units of Measure
a., acre
cc., cubic centimeter
cfs., cubic feet per second
cm., centimeter
fath., fathom
ft., foot or feet
gal., gallon
gpm., gallons per minute
in., inch or inches

km., kilometer
L., liter
lb., pound
lbs., pounds
m., meter
mi., mile
min., minute
ml., milliliter ($=$ cc.)
mm., millimeter
oz., ounce or ounces
ppm., parts per million (by weight)
sec., second
yd., yard

Bottom Types
Bo, boulder or boulders
BR, bed rock
C, clay
D, detritus
fP, fibrous peat
Gr, gravel
M, marl
Mk, muck
P, peat
pP, pulpy peat
R, rubble
Sd, sand
St, silt

Life History Stages
Ad., adult
Hl. gr., half grown
Iuv., juvenile
Mat., sexually mature
r., ripe
Yg., young

Species
sp., one species
spp., more than one species

Directions and Locations
E, east
N, north
S, south
W, west
T, township
R, range
Co., county
Sec., section

Miscellaneous
C., centigrade
F., Fahrenheit

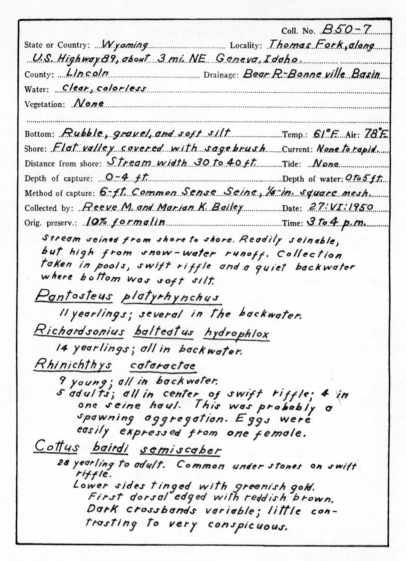

Coll. No. *B50-7*

State or Country: *Wyoming*   Locality: *Thomas Fork, along*
U.S. Highway 89, about 3 mi. NE Geneva, Idaho.

County: *Lincoln*   Drainage: *Bear R.-Bonneville Basin*

Water: *Clear, colorless*

Vegetation: *None*

Bottom: *Rubble, gravel, and soft silt*   Temp.: *61°F* Air: *78°F*

Shore: *Flat valley covered with sagebrush*   Current: *None to rapid*

Distance from shore: *Stream width 30 to 40 ft.*   Tide: *None*

Depth of capture: *0-4 ft.*   Depth of water: *0 to 5 ft.*

Method of capture: *6-ft. Common Sense Seine, ¼-in. square mesh.*

Collected by: *Reeve M. and Marian K. Bailey*   Date: *27:VI:1950*

Orig. preserv.: *10% formalin*   Time: *3 to 4 p.m.*

Stream seined from shore to shore. Readily seinable,
but high from snow-water runoff. Collection
taken in pools, swift riffle and a quiet backwater
where bottom was soft silt.

Pantosteus platyrhynchus
    11 yearlings; several in the backwater.

Richardsonius balteatus hydrophlox
    14 yearlings; all in backwater.

Rhinichthys cataractae
    9 young; all in backwater.
    5 adults; all in center of swift riffle; 4 in
      one seine haul. This was probably a
      spawning aggregation. Eggs were
      easily expressed from one female.

Cottus bairdi semiscaber
    28 yearling to adult. Common under stones on swift
    riffle.
    Lower sides tinged with greenish gold.
     First dorsal edged with reddish brown.
     Dark crossbands variable; little con-
     trasting to very conspicuous.

Fig. 1. COLLECTION RECORD. Sample fish collection blank and records made during a field study of fish distribution and ecology.

Use of Blank Forms

As an example of a form for recording fundamental investigational information, let us consider one in general use in the field in connection with the collection of fishes, primarily for distributional analysis (Fig. 1). The blank, however, also provides for the entry of key ecological information, which, when accompanied by detailed notes on each species encountered, will add up to a highly useful collection of data. The following paragraphs describe each item on this form, in order. Suggestions of value may also be found in later chapters dealing with lake and stream surveys.

Collection Number. A serial number assigned to each collection provides a ready means for identifying the collection, and for matching notes and specimens if the latter are accompanied by the number recorded in soft lead pencil or waterproof ink on good, heavy, bond paper or its equivalent.

State or country. These items serve to identify the general location of the collection and are of particular value when the data from many sets of observations are to be sorted according to political location.

Locality. In contrast to the above, this space calls for the most specific locality that it is possible for the worker to give. The statement should include an accurate reference both to a point on commonly available maps and to the exact spot at which the observations were made on the body of water. In some parts of the United States, the use of Township, Range, and Section numbers is very desirable.

County. Same as for State and country.

Drainage. Give major drainage affinity or watershed.

Water. Both true color and turbidity of the water are given here. When instruments to measure these characteristics objectively are not available, the best possible written description should be given. The following terms are weak but often used: as to color—colorless, light brown, brown, and dark brown; as to turbidity—clear, turbid, or very turbid. If chemical water analyses are made, the results should be given here also.

Vegetation. Intended here is a list of the species of aquatic vegetation and their distribution at the study location, with a description of the density of each (at least note sparse, medium, or dense).

Bottom. The character and composition of the bottom should be described in this space. Among the types frequently encountered are those in the preceding list of abbreviations. Particular reference to the bottom types over which each kind of fish or other organism is found may be entered along with the species list on the lower half of the form.

Temperature. The temperature of the air (in the shade, over the water), and of the water (at least just below the surface), as routinely taken with a good instrument, are to be recorded here.

Shore. The shore features, and those of the adjacent terrain which influence the aquatic habitat, are briefly described.

Current. Record here the exact or relative velocities of the current at the point of investigation, as investigational needs dictate. Instrument readings are customarily recorded in feet per second at bottom, mid-water, and just beneath surface. Subjective evaluation may describe surface velocities as stagnant, sluggish, slow, moderate, rapid, or torrential. Sometimes the entry will be "zone of wave action," or "surge zone," or "alternating pools and riffles."

Distance from shore (or stream width). In lake collections, the distance from shore at which the captures were made is written in this space; in stream operations the widths of the watercourse at the study station are recorded.

Tide. This blank calls for a note on the stage of the tide in habitats where it applies—such as rising, high, ebbing, or low.

Depth of capture—Depth of water. Both the depth at which the species were taken (or observed), and the maximum depth of the water, are called for here. This information discloses habits and bathymetric distribution.

Method of capture. If any collecting was done, the investigator should describe the gear he used, and how it was operated. For example, if a seine was employed, give its dimensions and mesh size, the number of hauls, and the extent of shore, stream or open water traversed. If observations were made, describe techniques and gear used.

Collected by. Name the person responsible for the work and notes first, and then the others in the party.

Date. It is well to avoid abbreviations, at least those which use Arabic numerals only. Some investigators give the month in Roman numerals (IV:14:56 or 14:IV:56).

Original preservative. "10 per cent Formalin" will be the most common entry here. Other fixatives are rarely employed. The importance of this notation lies in the cue it provides for subsequent treatment of the specimens. For example, the treatment for simple storage will differ from the treatment for histological study. This, too, is the place to indicate whether all collected specimens were preserved or whether the preserved specimens were selected from a larger collection—if so, the entry would be "selected collection."

Time. This blank calls for the actual clock-time spent in making the collection, the observations, or both.

As I said before, the investigator should guard against letting his powers of observation be strangled by the headings or the sizes of the blank spaces on his form. Any pertinent information should be recorded as opportunity allows or necessity demands, adding new headings or expanding the given headings elsewhere on the sheet. In collecting fish for general ecological studies, typical additional entries under the name of each species might be: actual numerical count, or relative abundance as "rare," "common," or "abundant"; life history stage as young, juvenile, adult, etc. (see previous list of abbreviations); habits; habitat "preferences"; descriptions, including coloration both when viewed in water and in hand; etc.

COLLECTING

Where to Collect Fish for Study

In collecting fish for study, it is of the highest importance to collect not only in places where fish are greatly in evidence or especially concentrated, but to collect in obscure spots as well. If fish are taken solely from locations in which they are very accessible, the investigator will almost certainly miss some of the species present in the body of water because different kinds have distinct habitat "preferences." A worker who is not careful to spread his effort may very easily obtain samples that are highly selective rather than representative in their composition. The best procedure is to try everything possible to obtain a representation of the fish from every habitat—and even then the sample will be influenced by the selectivity of the gear employed and the manner in which it was used.

Before collecting fish in any region, a worker should obtain written permission of the proper state or federal officials both as to locality and means of collection. A "collector's permit" with few limitations can often be obtained by a qualified person.

How to Collect Fish for Study

Fish may be collected in very many different ways. A few of the means most commonly used are described below.

Seining. For shore seining (Fig. 2) and collecting in streams a minimum standard combination of seines is the following:

Tied bag seine: 25 or 30 ft. long; 6 ft. deep; sides (wings) of 0.5-in. square mesh; bag, trailing 6 to 8 ft., of 0.25-in. square mesh; float line with sufficient buoyancy to assure that it will not submerge when the net is being drawn through the water; lead line "double-leaded" to make certain that it will stay on the bottom when the seine is being pulled. If the net is to be used in soft-bottomed, quiet waters, the extra leads may be omitted. Perishable parts of the gear should be protected from decay by treatment with a suitable twine preservative (e.g., copper napthenate).

Tied straight seine: 10 ft. long; 6 ft. deep; 0.25-in. square mesh; "double-leaded"; treated with preservative.

Minnow seine: Common Sense Brand, satisfactory; 6 ft. long; 4 ft. deep; 0.125-in. square mesh; number of leads ordinarily to be doubled after purchase.

Fig. 2. LAKE FISH COLLECTING. Upper photograph: 25-foot, tied bag seine in use along shore; lower photographs, charged, pendant electrodes for, and in use offshore (power supply is portable electric generator, 2500 watts, A. C. or D. C.) (see Electrofishing, p. 9).

Trapping. Some kinds of traps are very useful for sampling stream fishes. Most traps depend for success on fish movements or migrations. They range in size and portability from small minnow traps to semi-permanent weirs (Figs. 3 and 4). Types suitable for offshore use in large rivers and in standing waters are mentioned below, and shown in Chapters XIX, Figs. 100 and 101, and XXIV, Figs. 121–123.

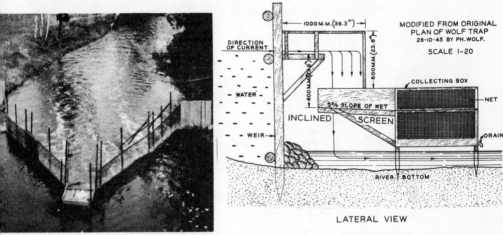

Fig. 3. FISH WEIR. Weir used in life history studies of sea lampreys for trapping upstream migrants during spawning run (Applegate, 1950). Stream flows toward top of page.

Fig. 4. INCLINED-SCREEN TRAP. Device used for the capture of fish and other organisms moving downstream (original design by Wolf, 1951; American adaptation by Applegate, 1950).

Electrofishing. Electrofishing (Fig. 5) is a means for collecting fish that is of particular value in streams and, to a limited extent, in standing waters.[1] A variety of electrical units have been assembled and found useful in different situations. Some are small and so light that they can be carried in a back-pack. Others are heavier and require two or more men to transport them. Both alternating and direct current can be used. A unit of intermediate weight (approximately 70 lbs.) and utility is a 500-watt, 110-volt, A.C. generator such as that manufactured by the Homelite Corporation of Port Chester, New York. This generator is driven by a contained, air-cooled gasoline engine. In a typical hook-up, the positive and negative poles of the generator are each connected to an electrode by No. 16 copper wire which is rubber-insulated and multistrand. Workable electrodes are various; a suitable one may be fashioned of a square foot of galvanized iron or copper hardware cloth with 0.25-in. or 0.5-in. square mesh, attached to a frame of wood or lightweight metal tubing. The copper wire from the power supply is soldered to the mesh and a 4- or 5-foot, non-conducting handle is secured to the frame. In operation, each of two workers carries an electrode and a dip net. Two operators customarily work upstream together and are

[1]The December, 1950, issue of THE CANADIAN FISH CULTURIST is devoted to the subject of electrofishing and should be consulted by anyone interested in the collection of fish by this means.

Fig. 5.   ELECTROFISHING.   Fish in field between the two electrodes, one of which is held by each man, are temporarily stunned and may be collected with a dip net. Portable generator in background has capacity of 500 watts, 110 volts, 60 cycles, A.C., and is suitable for work in small streams.

able to collect fish efficiently up to a distance as far as ten feet apart. The same 500-watt power supply will run an electrical seine of simple design (Funk, 1949).

Poisoning. The use of poisons has a place in the collection of fish. The substance most commonly used in North America is powdered *Derris* root with a rotenone content of 5 per cent (see Chapter XX). Such powder, mixed with the body of water from which a fish sample is desired, is lethal to fish in a concentration of one part per million parts of water (e.g., 1 lb. of powder containing 5% of rotenone to each million pounds of water). The mixture is harmless to warmblooded animals, but kills fish in a matter of minutes at 70° F. and up, requiring longer times at lower temperatures. It must be used with extreme caution in running waters because the toxic wave will sweep downstream for some distance before becoming diluted below the danger point.

Offshore netting. For collecting in the offshore parts of standing waters a variety of nets, traps, and trawls is used (see Chapter XXIV, "Freshwater Commercial Fisheries"). A commonly employed net is the so-called "Experimental Gill Net" (Fig. 99) which incorporates five mesh sizes in a single unit. Tied in nylon mesh and twine, with floats of aluminum or wood and sinkers of lead, such a net is constructed to fish on the bottom. However, this gear may be suspended by auxiliary floats to fish at any depth. One commonly used set of specifications for experimental gill nets follows:

Length: 125 ft. (41 2/3 yds.)

Depth: 6 ft. (2 yds.)

Mesh: 0.75-in. square, 25 ft. (8 1/3 yds.), No. 46 nylon thread
1-in. square, 25 ft., No. 69 nylon thread
1.25-in. square, 25 ft., No. 69 nylon thread
1.50-in. square, 25 ft., No. 104 nylon thread
2-in. square, 25 ft., No. 104 nylon thread

Nylon has superseded cotton and linen for these nets because it is more durable and appears to be more efficient in catching fish.

Of the various trap nets which may be employed for scientific collecting in lake waters less than 35 feet in depth, that described by Crowe (1950) is most successful (Fig. 121). The device is a modification and reduction of the submarine trap net used extensively in the commercial fisheries of the Great Lakes region. A leader, wings, hearts, and funnels of mesh guide the fish into the pots. The catch is removed from the second of the two pots by under-running the net with a boat. Underwater floats keep the hearts and pots open and hold the wings and leaders erect when the trap is anchored on the bottom.

Other methods. Besides the foregoing commonly employed means, there are many other ways to collect fish including the diversion of streams, the drainage of ponds or pools, begging, and fishing by hand or with explosives. In special situations a one-man push seine may be useful, as may be a cast net. Bow and arrow, spear, and harpoon each has its place, as has a variety of devices such as the "Arbalete," an underwater spear-gun for use while diving. For capturing fry, fine mesh nets have been used; to take fry and eggs from bottom nests, a suction tube will serve.

OBSERVING

The first step in making observations on the habits of an animal is to establish the correct identity of the subject. In aquatic work, this usually means the careful notation of characters of the organism as seen in the water, followed by collection and verification in hand. Once a reliable set of field characters has been worked out, observation of habits in nature may proceed on a sound basis.

Like other animals in their natural habitats, many fishes can be observed very successfully provided the investigator has patience and will remain reasonably quiet while watching (Reighard, 1910). Elaborate blinds are not necessary for hiding an above-the-surface observer, although sometimes a simple shield will facilitate note taking or picture making. I have seen excellent daytime photographs of spawning lam-

Fig. 6. PHOTOGRAPHY. Upper figure, daytime shot of spawning brook lampreys. Lower figure, nighttime shot of colony of bluegill nests with guardian males photographed by means of an underwater flash bulb. Note fine definition of bottom contours and nest depressions.

preys made by a worker who stood quietly near a nest (Fig. 6, upper part, was made so). Underwater photographs are easily taken by a properly equipped submerged photographer (Cross, 1954).

Records on some species can be obtained best at night (Fig. 7) with the aid of adequate illumination. I have used two kinds of very effective jacklights. In operation, either kind is placed beneath the surface of the water in order to eliminate glare. The electrical connections to the lamp need not be waterproof and will not short-circuit when submerged in ordinary fresh water. One light was fashioned from a reflector made of a 12-inch disc of 26-gauge galvanized iron. A 50-candlepower, 6-volt, automotive light bulb was mounted to pass through a hole in the center of the disc. The power supply was a 6-volt storage battery. A sealed-beam automobile lamp may be substituted for the homemade device for some purposes, but for general use its field of illumination is too restricted. The second type was powered by a 1500-watt generator (also useful for electrofishing). Two 500-watt photo-flood lamps or 150-watt reflector flood lamps were mounted on a bracket which could be held under the water by hand or secured to the bottom of a boat. The illumination is strong, and visibility in reasonably calm water is limited almost solely by turbidity.

Underwater television holds many real opportunities for fish watching, but equipment is costly (Cross, 1954), (Fig. 7).

Observers will do well to consider both around-the-calendar and around-the-clock opportunities (Carbine, 1939), particularly in monographic life history studies. Most of the relatively little that is known about fish habits stems from daytime studies in warmer seasons. Not even those fishes which are preeminently nocturnal in their habits, such as bullheads, have been carefully observed during the hours of darkness. Furthermore, the collection of fish, particularly along the exposed shores of larger bodies of water, can yield greatest returns after dark.

Few subjective observations of fish habits attain validity unless they are repeated and unless they are accompanied by as many objective measurements as possible. As previously indicated, adequate thermometers are very important to determine thermal conditions of the habitat, since these conditions may profoundly influence habits. For example, largemouth bass desert their nests when temperature drops suddenly by more than a few degrees. The possible influence of atmospheric pressure and light conditions on behavior calls for wider use of both barometer and submersible photoelectric cell or foot-candle meter. Stream work should perhaps never be undertaken unless a water current meter is at hand.

The exercise of ingenuity can yield striking results in life history studies. I recall the work of Lake (1936) in studying the reproductive habits of a darter which nests under stones. In order to observe the reproductive habits of this fish in natural surroundings, Lake merely installed a mirror under the water in such a position that he could sit comfortably on the bank, look into the mirror with a pair of binocular field glasses, and see everything that was going on in a nest. Recently, great improvements have been made in older methods of direct underwater observation and collecting. Modern self-contained underwater breathing apparatus (SCUBA)—such as the "Aqualung" and "Hydropak" now enables workers to conduct submerged studies, often without the need of an attending vessel and assistants. Although the depths attain-

Fig. 7. OBSERVING. Upper figure shows inexpensive face mask and snorkel for direct observation (and collection) of fish and other aquatic organisms. Lower figure is suggestive of use of underwater television and shows plastic cased T-V eye and floodlights being lowered through hole in ice; viewing screen is top center and generator for power supply is at right in distance.

able, and the amount of time spent safely in a dive, vary with the experience and capability of the individual, it is not uncommon for relative novices to spend an hour or more in the water at depths to 40 feet. Because of existing hazards, however, users of such equipment should be specially trained and physically qualified (Owen, 1955).

Observations once made must still be evaluated, correlated, and interpreted. Students of life histories are cautioned against making either undue generalizations (Gill, 1910), or anthropomorphic interpretations.

Much of the remainder of this book is devoted to descriptions of methods and reasons for studying various aspects of the life history and ecology of fishes. A monographic treatment of any species may include the features thus described, and any of the additional features in the following outline, as well as many other special items, for which see Gill (1910) and Koster (1955).

SUGGESTIVE OUTLINE OF MAJOR TOPICS FOR INCLUSION IN A MONOGRAPHIC TREATISE ON THE LIFE HISTORY AND ECOLOGY OF A FISH

Taxonomy

Range (general)
  Original
  Present
  Factors determining range

Distribution (specific in study region)
  Habitats
  Associations
  Factors influencing local distribution

Description
  Morphology
  Coloration
  Sexual dimorphism

Food and feeding
  Life history stages
  Selectivity of food
  Seasonal variations
  Food conversion
  Daily food requirements
  Periodicity in feeding
  Manner of feeding
  Factors influencing food eaten

Growth
  Age
  Length
  Weight
  Length-weight relationship
  Periodicity
  Factors influencing growth

Reproduction
  Attainment of sexual maturity
  Sex ratio
  Courtship
  Sexual recognition
  Breeding
  Fecundity
  Care of eggs and young
  Survival of young
  Fate of breeders
  Factors influencing reproduction

Embryonic development
  Germ cell cycle
  Fertilization
  Developmental period
  Hatching
  Larval development
  Factors influencing development

(cont.)

Behavior
  Movements
  Migrations
  Schooling
  Territoriality
  Learning
  Relations with associates
  Factors influencing behavior

Populations
  Instantaneous
  Rate of mortality
  Recruitment
  Factors influencing

Diseases

Predators and competitors

Relations to man
  Values
  Fisheries
    Methods
    Yields
  Conservation

STUDY PROGRAM

One of the basic factors in fish production is spawning success. Successful natural reproduction may sometimes be encouraged by environmental improvement, one of the tools of fish management. For this reason, the fishery biologist should know how to study the reproductive habits, and how to determine the spawning requirements of various species. Furthermore, such information is necessary when the stocking of fish in new waters is contemplated. Conditions unsuitable for reproduction have caused the failure of many plants of fish, and with it the waste of effort and funds.

Select a fish species that spawns during a season and in a place where it may be observed. Many stream fishes, including minnows, suckers, darters, muddlers, salmon, and trout are particularly suitable for study where they occur in clear water. Lake and pond dwellers such as the sunfishes and the basses are also excellent subjects of observation where the water is clear.

Before going into the field, read if possible Reighard's 1910 paper on methods. Take notebook, camera, ruler, seine, and other equipment to the spawning site. Also refer back to the life history outline earlier in this chapter to recall topics on which information may be gained, and to Koster (1955).

Approach the spawning location cautiously. Determine the response of the fish to various degrees of movement and other disturbances on your part.

Determine the exact identity of the fish of primary observation, and of associated forms, by (1) studying appearance in the water and (2) by careful seining to learn field characters. Watch for sexual differences and write descriptions.

Observe the various elements of behavior of the fish in all aspects of reproduction. Make repeated observations of the same features. Keep copious notes. Be analytical. Record dates, times, location of activities, water depths, strength of current (if any), and related information. A safe rule is that nothing is too insignificant to write down. When you begin to consider the continuity of the whole process, the separate elements will fall into their proper places and will be in true relation to one another.

Photographs are particularly valuable in augmenting written descriptions of the reproductive habits of fishes (Reighard, 1908).

Finally, compile your observations into a connected account of the reproductive habits of the fish studied. Compare your observations and conclusions with those of other workers on the same species and explain differences. How would you use information of this sort to set up the spawning requirements of a fish for management purposes? What additional information would you need?

REFERENCES

Applegate, Vernon C. 1950. Natural history of the sea lamprey, *Petromyzon marinus*, in Michigan. U. S. Fish and Wildlife Service Special Scientific Report — Fisheries, 55: xii, 237 p., 65 figs.

Carbine, W. F. 1939. Observations on the spawning habits of centrarchid fishes in Deep Lake, Oakland County, Michigan. Trans. Fourth N. Amer. Wildlife Conf., pp. 275-287, 5 figs.

Cross, E. R. 1954. Underwater photography and television. New York, Exposition Press, 258 p., illus.

Crowe, Walter R. 1950. Construction and use of small trap nets. Prog. Fish-Cult., 12 (4): 185-192, 4 figs., 1 text-fig.

Funk, John L. 1949. Wider application of the electrical method of collecting fish. Trans. Amer. Fish. Soc., 77 (1947): 49-60, 2 figs.

Gill, Theodore. 1910. A plea for observation of the habits of fishes and against undue generalization. Bull. U. S. Bur. Fish., 28 (2) (1908): 1059-1067.

Koster, William J. 1955. Outline for an ecological life history study of a fish. Ecology, 36 (1): 141-153.

Lake, Charles T. 1936. The life history of the fan-tailed darter Catonotus flabellaris flabellaris (Rafinesque). Amer. Midland Nat., 17 (5): 816-830, 3 figs.

Owen, D. M. 1955. A manual for free divers using compressed air. London-New York, Pergamon Press, 62 p., 13 figs.

Raney, E. C. 1939. The breeding habits of *Ichthyomyzon greeleyi*. Copeia, 1939 (2): 111-112.

Raney, E. C. 1939. Observations on nesting habits of *Parexoglossum laurae*. Copeia, 1939 (2): 112-113.

Raney, E. C. 1940. The breeding behavior of the common shiner, *Notropis cornutus* (Mitchill). Zoologica, 25 (1): 1-14, 4 pl.

Reighard, J. R. 1908. The photography of aquatic animals in their natural environment. Bull. U. S. Bur. Fish., 27 (1907): 41-68, 9 figs., 4 pl.

Reighard, J. R. 1910. Methods of studying the habits of fishes, with an account of the breeding habits of the horned dace. Bull. U. S. Bur. Fish., 28 (2) (1908): 1111-1136, 5 figs., 7 pl.

Reighard, J. R. 1943. The breeding habits of the river chub, *Nocomis micropogon* (Cope). Pap. Mich. Acad. Sci., Arts, and Lett., 28 (1942): 397-423, 1 fig.

Sigler, William F. 1953. The collection and interpretation of fish life history data. Logan, Utah, Author and Wildlife Mgt. Dept., Utah St. Agric. Coll., 46 p., 7 figs.

Timmermans, J. A. 1954. La pêche electrique en eau douce. Trav. Sta. Recherche Groenendaal, Ser. D, 31 p., 12 figs.

Wolf, Philip. 1951. A trap for the capture of fish and other organisms moving downstream. Trans. Amer. Fish. Soc., 80 (1950): 41-45, 3 figs.

Chapter II

Freshwater Fishes of North America, North of Mexico

The basis of work in fishery biology is an exact knowledge of the kinds of fishes composing the fauna under investigation. This book presupposes an acquaintance at least with elementary ichthyology.

There are about two hundred kinds of freshwater fishes of common occurrence in North America north of Mexico. In addition, there are about five hundred less common or rare ones. All of these species are currently grouped into thirty-three families, not including cavefishes or marine groups with occasional wanderers into fresh water. There follows an arrangement of the freshwater families into four contrasting systems of classification which will be useful for reviewing natural groups of fishes and their composition.

Besides being able to recognize all of the fishes of frequent occurrence, a fishery biologist should know them by both technical and common names, and he should be acquainted with the fundamentals of their life ways, requirements, and management. Knowledge of generally acceptable common names and their colloquial equivalents is of particular value in dealing understandingly with lay conservationists, commercial fishermen, and anglers. For purposes of orientation, it is further desirable that the worker know the general range of each of these key forms and something of their primary economic status. In Appendix F will be found a list of common freshwater fish species for the United States, Canada, and Alaska. In so far as practicable, I have followed the names used in Special Publication No. 1 of the American Fisheries Society and its official emendations.

LAMPREY FAMILY—PETROMYZONTIDAE

The lampreys are easily recognized by their eel-like body shape, the sucking-disc mouth which lacks ordinary upper and lower jaws, the absence of paired fins, and the presence of seven external gill openings on each side of the body. Lampreys are found in North America from the Arctic to Mexico. They also occur in Eurasia and in the Sub-antarctic. The group is not large and through its entire range contains only about two dozen species. It is particularly well represented in the fresh waters of eastern North America.

Lampreys inhabit creeks, rivers, and lakes as well as the oceans. All species ascend streams to spawn and ordinarily build nests on gravelly

OUTLINE CLASSIFICATION OF FAMILIES OF FRESHWATER FISHES OF NORTH AMERICA, NORTH OF MEXICO

Saltwater families with occasional wanderers into fresh water and cavefishes are omitted.

FAMILIES	ORDERS (And Major Groups) FOLLOWING JORDAN, 1923	ORDERS (And Major Groups) FOLLOWING REGAN, 1929	ORDERS (And Major Groups) FOLLOWING BERG, 1940	PROPOSED ORDERS (And Major Groups*)
	(Class Marsipobranchii)	(Class Marsipobranchii) (Subclass Cyclostomata)	(Class Petromyzones)	(Class Monorhina) (Subclass Cyclostomi)
PETROMYZONTIDAE Lamprey Family	Hyperoartia	Hyperoartia	Petromyzoniformes	Petromyzontida
	(Class Pisces) (Subclass Actinopteri)	(Class Pisces) (Subclass Paleopterygii)	(Class Teleostomi) (Subclass Actinopterygii)	(Class Osteichthyes) (Subclass Teleostomi)
ACIPENSERIDAE Sturgeon Family	Glaniostomi	Chondrostei	Acipenseriformes	Acipenserida
POLYODONTIDAE Paddlefish Family	Selachostomi			
		(Subclass Neopterygii)		
AMIIDAE Bowfin Family	Halecomorphi	Protospondyli	Amiiformes	Amiida
LEPISOSTEIDAE Gar Family	Holostei	Ginglymodi	Lepisosteiformes	Lepisosteida
CLUPEIDAE Herring Family	Isospondyli	Isospondyli	Clupeiformes	Clupeida
OSMERIDAE Smelt Family				
THYMALLIDAE Grayling Family				
SALMONIDAE Salmon Family				
COREGONIDAE Whitefish Family				
HIODONTIDAE Mooneye Family				
UMBRIDAE Mudminnow Family	Haplomi	Haplomi		
ESOCIDAE Pike Family				
DALLIIDAE Blackfish Family	Xenomi			

*Major groups following system proposed in report of American Society of Ichthyologists and Herpetologists Committee on Fish Classification (Copeia, 1950, No. 4: 326-327) but later abandoned by same Committee (Copeia, 1953, No. 4: 251-252).

OUTLINE CLASSIFICATION OF FAMILIES OF FRESHWATER FISHES OF NORTH AMERICA, NORTH OF MEXICO (Continued)

Saltwater families with occasional wanderers into fresh water and cavefishes are omitted.

Family	Suborder	Order	(-iformes)	(-ida)
CHARACIDAE — Characin Family	Heterognathi	Ostariophysi	Cypriniformes	Cyprinida
CATOSTOMIDAE — Sucker Family	Eventognathi			
CYPRINIDAE — Carp Family	Eventognathi			
ICTALURIDAE — North American Freshwater Catfish Family	Nematognathi			
ANGUILLIDAE — Freshwater Eel Family	Apodes	Apodes	Anguilliformes	Anguillida
CYPRINODONTIDAE — Killifish Family	Cyprinodontes	Microcyprini	Cyprinodontiformes	Cyprinodontida
POECILIIDAE — Livebearer Family	Cyprinodontes			
GADIDAE — Cod Family	Anacanthini	Anacanthini	Gadiformes	Gadida
PERCOPSIDAE — Trouperch Family	Salmopercae	Salmopercae	Percopsiformes	Percopsida
APHREDODERIDAE — Pirateperch Family	Xenarchi			
ATHERINIDAE — Silverside Family	Percomorphi	Percomorphi	Mugiliformes	Percida
SERRANIDAE — Bass Family	Percomorphi		Perciformes	
CENTRARCHIDAE — Sunfish Family	Percomorphi		Perciformes	
PERCIDAE — Perch Family	Percomorphi		Perciformes	
SCIAENIDAE — Drum Family	Percomorphi		Perciformes	
EMBIOTOCIDAE — Seaperch Family	Percomorphi		Perciformes	
CICHLIDAE — Cichlid Family	Percomorphi		Perciformes	
COTTIDAE — Sculpin Family	Cataphracti	Scleroparei	Gasterosteiformes	Gasterosteida
GASTEROSTEIDAE — Stickleback Family	Thoracostei			

riffles. Their nests are shallow depressions dug into the bottom. The eggs are buried in gravel; when the young hatch they work their way up through the gravel into the free-water of the stream and then drift with the current. They stop their downstream drift to burrow into soft-bottomed areas in the water course. Here they spend one or more years as larvae, feeding on materials which they strain from the water and from the oozy layer on the bottom. Species that are non-parasitic as adults transform into the adult stage at metamorphosis, and soon attain sexual maturity, spawn, and die. The parasitic sea lamprey, however, metamorphoses into a blood-sucking parasite which attacks other fishes for about a year and a half until it attains sexual maturity. It, too, then spawns and dies.

Non-parasitic species are of little importance in fishery management. The parasitic ones, however, are able to kill their host fishes or to leave unsightly scars upon them. Lamprey injuries destroy the value, both aesthetic and monetary, of food fishes which have been so attacked, and make game fishes unpleasant for most anglers to see. The disappearance of valuable components of the fisheries of the upper Great Lakes, such as the lake trout and whitefish, is blamed on the depredations of the parasitic sea lamprey. Control of this relatively recent intruder into the upper Great Lakes is one of the most interesting and pressing problems in current freshwater fishery management.

STURGEON FAMILY—ACIPENSERIDAE

The sturgeons are characterized by rows of bony scales, or bucklers, along the sides and top of the body. Like the paddlefish, the upper lobe of the tail fin is strongly upturned, and part of the tail base is scaled. The mouth is situated below and behind the tip of the snout and has ·dant barbels in front of it. There are not many species. The principal genus is *Acipenser*. Sturgeons occur in the northern parts of North merica, in both Atlantic and Pacific marine and fresh waters, and in Eurasia.

As the ventral mouth suggests, sturgeons are bottom feeders and use many different kinds of organisms as food. The fish are very slow-growing, and some species appear to require a dozen or more years to attain sexual maturity. Spawning is usually in the late spring or early summer, in streams or in shallow waters of some large lakes. Although growth is slow, weights up to 1800 pounds have been recorded (for the white sturgeon).

Sturgeons are very desirable food fish, for their flesh is tasty, white, and flaky, and their roe can be made into costly caviar. Once very abundant in inland waters and coastal streams, sturgeons are now moderately scarce everywhere. They still contribute to local commercial fisheries, as for example in the Mississippi Valley; and in some inland waters they are speared through the ice in the winter to afford some sporting enjoyment.

PADDLEFISH FAMILY—POLYODONTIDAE

The paddlefish is marked by its elongated, canoe-paddle-shaped snout. Like the sturgeon, it has a strongly upturned tail. It lacks scales, except on the tail base. In North America, the range of the paddlefish is the Mississippi Valley, and presumably it once occurred in the Great Lakes.

The single American species in this family is essentially an inhabitant of open waters of large, silty rivers, and of oxbow and flood-plain lakes. Its spawning habits are imperfectly known. It feeds by straining plankton from the water by means of numerous fine gill rakers. The size it attains may exceed 6 feet in length and 150 pounds in weight.

Formerly, the fish was very abundant in the Mississippi Valley and had considerable commercial significance. It was excellent as food, and its roe was used for the manufacture of caviar. Its scarcity now makes it of relatively little importance in the North American freshwater fisheries of today.

BOWFIN FAMILY—AMIIDAE

Like the American paddlefish family, the bowfin family has only one living species. This fish can be told from all other North American freshwater fishes by the long fin which arches in a bow over much of the length of the back. The covering scales are cycloid, and there is a dark or dusky spot (ocellated with yellow-orange in adult males) near the slightly upturned base of the tail fin. The bowfin is found only in North America, and here only in those parts of the country that lie east of the Rockies.

Bowfin

The bowfin inhabits quiet waters, and feeds on fish, amphibians and crayfish. Spawning takes place in the spring in shallow water amongst the vegetation. Here the male clears a circular area for a nest, then spawns the female and remains on guard. The eggs hatch eight to ten days after they are laid, and after another eight to ten days the fry are ready to leave the nest. When a young bowfin starts swimming about, it is approximately 1/2-inch long and is coal-black. The male convoys his brood of little black fish about in search of food. The young in the school keep on being guarded and guided by the male until they are as much as three inches long. They usually attain this length at the end of the first summer; beyond this, their rate of growth is not known. Their age cannot be determined from their scales, as it can with other fish. Weights up to 8 pounds have been recorded.

The bowfin is not extensively used for food, nor is it much sought after as a sport fish. In the past, it has been controlled, like gars, in an effort to bolster. populations of preferred warm water food and game fishes. At present, however, its value in preventing overpopulation and stunting in preferred fishes is coming into higher and higher regard.

GAR FAMILY—LEPISOSTEIDAE

Gars are archaic-looking fishes, marked by a heavy armature of more or less diamond-shaped, fixed scales that cover the body. Jaws and face extend forward into a beak; teeth are strong, sharp, and conical and are a prominent feature. The family is exclusively American, with species ranging from the North Central region of North America to Central America and Cuba. About ten kinds of gars are known, all of them from fresh waters. The species frequent quiet, warm waters in lakes and in large, slow-moving streams. Unless pursuing their food— which is most often fish—they are sluggish. Spawning takes place in the spring. Their growth in early life is very rapid. The alligator gar is the largest of all species, and is said to reach canoe size.

The food quality of the gars is low. For many years they were controlled in inland waters in an effort to protect stocks of preferred food and game fishes. More recently, in warm water lakes at least, they have been considered of value in controlling the numbers of fishes, such as the bluegill and perch, which are prone to overpopulate and stunt.

HERRING FAMILY—CLUPEIDAE

True herrings of this family have a strong, sharp-edged row of spiny scutes along the midline of the belly which gives a saw-toothed appearance that serves to characterize the silvery, slab-sided fishes. Many species of the family are marine (Atlantic and Pacific herrings, sardines), and abound in the oceans of the world. Some species however, are exclusively freshwater, whereas others enter fresh waters from the sea for spawning (American shad) or other purposes. The freshwater herrings of North America include such species as the skipjack herring, the gizzard shad, and the alewife of the Great Lakes-St Lawrence and Mississippi River systems. In these waters, the herrings dwell in large lakes and the sluggish portions of large rivers. Many feed extensively on plankton. Spawning is in the spring, in open water.

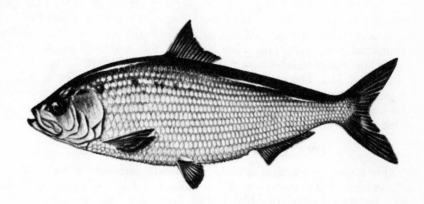

American shad

Although the species in fresh waters have little food or commercial value, they do figure in the diet of predacious game and food fishes. Some become nuisances as, for example, the gizzard shad, which is able to preempt the fish production capacity of certain warmwater ponded areas in the Mississippi Valley, and the alewife which each year dies in huge numbers in Lake Ontario, littering many beaches with decaying carcasses. The alewife is currently penetrating the upper Great Lakes, presumably having gained access, like the sea lamprey, through the Welland Canal.

SMELT FAMILY—OSMERIDAE

Like whitefish, grayling, salmon, catfish, trout, and troutperch families, the smelts, in addition to ordinary fins, have on their backs an adipose fin lacking fin rays. Smelts are easily told from their salmonoid relatives, however, by their scales (Fig. 146) and by the absence of the gristly process in the angle of pelvic fins. Although essentially a marine family with some representatives that run into fresh water to spawn, the American smelt has become land-locked in some fresh waters. There are fewer than two dozen species in the whole family, all of which are Arctic or North Temperate in range.

Spawning of the American smelt takes place in early spring. The exact date depends on climatic conditions and especially on temperature. The peak of the activity is during the night. Sea-run American smelt of the East Coast ascend streams to spawn, and land-locked populations (as in the upper Great Lakes) run up tributaries. The eggs are broadcast on the bottom and stick there. The maximum growth attained is about 14 inches, the average length 8 to 10 inches is reached in a period of a few years. Principal foods are plankton and occasionally a small fish.

The flesh of the American smelt has an excellent flavor and is often prepared for the table simply by deep-frying the whole fish. This smelt is most eagerly sought by fishermen during its spring spawning runs, but is also taken during the winter through the ice, for sport and for commercial purposes. The relationship of the American smelt to other species of commercial importance such as lake trout is as yet little understood. It is known to be a predator, but it also serves as food for the predacious food and game fishes. Whether or not it does more good than harm in the economy of water areas such as the Great Lakes (into which it was introduced) or Lake Champlain, is not known.

GRAYLING FAMILY—THYMALLIDAE

The Arctic grayling, the sole continental species in its family, is distinguished from members of the salmon family, whom it resembles most, by its enlarged flag-like dorsal fin which has more than fifteen soft-rays, whereas that of the salmon and trout has fewer than fifteen. The grayling family ranges throughout the northern parts of North America (being most abundant in Alaska) and Eurasia, but in the United States only a single center of distribution, the Montana-Yellowstone area, remains today. Another locus of occurrence, in Michigan, can no longer be included in the range of the species, because it became extinct there about 1936. The principal habitat of the Arctic grayling is similar to that of brook trout and cutthroat trout. Spawning is in the early spring. The eggs are laid in the shallows over sand and fine gravel. The principal foods are aquatic insects, invertebrates, and sometimes small fish.

Arctic grayling

Grayling have been artificially propagated and stocked successfully in some waters of the Yellowstone country. Apparently this and other conservation measures are necessary if the grayling is to survive in the southern remnants of its range. It is truly the vanishing American game fish!

SALMON FAMILY—SALMONIDAE

Salmon and trout are characteristically coldwater fishes. The salmonids are fine-scaled. Behind the ordinary dorsal fin they have an adipose dorsal fin without rays and there is a curious little process in the axilla of each of the two pelvic fins. The family as it is interpreted here does not include the whitefishes but embraces the salmons and trouts. These are Arctic and North Temperate fishes that either live in fresh water through their life, as do most of the trouts and chars, or else grow in the sea but run into streams to spawn, as do most of the salmons. Species are not very numerous but of considerable sporting and commercial significance. As an addition to the kinds native to American waters, the brown trout has been widely introduced from Europe. Details on important species in American fresh waters follow.

Chinook salmon

Pacific Salmons

The five Pacific salmons—pink, chum (dog), coho (silver), sockeye (red), and chinook (spring, king)—hatch in fresh water, grow in the ocean, return to fresh water to spawn once, and then die. They have a very highly developed homing ability. As they attain sexual maturity in the ocean, they begin to seek out freshwater streams to ascend for spawning. It would appear that each fish makes a try at returning to the very stream in which it hatched. Marking experiments have shown that many of them actually succeed, after going a thousand miles downstream, traveling other thousands about the ocean, and returning some years later over the first thousand miles back upstream.

The hazards that beset both downstream and upstream migrants are many, and are of real concern to the fishery manager. There are waters polluted by industry, domestic sewage, and erosion soil. There are also the twirling blades and churning currents of boat propellers and turbines, water falls, and an increasing number of high dams. The effectiveness of fishing by both sport and commercial operators, too, constitutes a hazard to migrating salmons.

The sex of a salmon is readily distinguishable externally as spawning approaches. Besides showing color differences, the males are ordinarily distinguishable from the females by their more or less humpback conditions, and by the hooked nose or upper jaw they develop. Different species spawn at different ages during the season from late summer to late fall. The sockeye ordinarily nests in its fourth year of life, whereas the chinook nests any time from the third to the eighth year, usually in the fourth or fifth. The cohoes usually spawn in their third year, and chums in the third to fifth. Only the pink normally spawns in its second year of life. Young with yolk sacs are called alevins, and when the yolk has been absorbed, they are named fry. Post-spawners are kelts. All species exhibit much more rapid growth in the oceans than in the streams. However, the Kokanee, a sockeye variety, is landlocked.

High sporting and very high commercial values are attached to the Pacific salmons. Conservationists have grave concern over the future of the Pacific salmon resource because of the effects of the march of civilization on the habitat of these valuable fishes. Salmon has been called "the real gold of Alaska." Attempts to establish the Pacific species in Atlantic waters and in the Great Lakes have apparently failed. These fishes are extensively propagated in hatcheries and stocked in the hope that this practice will help maintain the supply. They are also transported over dams and other obstacles in the way of their migration, either directly or by means of ingenious fishways.

Atlantic Salmon

The Atlantic salmon is a fall spawner. It uses the clean gravel and rubble in riffles of streams. The young hatch in the spring and work up through the gravel as they gain size. Four to six weeks after their emergence they begin to prey on the stream life. Although these young salmon (soon called parr) show some growth during their life in fresh water (last stages called smolt), much more rapid growth occurs during their life in the sea. While in the stream, young salmon especially are set upon by many natural enemies. The kingfishers and the American Merganser have been shown to be two of the worst offenders. In some western Atlantic tributaries, there are recognizable cycles of abundance that can be correlated with dry periods. It seems probable that low waters during dry spells so concentrate the young salmon in the shrunken streams that they are made unusually subject to the depredations of their enemies.

Atlantic salmon

Atlantic salmon grow in four years to an average of about 30 inches, weighing about 10 to 20 pounds. Five-and six-year-olds may attain 35 inches and about 18 pounds. Unlike the Pacific salmon which spawn only once and then die, the Atlantic salmon may spawn annually for many years after it has attained sexual maturity. The first spawning run is usually made after two or three years of stream life followed by two years of ocean life, but a few individuals, called grilse, return after only one year in the sea.

The Atlantic salmon is sought by both sport and comercial fishermen. Commercial operators still take several million pounds annually from the waters of Canada and Newfoundland. United States waters, however, yield only a few tons. Artificial propagation and stocking are carried on in an effort to maintain the supply of Atlantic salmon. Dams such as those in the Penobscot River in Maine are equipped with fish ladders so that they may be negotiated by the upstream migrants.

A popular game fish of some inland waters of New England and New York is the lake Atlantic salmon (so-called landlocked salmon, or Sebago salmon) which is merely a landlocked variety of the Atlantic salmon. This fish moves to its breeding grounds in the early fall, and spawns from October to November. The eggs of the species are buried in clean gravel, like those of other salmonids. The nests are usually in tributary or outlet streams, often near the bases of dams. Sometimes they are made on the wave-swept shoals of the lakes themselves. Growth differs markedly from lake to lake; however, the landlocked Atlantic salmon normally attains 14 inches of length during its fourth year of life. In some lakes, lengths of 25 inches are reached in the fifth year, with weights as high as 6 pounds. The lake Atlantic salmon is artificially propagated and stocked in inland lakes of New England and elsewhere, in an effort to maintain the supply. Introductions into some waters such as the upper Great Lakes have failed to take hold.

Cutthroat trout

Cutthroat Trout

The cutthroat trout is a spring spawner. Inland subspecies usually spawn from one to six weeks after the ice has gone out, with breeding activities at high elevations being delayed until July or August. The Pacific Coast subspecies, which ranges from California to Alaska, spawns from December to May. The redd is made by the female in gravel riffles in streams. Females weighing 4 pounds produce 3,000 to 4,000 eggs, 5-pounders 5,000 to 6,000 eggs. Under average conditions, the cutthroat attains sizes between 8 and 12 inches in 3 years. Specimens weighing more than 40 pounds are on record. Inland subspecies are highly prized as fighting game fish and as food.

Rainbow Trout

In its natural environment of the swift streams of the western mountains, the rainbow trout thrives best in temperatures ranging from 38° F. in the winter to 70° F. in the summer. It can withstand higher and lower

Rainbow trout

temperatures if it is acclimated gradually, but its growth is impeded by extremes of temperature, as for example those in the low 80's which it can tolerate only for short periods of time.

The rainbow spawns between early winter and the beginning of summer, depending on climate, elevation, and genetic strain. Spawning is usually accompanied by at least some upstream migration. Long journeys of this kind may be made by lake- or ocean-run rainbow steelheads. The nest site is often located at the tail of a pool where the water is swift and the gravel clean. Females dig pits in the gravel and later spawn in them with the males. As much as two days may be spent in digging a single pit. Eggs are covered with loose gravel to depths of 8 inches and even more. If the stream temperature averages 45° F., eggs will hatch in about 48 days. Males may be good breeders at 2 years of age, but few females produce until their third year of life.

Young rainbows attain fingerling size of about 3 inches by the end of their first summer. In succeeding years, lengths may range between 7 and 8 inches at the end of the second, 11 and 15 inches after the third, 14 and 16 inches after the fourth, and 16 or more inches after the fifth year of growth. Lake- and ocean-run rainbows may grow over twice as fast as this. Under favorable conditions of artificial propagation, yearlings average about 1 ounce, 2-year-olds about 9 ounces, 3-year-olds between 1 and 2 pounds, and 4-year-olds between 3 and 4 pounds. Returning sea-run individuals weigh up to 40 pounds, or even more, but usually between 3 and 20 pounds with the majority weighing less than 12 pounds.

Although the native range of the rainbow is North America west of the Rockies, and the Pacific Ocean, the species has now been introduced into all parts of the continent. It is easily propagated, and is quite tolerant of the intensive feeding procedures and crowded conditions in hatcheries. Brood stocks are readily held, and eggs and milt easily stripped by hand when the fish are ripe. In many parts of the United States, trout fishing is to a large extent dependent on stocking of such hatchery-reared fish. This is due to the inadequacy of natural reproduction and survival rates to meet the intense angling pressure. The rainbow is more tolerant of warmwater conditions than brook trout.

Brown Trout

Brown trout spawning time varies with the locality, but usually falls within the period from October to February. Like the rainbow trout, the female brown trout digs a pit in the gravel of a cool stream. This pit is usually longer than the female, and as deep or deeper than her greatest depth. She sheds her eggs in the bottom of the nest in company with a single male shedding sperm simultaneously. After spawning, the female completes the redd by moving upstream and churning gravel down over the eggs to cover them with a few inches of the bottom material.

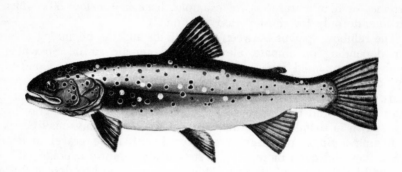

Brown trout

The older and larger the female, the more eggs she produces. A few brown trout females mature at 2 years of age, and produce between 400 and 500 eggs. Four- and 5-year-olds are known to hold as many as 6,000 eggs. The length of the incubation period varies with water temperature, as it does in other fishes. At 57° F., 30 to 33 days are required from spawning to hatching.

By the end of the first summer's growth, the brown trout ranges from 2 to 4 inches in length. At the second fall, it may be from 6 to 8 inches. Successive years of growth may find it at approximately the following lengths and weights: third year, between 7 and 8 inches, weighing about 3 ounces; fourth year, between 10 and 11 inches, weighing between 6 and 7 ounces; fifth year, between 11 and 12 inches, weighing between 9 and 10 ounces; and sixth year, 14 inches or more, weighing about 1 pound.

The brown trout, like the rainbow, is more tolerant of adverse environmental conditions including higher water temperatures than is the brook trout. For this reason, among others, the brown trout is in some situations thought to compete dangerously with the brook trout. Certainly, the brown is more difficult to catch than the popular rainbow, brook, or cutthroat. The brown trout is not native to North America, but was first introduced from Europe in 1883.

Lake Trout

The lake trout which ranges widely in northern North America, from Alaska to the central and northeastern United States, is a fall spawner, breeding in the southern part of its range, mostly during October and November. The eggs are heavy and are shed on the bottom, usually on rocky reefs or shoals of larger lakes. In smaller lakes, gravelly shallows and sometimes tributary streams are used. Lake trout may attain a length of 13 inches at 3 years, nearly 16 inches at 4 years, about

Lake trout

20 inches at 5 years, and about 24 inches at 6 years of age. A 24-inch fish weighs from 4 to 5 pounds. In the Great Lakes, sexual maturity is not reached until a length of about 20 inches and/or an age of 7 years or more have been attained. Average weights encountered are from 3 to 10 pounds, but old records run over 100 pounds.

Lake trout have the usual complement of fish diseases and parasites. In the Great Lakes, however, the sea lamprey is an exceptionally effective parasite of the species.

In many waters such as the Great Lakes and the large lakes of Canada toward Alaska, both commercial and sport fishermen pursue the lake trout. Consequently it is a very valuable species in the inland fisheries of northern North America. Through the years overfishing and other causes have depleted the supply in the southern parts of its range. Some artificial propagation and stocking, as well as legal restrictions, have been used in an effort to maintain the supply in widely ranging waters.

Brook Trout

The breeding season of the brook trout comes in the fall, when the waters grow cooler and the days shorter. Depending on the water condition and location, this species spawns usually between October and December, in the shallows of headwater streams. The size of the redd pit constructed by the female in gravelly bottom varies with her own size; it may be as much as 2 feet long and 10 inches deep. After the eggs are spawned and fertilized, the female covers them with gravel and, as do other trouts, she and the male then desert the nest. At breeding time, the males can be distinguished from the females by the hook which they develop at the midpoint of the lower jaw, and by their darker color. Yearling brook trout females may produce 150 to 250 eggs, 2-year-olds 350 to 500, and older fish from 500 on up. Fertilization in natural redds has been found to be about 80 per cent efficient. At 50° F. the eggs require about 50 days to hatch.

Brook trout

The young fry absorb their yolk sacs in from one to three months, depending on the water temperature. During this interval, they will have worked themselves free from the gravel and have started feeding. Average length attained at various ages may approximate: first year, 3½ inches; second, 6 inches; third, 9 inches; fourth, 12 inches; and fifth, 13 inches. Growth is extremely variable, depending on the suitability of the environment.

The brook trout is propagated in hatcheries and stocked in many streams to afford angling, not only in the eastern part of the country of their native range, but widely through the West. As for other stream trout, the passage of years has seen an increase in the size to which the fish are reared before being planted.

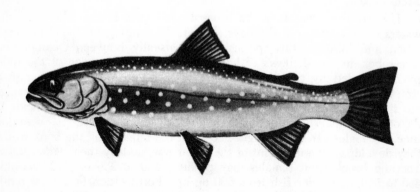

Dolly Varden

Dolly Varden

The Dolly Varden trout is a fall and winter spawner. Ocean-run spawners run upstream from the Pacific into tributaries. When they are spent, they return to sea or, if they are stream resident fish, drop back downstream into likely pools. In some streams, regular seaward migrations are reported to occur in the spring, and upstream movements in the autumn.

The Dolly Varden has been accused of being an important predator on salmon eggs and young. For many years, Alaska paid a bounty of several cents for each Dolly Varden tail. However, research revealed that many of the tails so turned in were from salmon and other trout and the practice was discontinued. Control of the Dolly Varden has been shown to increase the escapement of young salmon from some nursery lakes.

WHITEFISH FAMILY—COREGONIDAE

The whitefishes and their relatives, like the members of the trout and the grayling families, have a rayless adipose fin behind the regular dorsal fin, and possess an appendage at the base of each pelvic fin. There is a recent tendency in North America to follow the long-time practice of European workers by combining in the family Salmonidae fishes formerly placed in the separate whitefish family. Fishes of the whitefish group are told from the salmons and trouts by their larger scales and their much smaller mouth with no or very weak teeth, as well as by other characteristics. Like the Salmonidae, the Coregonidae are limited in distribution to northern parts of North America and Eurasia. Their range corresponds approximately to the glaciated areas. All coregonids spawn in fresh water, and all but a few are throughout their lives confined to cool waters of lakes and relatively coldwater streams. Principal components of the whitefish family are the whitefishes, ciscoes, round whitefishes and the Arctic inconnu. Because of their plasticity, species and their subdivisions in ciscoes offer many problems to taxonomists as well as to fishery workers.

Most coregonids are fall spawners, broadcasting their eggs on the bottom in shoal areas. Exceptions are among the deepwater ciscoes or chubs which spawn at various times of the year. In fact, it has been said one or the other species of chubs is spawning in every month of the year except July.

Lake Whitefish

Of all the members of the family, the lake whitefish is the finest for food. It ranges widely throughout the Great Lakes region and central and eastern Canada. Throughout most of this range, the lake whitefish spawns in November and December, with the females scattering their eggs over rocky or sandy shoals. In some areas, streams are ascended for spawning purposes. Spawners are ordinarily three years of age or over. Females lay 10,000 to 75,000 or more eggs, depending on size. The rate of growth is quite rapid, especially in the southern part of the range where a weight of 2 pounds is reached in 4 to 5 years. Lake whitefish use a wide variety of food, including plankton, aquatic insect larvae and other bottom organisms, and occasionally small fish.

For many years, the species was propagated artificially and stocked in many continental waters in the hope of aiding natural reproduction to meet fishing pressure. These operations have never been proved to be of value and are being abandoned.

Rocky Mountain Whitefish

Rocky Mountain whitefish are fall and early winter spawners. To breed, the adults usually leave the lakes or quiet parts of large streams which they inhabit, and ascend tributaries. With water temperature in the high 40's F., the eggs hatch in about four weeks. Eggs are smaller than trout eggs and run about 900 to the fluid ounce. The average yield is nearly 7,000 eggs per pound of female. Interestingly, at least part of the food of the breeders of the species is reported to be their own eggs. In the Green River of Wyoming, and elsewhere where the Rocky Mountain whitefish is abundant, some concern is felt over its relation to trout. It is thought that this whitefish may in certain situations compete unfavorably with trout.

MOONEYE FAMILY—HIODONTIDAE

This is another small family of North American freshwater fishes. It is made up only of the mooneye and goldeye. Both these species look like true herrings in that they are slabsided and silver to gold in hue. However, they lack the row of sharp, spiny scutes down the midline of the belly which characterizes true herrings, and possess prominently large eyes. Members of this family occur only in the fresh waters of parts of eastern and central North America, in larger lakes and quiet streams.

The species are spring spawners in shallowwater areas. It is presumed that the eggs are broadcast over the bottom. Sizes of 4 to 6 inches may be obtained at the end of the first summer. They are occasionally taken by fishermen at lengths of 12 to 14 inches.

Although the flesh is edible it is not of very good quality. The fish are not sought after very extensively by commercial fishermen. However, the goldeye is delicious when smoked, and is harvested commercially for this purpose from large lakes in Manitoba and Ontario. Both the mooneye and goldeye may have some importance as food for predacious game and food fishes in certain waters.

MUDMINNOW FAMILY—UMBRIDAE

Mudminnows are fingerling-sized fishes of dark coloration with a vertical fin position resembling that of pike, prone to dive into bottom materials for escape. Only four species in the family are known: *Umbra limi* of central North America, *U. pygmaea* of lowland fresh waters of the central and southern Atlantic Coast, *U. krameri* of Europe, and *Novumbra hubbsi* of a small drainage in the state of Washington. American species are spring-spawning, inhabiting principally soft-bottomed, quiet, and often stagnant waters. The species are carnivorous and very hardy. They are eaten by predacious game fishes, and used as bait by anglers.

PIKE FAMILY—ESOCIDAE

Members of the pike family, when looked at from above, are marked by having the front of the head shaped much like a duck's bill. In addition, they have stout, sharp teeth, and dorsal and anal fins set well back on the body. The pike family has a circumpolar distribution in the Northern Hemisphere. Only one genus, *Esox*, is present in the family.

Northern Pike

The northern pike itself is the most wide-ranging species of the family. In North America it is found from Alaska to Labrador, south through New England and much of New York, the northern part of the Ohio Valley, the Great Lakes region, and on to Missouri and Nebraska. Its most frequent habitats are cool to moderately warm and generally weedy, rivers, ponds, and lakes. The pike spawns early in the spring, from March to June, depending on the latitude. The activities of this season are initiated by movement into shallow waters, and particularly into marshes if these are accessible. Here spawning takes place accompanied by wild, thrashing movements; the eggs are broadcast upon the bottom and then deserted. A 10-pound, 3-foot-long female may produce as many as a hundred thousand eggs, whereas a 16-inch fish, weighing about 3/4 pounds may have between 9 and 10 thousand eggs. Soon after hatching, pike are growing at the rate of 1/10 of an inch per day. By the end of the first summer, they measure from 7 to 12 inches and weigh from

Northern pike

1/2 to 3/4 pounds. In later years, they run as follows: second year, 13 to 18 inches, 1 to 1½ pounds; third, 19 to 26 inches, 1½ to 3½ pounds; fifth, 26 to 36 inches, 3 to 12 pounds; and tenth, 40 to 48 inches, 16 to 26 pounds. Twelve-year-old fish have measured as much as 40 inches in Minnesota and 53 inches in Michigan. Old records in Europe go well over a hundred pounds; in large aquaria at zoos, pike have been kept as long as 75 years.

The northern pike enters the commercial and sport fisheries in waters of the northern United States, and in southern and central Canada where it is particularly common. There is a growing interest in the preservation and encouragement of the species in warmwater habitats that involve association with sunfishes and perch. In these waters, it is thought, pike might be very significant in keeping the numbers of the other species under control and so prevent them from stunting as a result of over-population.

Muskellunge

The muskellunge, like the northern pike, is a spring spawner, breeding usually in April and May, earlier in the southern part of its range and later in the North. Like pike, male and female muskies move into the shallows and drop their eggs over soft bottoms, sometimes in marshy situations. The females usually run larger than the males; males become sexually mature at about three years of age, females at four. The eggs of muskellunge are small, going about 74,000 per quart. The reproductive capacity of females is huge and increases with the size of the fish. A single female may deposit as many as 300,000 eggs in one season; more specifically, a 35-pound fish is said to have contained 225,000 eggs. Such high productivity may compensate for the fact that the eggs are scattered over the bottom and are left without parental protection for hatching. With water temperatures in the low 50's F., eggs hatch in from 10 to 15 days. In about 2 weeks after hatching, the fry have absorbed their

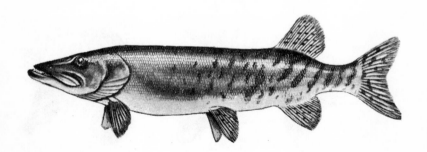

Muskellunge

cumbersome yolk sacs and begin to move about in search of food. Even the first food of muskies is likely to be animal matter, and this carnivorous habit normally stays with the fish until its death.

Muskies are reported to have reached lengths of 8 feet and weights exceeding 100 pounds, although official sporting records are smaller. As in all predacious fishes, growth shows great individual variations. Fish approaching their tenth year of life may range from 3 to 4 feet in length. In successive years of life, lengths may approximate the following: first year, 7 to 9 inches; second, 13 to 16 inches; third, 17 to 24 inches; fourth, 21 to 27 inches; fifth, 26 to 30 inches.

The muskellunge is among the most highly esteemed of North American freshwater trophy fishes, perhaps because it is nowhere abundant. Because of its great esteem as a game fish, the species is propagated and planted in some waters and variously protected in others. The principal means of protecting the muskellunge is to permit it to attain a substantial size so that it may breed more than once before it may be taken by anglers. The species is not harvested commercially. In some waters of Northern Wisconsin, pike control is practiced to favor survival of muskellunge.

Pickerels

Besides the muskellunge and northern pike, there are three kinds of pickerels in the pike family—chain, redfin, and grass. All are spring spawners, although there is evidence that the grass pickerel may occasionally spawn in the fall as well. The eggs are scattered in shallow waters, spawning usually taking place over soft bottoms away from any current. The eggs are adhesive and stick to bottom materials. They are deserted as soon as they are laid. A week or two later, depending on the water temperature, they hatch into young which in another fortnight embark on their predacious and often cannibalistic lives. None of these three species attain the sizes that pike and muskies reach.

Chain pickerel

The chain pickerel does afford some angling pleasure, but redfin and grass species do not grow very large. The grass, for example, seldom exceeds a length of 16 inches. It may in some situations be regarded as a nuisance fish.

BLACKFISH FAMILY—DALLIIDAE

Closely related to the pike and mudminnow families, and grossly resembling them, the blackfish family is confined to the freshwater streams and ponds of northern Alaska and Siberia. The sole living species, the Alaska blackfish, abounds in sphagnum ponds and is very tolerant of adverse environmental conditions. Reputedly it can remain frozen for days, and when thawed will be as lively as ever. Although ranging up to only 8 inches in length, the blackfish has some value as food for natives and their dogs.

CHARACIN FAMILY—CHARACIDAE

The characins compose a large freshwater family of several hundred species. In South America and Africa, where they are most numerous, they take the ecological place of the Cyprinidae and Salmonidae of the Northern Hemisphere. Of the few dozen species occurring north of the Isthmus of Panama, only one, the banded tetra, now ranges northward as far as Texas and New Mexico.

SUCKER FAMILY—CATOSTOMIDAE

The suckers are fishes with none but soft-rays in their fins, and with extensible sucking mouths that oft-times have fleshy lips. The species are sometimes difficult to tell apart. Nearly one hundred of them occur in North America, one occurs in Siberia, and one in China. All live on the bottom of lakes, ponds, and streams, and most of them ascend tributaries to spawn in the spring, though some use the shallows of larger lakes. Feeding is by suction, and bottom organisms are the food. Growth may be very rapid in warm waters, with some of the buffalo fishes attaining sizes of three feet and more in length. Suckers make up a small but significant part of the inland freshwater fisheries of both the commercial and recreational kinds. In certain waters, they may become obnoxious through overabundance, and some are known to eat the spawn of more highly prized fish. Some of the young are eaten by predatory food and game fish. Suckers are quite bony, though edible.

White Sucker

The white sucker is a spring spawner and characteristically moves into the shallows around the gravelly riffles for spawning. Its eggs are normally buried in loose gravel, and there the fry hatch in about three weeks at approximately 50° F. Females from 16 to 21 inches long have been found to hold from 22,000 to 48,000 eggs, whereas larger females may have as many as 100,000.

At hatching, the young are little more than a quarter of an inch long. As soon as they have absorbed their yolk sacs, their mouths open and they begin feeding on microscopic organisms. In some Wisconsin waters, sizes attained in successive years have been recorded to average: first year, 2½ inches; second, 4 inches; third, 5½ inches; fourth, 7 inches; fifth, 8 inches; seventh, 10 inches, and ninth, 12 inches. In other waters, sizes of 13 to 15 inches have been reached in the seventh year.

In some inland lakes and streams, the white sucker has been considered a nuisance fish because of the way in which it may usurp the productive capacity of the area in terms of pounds of fish flesh. This sucker is also known on occasion to be an egg predator. In general, however, the problems revolving around this and other species of the family vary with the lakes and streams where they exist, and must be identified and solved from case to case.

The white sucker makes up a part of both inland commercial and recreational fisheries. It is also reared sparingly for use as bait, for which purpose it is quite good because of its resistance.

CARP FAMILY—CYPRINIDAE

Although in loose parlance, the young of many fishes are called "minnows," there is only one true minnow family, or carp family as it is best called. All the members of this family are soft-rayed fishes, have toothless jaws like the suckers, and grow teeth in the throat only. As this is probably the largest of the recognized freshwater fish families, many of the species are difficult to tell apart. The many hundreds of species occur in almost all fresh waters in the North Temperate Zone and throughout Africa. The North American fauna includes several hundred kinds closely resembling one another.

Minnows occur in all kinds of water—lakes, ponds, or streams, warm or cool. A few kinds, however, have very select habitats and are confined to pelagic or standing water situations; others are entirely stream dwellers. Minnows exhibit a variety of spawning habits. Some species (bluntnose minnow and relatives) make nests under boards, stones and other ob-

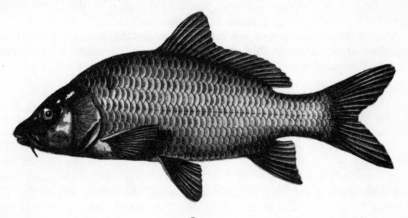

Carp

jects; and the male guards the eggs. Others (creek chub) bury the eggs in gravel and give no further care to them or to the young. Still others (carp) broadcast the eggs on the bottom or among vegetation and then desert them. Most species are very short-lived and attain sizes of only a few inches. Others, such as the squawfish and the introduced carp, may become veritable giants in the freshwater fish world.

Minnows are very important in the food chains of most predacious fishes. They also are used as bait by sport fishermen, and support a substantial industry in bait culture. Minnows themselves are interesting to catch on rod and line, and larger forms such as the carp afford considerable sport to spear and to bow-and-arrow fishermen. The introduced carp figures in the inland commercial fisheries of the Mississippi Valley and Great Lakes regions. Although its flesh is edible, it is not sought after by many people, and the market demand is not great.

NORTH AMERICAN FRESHWATER CATFISH FAMILY— ICTALURIDAE (= AMEIURIDAE)

The freshwater catfish family of North America is entirely made up of scaleless fishes, with a stout spine at the beginning of the dorsal fin and at the beginning of each pectoral fin. In addition, some members of this group have prominent whisker-like barbels which give them their cat-like appearance. As the name suggests, this family is restricted to North America, ranging in fresh waters from Canada to Guatemala. There are fewer than fifty species in the family, some of them blind cave-dwellers. Most catfishes of inland waters belong to one of two groups. One category is made up of the large cats and the bullheads, which are edible and provide food for man; the other includes the little madtoms which have poison glands at the bases of their pectoral fin spines that can inflict a very painful wound. With the exception of a very few species (such as the channel catfish), the members of this family generally inhabit quiet or slow-moving waters. All are spring spawners and more or less omnivorous feeders. Some kinds, such as the flathead catfish, get as large as 100 pounds in weight.

All of the larger species are esteemed as human food. Bullheads and catfishes afford considerable angling pleasure in the central and eastern part of the continent.

Channel Catfish

The channel cat is a spring spawner, typically choosing the rapid waters of streams as a breeding site. The spring spawning season is accompanied by upstream movements, as attested by the large numbers which are caught at this time below dams and other obstructions. The young are presumed to hatch in about a week, and by the end of their first summer's growth may be 2 to 4 inches long. Although small channel cats are quite blond in their coloration, the adults are dark. The species is perhaps the most active of all in the family, particularly so during daylight hours.

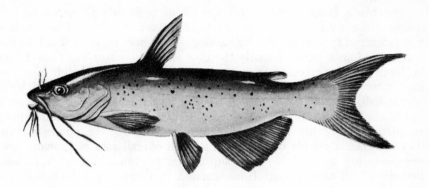

Channel catfish

Channel cats have been successfully reared in hatchery ponds using nail kegs for nests, although studies currently in progress in Oklahoma seek to improve older methods of artificial propagation. The species has been stocked in many streams, within its native range as well as elsewhere, including waters of the Pacific Coast states and Europe.

Blue Catfish

The blue catfish, like the channel cat, is a spring spawner, although details of its habits and growth are relatively unknown. It is said to be the most migratory member of this family, making long seasonal movements, upstream in spring and downstream in fall. The center of its abundance is the Mississippi Valley. It grows to large sizes and is a favorite sport catfish.

Blue catfish

Bullheads

The **black, brown, and yellow** species of bullheads all spawn in late spring and early summer. The nest is sometimes constructed in a naturally protected spot, such as a hollow log, but it may be tunnelled into the bottom or into a bank. Usually the nest site is in water less than 4 feet in depth and is protected from strong currents. The fry hatch in a few days after the eggs are laid and are convoyed about as a school by a parent fish. Such aggregations of tiny black catfishes may often be seen in the shallows or among the weeds, milling and swarming about their guardian. Before the first summer has passed, they are on their own; they are then a couple of inches long, with overall rate of growth varying according to available food supply, temperature, and other factors. Perhaps of all of the sport fishes treated in these pages, bullheads are most tolerant of adverse environmental conditions. They are sometimes

Brown bullhead

found in waters from which all other kinds of fishes have vanished. Bullheads feed extensively by taste and are quite nocturnal in their activities.

Bullhead fishermen have best luck after dark, with baits that readily impart flavors and/or odors to the water. The species are not harvested very vigorously, and in some waters tend to overpopulate and call for measures of control. Overpopulation leads to stunting and loss of angler interest in the myriads of runty individuals which may result.

FRESHWATER EEL FAMILY—ANGUILLIDAE

Members of this, the true eel family, can readily be told from all other American freshwater fishes (except the lampreys) by their snake-like shape and movements. From the lampreys, they are set apart by their true jaws, which contrast with the sucking disc of the lamprey mouth. Interestingly, although not easily seen and often ignored, eels have scales imbedded in the skin. Throughout the world in this family, there are about a dozen species, but only one of them occurs in American fresh waters. The American eel is chiefly found shorewise along the Atlantic and Gulf coasts of North America, and in tributary waters which it ascends for growth and maturation. In the Great Lakes, it is native only to Lake Ontario, like the sea lamprey; it was introduced once years ago into the upper lakes, to which it nearly ascends by natural means via the Mississippi River. Spawning takes place in the vicinity of the Sargasso Sea and after hatching the transparent, ribbon-shaped young (called leptocephalus larvae) move in the direction of the North American continent. As they approach the coast and mouths of streams they metamorphose into pencil-shaped elvers, and many ascend the streams to grow to sexual maturity. Sizes attained at time of the seaward spawning migration may be as much as 6 feet, but the majority achieve less than half this length. Males are much smaller than females, and both die after they reproduce. Eels are reported to be the most voracious of all carnivorous fishes and are principally nocturnal feeders.

The pleasant white flesh of the American eel is highly esteemed, whether fresh or smoked or otherwise cured. Eels are sought by anglers in the streams in which they grow, and are taken in large numbers in weirs during their downstream migration in certain waters such as the Susquehanna River.

KILLIFISH FAMILY—CYPRINODONTIDAE

The killifish ("topminnow") family is composed of small soft-rayed fishes, characterized by a head that is flattened on top toward the snout and a mouth opening along the upper front edge of the head. These features are adaptations to the feeding habit of the group, which characteristically seeks its food at the surface of the water. Killifishes occur in temperate and tropical parts of North America and South America, and in other continents. There are many species in both fresh to salt waters. All are egg-layers and common inhabitants of shoal waters. They have some value as forage fish and as live bait for anglers, but are not food or sport fishes.

LIVEBEARER FAMILY—POECILIIDAE

All poeciliids are small fishes, looking much like killifishes but bearing their young alive. The well-known guppy of aquarists is an example. The family is exclusively American, ranging from the upper Mississippi Valley to Argentina. Fertilization is internal. The gravid females are easily recognized by the young which they contain, and adult males by the conspicuously elongated anal fin which is used as an intromittent organ for guiding spermatozoa into the female. An economcially outstanding member of this family is the "mosquitofish," *Gambusia*. This fish has been widely used in North America and elsewhere for controlling the mosquito larvae or wrigglers which suspend themselves from the surface film of the water and are ready prey for properly adapted predators. Poeciliids are of value in the control of malaria.

COD FAMILY—GADIDAE

This family is primarily marine. The New England cod is its out-standing example. In inland waters of eastern and northern North America (and northern Eurasia), the burbot ranges as a freshwater representative of the family. In Quebec, there are landlocked populations of the tomcod. The burbot is easily told from other fishes of the inland waters of the American continent by the single prominent barbel on the underside of the chin, near its tip.

The burbot is a fish of northern waters, living in large deep inland lakes and also in cooler streams both sluggish and rapid. In the Great Lakes, it is taken up to the great depth of seven hundred feet where it lives with some of the deepwater ciscoes of the whitefish family. The burbot is a winter spawner with an average size of about 20 inches and average weight of about 1 pound. It enters the commercial catch in a small way in the Great Lakes and upper Missouri River basins, but has relatively little market value. Interestingly, it is spurned as food in the Great Lakes region, but quite highly esteemed along the upper Missouri.

TROUTPERCH FAMILY—PERCOPSIDAE

Troutperches, as the name implies, combine some of the gross characters ordinarily associated with trout and some characters of the perch-like fishes. They are spotted, like a small trout, and have an adipose dorsal fin. But, like a perch, they have ctenoid scales and spined fins. Troutperches are spring spawners found in the shoal waters of the Great Lakes and in a few of the larger inland lakes and streams in northern North America. There are only two species in the family, one in the Great Lakes region and the East, the other in the Columbia River system. These are obviously remnants of a group that is now largely extinct. The place of these small species (usually less than 6 inches long) in the economy of waters is not fully known, but they appear to be of some value as forage fish for predacious food and game species.

PIRATEPERCH FAMILY—APHREDODERIDAE

The pirateperch is marked by the location of the anus in the throat region rather than farther back in the position usual in a fish. Sizes run most often less than 5 inches. There is today only one living species in the family which ranges from Minnesota to southern Lake Ontario tributaries and on southward, west of the Appalachian Mountains, to the Gulf Coast as far as Texas. The pirateperch is nowhere abundant, and occurs in certain warmwater creeks, rivers, and lakes. It is distinctly a lowland, spring-spawning form and appears to have no importance for recreational or commercial fisheries.

SILVERSIDE FAMILY—ATHERINIDAE

Silversides are mostly marine fishes, but there are a few freshwater species in North America. All are stream-lined and in life very transparent, with a tiny, spinous first dorsal fin which escapes notice unless carefully sought. Scales are very thin and fall off readily. The species, including the brook silverside, are surface swimmers in lakes and quieter parts of large streams. They often skip into the air for a short distance, and their common colloquial name derived from this habit is "skipjack." Breeding takes place in the spring in open waters. Growth is rapid but the life span is short. Young quickly attain the adult size of a few inches, and spawn at ages of one or two years depending on the species.

The American freshwater atherines are not sport or commercial fishes, but are eaten by predacious fishes including game kinds. They can be used as bait minnows, but are very tender and do not survive well in a live-pail.

BASS FAMILY—SERRANIDAE

Two of the three representatives of this, the true bass family, in the inland waters of North America, are distinguished by prominent horizontal dark lines on the upper parts of their sides; the third is a silvery, perch-like fish. Most members of the family are tropical and subtropical marine fishes. In inland waters only the white, and the yellow basses, and the white perch represent the group. The general habitat of these three species is deep, quiet water over sand and gravel bottoms in medium or large lakes and in large, deep rivers. The species are notably gregarious, often schooling at or near the surface, and thus are easily seen and pursued by anglers.

White Bass

The white bass is a spring spawner utilizing the open shores of lakes or streams. The eggs and milt are scattered simultaneously in shoal water and then deserted by the parents. The eggs are small and reportedly run 1½ million per quart. Hatching requires only about two days at a water temperature of approximately 60° F. In Lake Erie, the growth averages about as follows at successive birthdays: first, 6 inches (1

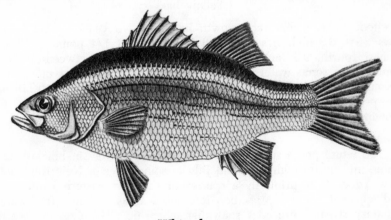

White bass

ounce); second, 8 to 9 inches (1/4 pound); third, 10 to 11 inches (1/2 pound); fourth, 12 to 13 inches (3/4 pound); and fifth, 13 to 14 inches (1 pound). Growth in southern impoundments and in large warm rivers may be more rapid.

The white bass enters the commercial catch in the Great Lakes, particularly in Lake Erie, and in some of the larger waters of the upper Mississippi basin. It ranges in interior waters from the Great Lakes region south to the Gulf, and is doing particularly well in building up populations in some of the growing number of large impoundments. In the sport fisheries it is not uncommon for an angler to catch double and triple headers, using live minnows as bait.

Yellow Bass

The yellow bass spawns in the spring. It is a smaller fish than the white bass. Its range is quite similar to that of the white bass in interior waters, with a concentration in the upper waters of the Mississippi Basin. In

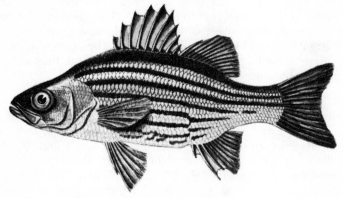

Yellow bass

Reelfoot Lake, Tennessee, growth in successive years averages as follows: first, 3.9 inches; second, 7.8 inches (about 1/4 pound); third, 8.8. inches; fourth, 9.9 inches; and fifth, 11.6 inches (between 3/4 and 1 pound). In some waters, the yellow bass can become a nuisance fish because of its proclivity to overpopulate and stunt and thus to fall under the protection of laws written primarily to protect the larger, faster growing white bass which occurs in many of the same waters.

White Perch

The white perch spawns mostly in April and May in brackish or salt water, and on through June and July in some lakes of New England and New York. It is primarily a species of the northeastern United States and adjacent waters. Migration into shoal areas and into freshwater or tributary streams precedes spawning in spring. The eggs are scattered on the bottom and left without parental care. They hatch in about two

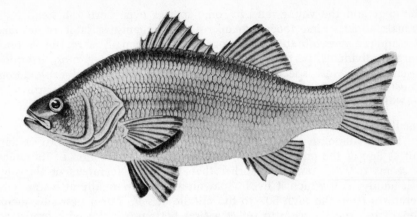

White perch

days with water temperatures approximately 60° F. Average lengths of white perch in Maine lakes at the end of each year of life are about as follows: first year, 3 inches; second, 4 inches; third, 5 inches; fourth, 6 inches; fifth, 6½ inches; sixth, 7 inches; seventh, 7½ inches; and eighth, 8 inches. An 8-inch white perch weighs on the average close to 1/2 pound. Specimens in the seventeenth summer of life in some eastern lakes average little more than 10 inches in length and less than 1 pound in weight. In other lakes, this length and a weight of 1 pound and more are attained during the sixth and seventh summers.

The white perch is an important recreational species in many of the inland lakes and reservoirs in its range in New England and New York. Often large strings are taken with relative ease by sport fishermen.

SUNFISH FAMILY–CENTRARCHIDAE

The sunfish family, like the perch family, is a group of spiny-rayed fishes. It may be distinguished from most other spiny-rayed freshwater fish families by the fact that the spinous and soft-rayed parts of the dorsal fin elements are united into a single fin rather than separated into two distinct fins. Included in the sunfish family are the following kinds of exclusively North American freshwater fishes: largemouth, smallmouth, spotted, and redeye basses (the common black basses of anglers); the true sunfishes; crappies and round sunfish and rock bass, warmouth, and Sacramento perch. The number of recognized species approximates twenty-five in the endemic North American distribution of the group. Throughout its natural range, and through the extension of this range by widespread introduction in continental North America as well as elsewhere, members of this family inhabit very many kinds of waters both flowing and standing.

Centrarchids are spring spawners and utilize for their nests shallow depressions of varying depths, excavated by the males. The males guard the eggs and the young, and in some species even herd the small individuals about. First foods are microscopic organisms; later come various aquatic invertebrates, fish, frogs, and occasionally a reptile or bird. Large individuals, particularly of the bass and crappie groups, are quite piscivorous. Most species are protected from commercial exploitation. Together they are the chief components of North American warmwater sport fisheries.

Smallmouth Bass

The smallmouth bass spawns early in the spring in southern waters, but as late as the end of June in Ontario, the northern limit of its range. It seems to nest somewhat earlier than the other members of the sunfish family with which it lives. Spawning occurs normally at water temperatures from the high 50's to the middle 60's F. For a nest site, members of the species seem to select a firm bottom, usually with gravel, in shallow water, in contrast to the largemouth bass which is more tolerant of soft-bottomed nest sites. More often than not, the location of the nest is adjacent to a protecting bank or other object of shelter. The male, of course, prepares the excavation and may spend from half a day to more than two days in the process. A temperature drop below the 60's F. during this work may cause him to desert his job. If he deserts for temperature-drop reasons while guarding the eggs, all of them may be destroyed. The completed nest of a smallmouth is usually a saucer-shaped depression, a few inches deep and 2 or 3 feet in diameter. Such nests are very conspicuous—most fishery workers and anglers have seen them. The male brings one or more females to the completed nest for spawning and may bring off more than one batch of eggs in a season. The eggs stick to the clean stones or other material in the bottom of the nest.

The eggs of the smallmouth bass hatch a few days after being laid. The hatchlings only remotely resemble their parents. Their eyes, fins,

Smallmouth bass

and other characteristics are feebly developed, and they are pot-bellied because of the yolk sac in the abdomen. At hatching, the sac fry cannot swim, but can only wriggle into the crevices of the materials in the bottom of the nest. Here they grow on their yolk for a few days, but soon begin feeding upon tiny organisms. After begining to feed, and with the disappearance of the yolk, they rise from the nest and swim away, convoyed by the male, in the pursuit of larger food items.

As they near the end of their first summer of life, young smallmouths are normally of good fingerling size, ranging from 2 to 5 inches, depending on water temperature, food, and other factors. Only a small percentage of the original number of the young which hatched survive to become fingerlings; as with fish in general, most die very early in life. One of the tasks of fishery managers is to increase this survival rate, where desirable, to produce better fishing.

The smallmouth bass in northern waters usually approximates the following sizes in successive years of life: 1 year old, 3½ to 4 inches; 2 years, 5½ to 6½ inches; 3 years, 8 to 9 inches; 4 years, 10 to 11 inches; 5 years, 12½ to 13½ inches; 6 years, 13½ to 14 inches; 7 years, 15 to 16 inches. The species does not ordinarily attain sexual maturity until the fourth birthday. A 10-inch smallmouth averages about 1/2 pound in weight, and a 1-pound specimen is usually about 13 inches long.

This bass has for a long time been successfully pond-cultured in North America. As a result, it has been stocked widely in this country and abroad. The species ranges a little farther north than the largemouth and, in clear and cool streams, as far south. From the point of view of anglers, it is an often sought and most vigorous game fish. The flesh is highly edible.

Spotted Bass

The seasonal spawning habits of the spotted bass by and large resemble those of the smallmouth. However, since the spotted species can

Spotted bass

survive adverse conditions, and since it is reputedly very prolific, it shows promise of being worthy of transplantation into fitting species-aggregations. Hatching time of spotted bass is reported to be about half that of the smallmouth. This factor may be exceedingly important in favoring survival in areas where cold snaps lead to egg or fry losses of the other bass species. The spotted bass is southern in its distribution, ranging from the upper Mississippi Valley south to the Gulf states. It is a fine sport fish.

Largemouth Bass

The largemouth is a spring and early summer spawner. The male selects the nest site, and with its tail sweeps away the silt and debris from a more or less circular area of the bottom. The depth of the water over the nest may be from one to a few feet. When the nest is ready,

Largemouth bass

one or more females are spawned in it by the attendant male. A nest may hold from 1,000 to more than 11,000 eggs, the average being between 4,000 and 5,000. Adult females may yield more than twenty thousand eggs in a spawning season. Obviously, it does not take many successful nests to populate an average body of water. As previously indicated, the male remains on guard over the eggs, driving away marauding insects and other fishes and also periodically fanning the eggs, apparently to keep them silt free and aerated. The eggs hatch in two or more days, depending on the water temperature. For a while, the young fish are very clumsy and cannot leave the nest as sac fry, because they are more or less anchored there by the heavy yolk. While they remain, the male continues to guard them. As the yolk is absorbed, the young begin to feed, and soon rise from the bottom and leave the nest.

Growth of the largemouth bass under ordinary conditions is not very rapid. Lengths attained, on a rough average in successive years of life, are approximately as follows: first year, 3 to 4 inches; second year, 5 to

7 inches; third year, 8 to 9 inches. Sometimes a length of a little more than a foot is attained by the fifth birthday. If food is abundant and space is adequate, however, the foregoing growth rate may be very nearly doubled; on the average it is more rapid in the South than in the North. Twenty-inch bass in Louisiana are reported to be only 5 years old but in northern states they may be 12 or more years of age. Ten-inch individuals average about 1/2 pound in weight, whereas a 13-inch specimen may weigh as much as 4 pounds.

In management, the largemouth bass was until recently protected extensively by law, and was artificially propagated and planted in many waters of the United States. By the middle of the twentieth century, however, general stocking had been abandoned, and in many parts of this country the formerly rather stringent season, size, and bag limits had been removed. The largemouth bass is perhaps the most popular and widely pursued North American freshwater game fish. Obviously, this is due in part to its wide distribution which extends from southern Canada to the Gulf and, by introduction, to warm waters of the Pacific slope. The largemouth bass is an exciting fish to catch on light tackle, and is very edible when taken from any but extremely stagnant waters.

Bluegill

Of all of the North American sunfishes, the bluegill is perhaps the most important one as a panfish. It is a spring spawner, with the male scooping out a typical saucer-shaped depression in the bottom in shallow water. Most nests are from 1 to 2 feet in diameter and about 6 inches in depth. Whereas the nests of other members of the sunfish family are often well separated or isolated, those of the bluegill are usually grouped in tenement-like colonies. The male spawns the females in his nest, guards the nest and eggs, and may bring off more than one

Bluegill

brood of young in one nesting season. Sexual maturity in this species may be attained in a single year if feeding conditions are good.

Lengths of the bluegill in northern waters in successive years of life are approximately as follows: first, 1¾ inches; second, 3 inches; third, 4¼ inches; fourth, 5½ inches; fifth, 6¾ inches; seventh, 7¾ inches; tenth, 8½ inches. In small, properly managed ponds, as exist in the South, this rate of growth can be more than doubled. A typical bluegill between 4 and 5 inches long weighs about an ounce, whereas 9-inch ones average about 1/2 pound.

Interestingly, bluegills as small as 2 inches in length that are stunted from overcrowding, may breed successfully. More than 60,000 eggs have been counted from a single nest, presumably the eggs of several females. The reproductive capacity of this species has often led to overcrowding and consequent poor growth. Bluegills, as other sunfishes, will sometimes mate with individuals not of their own species, particularly when there is competition for nest sites. The resulting hybrids are mostly males, grow more rapidly than both parent species, and are fertile.

For many years, the bluegill was reared in great numbers in hatcheries. The young were planted widely throughout the native range of the species, and also introduced into faraway waters where they were not native. By the middle of the twentieth century stocking for maintenance was being abandoned and season, size and bag limits were being removed, as more and more was learned about the remarkable reproductive potential of this fish and about its hazards of overpopulating and stunting.

Rock Bass

The rock bass is a prolific and environmentally tolerant species. It spawns from early spring to summer, depending upon the latitude. As in other centrarchids, the male prepares the nest in the shallows, but he

Rock bass

does this on almost any bottom type. A site containing plant roots or other large pieces of debris is not rejected. Nests usually lack the size and symmetry of those made by other members of the family. Sometimes they are so poorly constructed that they are difficult to locate. After spawning the female, the male faithfully guards the eggs until they hatch.

In northern states, the young average between 1½ and 2 inches in length at the end of their first year of life, at 3 years between 4 and 5 inches, at 5 years between 5 and 6 inches, and at 10 years between 10 and 11 inches. A 7-inch fish averages approximately 1/4 pound in weight, a 9-inch fish averages 1/2 pound, and the rare 11-inch specimen may go 1 pound.

Like other sunfishes, the rock bass tends to overpopulate and become stunted unless it is harvested in substantial numbers by fishermen or natural predators. Stunted individuals are not attractive to anglers. Unlike bluegills and basses, the rock bass has never been artificially propagated to any extent, nor stocked in great numbers.

Crappies

Two kinds of crappies, the black and the white, have almost identical ranges in the central part of North America, straggling elsewhere. The black crappie spawns in late spring, and in the northern part of its range sometimes on through the early part of the summer. The male selects the nest site, then guards it and the eggs which he causes to be deposited there. By the end of the first summer, the young are between 2½ and 3 inches long. The length is doubled during the second summer and at 3 years of age the fish are often from 6 to 8 inches long, at 4 years between 8 and 10 inches, and by 7 years, possibly 12 inches. In southern very fertile waters, such as those of new impoundments,

Black crappie

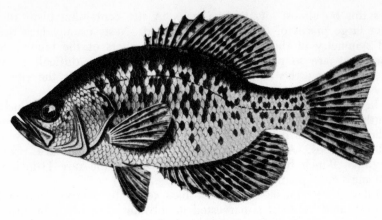

White crappie

lengths of 1 foot may be attained in 5 years. A 9-inch black crappie may weigh 1/2 pound, a 12-inch one, 1 pound.

A favorite of many anglers, the black crappie typically moves into shallow waters to feed at night in the warmer months. As autumn comes on, it retires to deeper water, and when the ice cover forms on northern lakes it returns once more to the shallows to feed. These habits are generally known by anglers and the responsiveness of the black crappie to small minnows as bait makes it rather easy to catch. It is good to eat.

In general, the habits and growth characteristics of the white crappie closely resemble those of the black species. The two kinds often live together, and in this situation hybrids sometimes result, as in the western end of Lake Erie. When the two species do live together, one is usually dominant over the other, with the white said to have a better chance to dominate in the South, the black in the North.

PERCH FAMILY—PERCIDAE

The perch family is a spiny-rayed group of fishes which has two distinct dorsal fins, along with only one or two spines in the anal fin. Scales of all of the contained species are moderately to strongly ctenoid. The group is typified rather well by the yellow perch. There are, however, three subgroups in the family: (1) the yellow perch; (2) the walleyes and saugers; and (3) the small, colorful darters. Members of the first two groups are inhabitants of large lakes in central and eastern North America as well as in large streams. Most of the darters are stream dwellers, but a few, such as the Iowa darter, are mostly lake or pond species. Both the perch and the walleye groups, with fewer than a dozen species between them, occur in Europe as well as in North America. The darters, however, are exclusively North American and comprise several dozen species.

All members of this family are spring spawners and exhibit a great diversity of nesting habits. The perch lays a zig-zag "rope" of eggs in moderately shallow water. The walleye scatters its eggs on the bottom in shoal areas. Some of the darters leave their eggs ungarded, scattered on the bottom (Iowa darter, logperch); others bury them in fine gravel on riffles and desert them, much like trout (rainbow darter); still others have males that make nests beneath flat stones or other objects on the bottom and guard them until they hatch (Johnny darter, fantail darter).

Yellow Perch

The yellow perch, as indicated above, spawns in the spring and moves into the shoal water of its breeding grounds in March through May, depending on the latitude. Breeding takes place when the water temperature approximates 50° F., with the eggs being fertilized by males while they are being laid by the female in a zig-zag gelatinous rope. Usually these egg masses are to be found where the bottom is clean in

Yellow perch

the shallows and often in the quiet protection of stands of bulrushes. In a week or so the young hatch and soon begin feeding on tiny water organisms. Rate of growth differs considerably according to environment and population density. Average lengths in successive years of life for Great Lakes' perch are: first year, 2½ to 3½ inches; second year, 4½ to 6½ inches; third year, 6 to 8 inches; fourth, 7 to 9½ inches; fifth 8 to 10½ inches; and sixth, 10 to 12 inches. Sometimes when a perch population is overcrowded, growth may be less than half these figures. In inland waters average perch of about 11 inches in length will weigh ½ pound, whereas between 13 and 14 inches, 1 pound may be attained. Normal life expectancy appears to be between 6 and 8 years, although individuals as old as 12 years have been recorded.

The yellow perch is important in the commercial as well as the recreational fisheries at various points within its range. This is particularly true for the Great Lakes and surrounding waters. In earlier years some pond culture was carried on, and there was stocking of perch as a conservation measure. In the early 1900's, the species was introduced in the many western and midwestern states where it was not native. Reproductive potential is high, and once the perch is established subsequent stocking is usually not needed, although its introduction, as the introduction of any exotic species, must be approached with caution.

Yellow walleye

The yellow walleye, like the yellow perch, is a spring spawner in both lakes and large rivers. In rivers, impressive upstream migrations and in lakes, shoreward movements, accompany the advent of the breeding season. In Lake Erie, males mature at 4 years of age and females at 5. At spawning, the female dashes along the shore rolling and twisting while strewing the eggs at random, the male following in her wake, scattering milt. The eggs are deposited in shallow waters, typically on clean, hard, often rock bottoms. They are small, about 1/20 inch in diameter, numerous, and have been reported to average between 50,000 and 60,000 per female. They hatch in about three weeks when the water temperature ranges around 50° F. Within ten days, the yolk sac is absorbed and the fry begin feeding on tiny aquatic organisms. Soon, more predacious feeding commences and sometimes small fish are eaten, including, on occasion, other little walleyes.

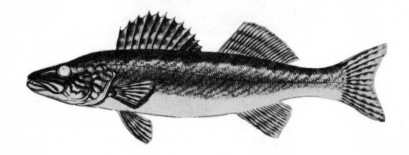

Yellow walleye

Growth is variable, depending on such factors as available food and length of growing season. In northern inland lakes of Minnesota, lengths at various ages have been averaged as follows: first year, 4.6 inches; second, 8.6 inches; third, 12.0 inches; fourth, 15.0 inches; fifth, 18.1 inches; eighth, 25.2 inches. In certain large impoundments such as in Norris Lake, Tennessee, growth is more rapid.

The walleye is important in both commercial and recreational fisheries of inland waters of the northern United States and Canada. It has been extensively propagated and stocked by federal, provincial, and state hatcheries, in an effort to bolster sagging catches, as in the Great Lakes. This species has been stocked mostly as fry, because individuals are so very cannibalistic that large numbers can be kept in rearing enclosures for only a short period of time after hatching. In some central states, walleyes are now successfully propagated to larger sizes, using natural inland ponds as rearing waters. Stocking of large young and yearlings is held to be successful both from the point of view of introduction and maintenance. There is no evidence that stocking of tiny young walleyes in large numbers—such as was done in the Great Lakes for many years—has very beneficially affected subsequent catches of the species.

DRUM FAMILY—SCIAENIDAE

The drums are distinguishable from all other bass-like spiny-rayed fishes by the fact that the lateral line extends all the way across the tail fin. They make a characteristic purring, drumming sound. Drums, with few exceptions, are marine fishes. In the freshwaters of North America, only one species represents this otherwise tropical and temparate saltwater group. This inland species is the freshwater drum, which ranges from the Hudson Bay drainage of Manitoba and east central Ontario, the Great Lakes, and Quebec, southward through the Mississippi lowlands from Montana and Nebraska to the Gulf states and eastern Mexico and on into Guatemala. The principal habitats are large rivers and lakes, often in silty waters.

Like most other warmwater food and game fishes, the freshwater drum is a spring spawner. It is generally from April through June that males and females move into the shallows to scatter their eggs and milt over gravelly and sandy bottoms. The eggs are very numerous. They sink and stick to the substrate. They are deserted by the parents. By the end of the first summer the young are of fingerling size. Both young and adults are often found in sizable schools.

Rate of growth and relation of weight to length are variable according to different waters. Rough averages estimated by combining growth records for Lake Erie with those for smaller bodies of water are about as follows at successive birthdays: first, 4.5 inches; second, 8 to 10 inches (1/4 to 1/2 pound); third, 10 to 12 inches (1/2 to 1 pound); fourth, 12 to 15 inches; fifth, 13 to 16 inches. Specimens as old as 17 years have been recorded in Lake Erie with a weight of nearly 8 pounds and lengths of slightly over 27 inches. In Reelfoot Lake, Tennessee, fish of only 11 or 12 years have been recorded to measure 27 inches and weigh 11½ pounds.

The earstones of the freshwater drum are said to be the original "lucky stones." There is one on each side of the head, deep in the bone work of the skull. They were fancied by Indians as well as successive generations of American youths. This drum is edible but not highly re-

garded as food. Large sizes are reported and in early years weights
approaching 100 pounds were attained. Pharyngeal (throat) bones bearing molar teeth, found in camp sites of early Indians, indicate that in
primordial times sizes of about 200 pounds were reached. The species
has only little recreational value. Most of the commercial take is from
Lake Erie and the Mississippi Basin's big waters. The species constitutes a resource which is managed essentially only by encouraging its
use (as is true for coarse fishes in general).

SEAPERCH FAMILY—EMBIOTOCIDAE

The seaperch family dwells largely in the bays and surf of the Pacific
Coast of North America. Only one species, the freshwater viviparous
perch of California, departs from the marine habitat.

CICHLID FAMILY—CICHLIDAE

The cichlids are a numerous family of freshwater fishes resembling
the North American centrarchilds in form, size, appearance, habits and
ecology. About 150 species inhabit the waters of Africa and tropical
America and many are of importance as human food. Of the sixty some
species of Middle America, only one, the Rio Grande perch occurs in
the United States, and that alone, in Texas.

SCULPIN FAMILY—COTTIDAE

Cottids of inland freshwaters are characterized by their enlarged, flattened heads and their expansive pectoral fins. Scales are lacking in most
species, though in a few they are represented by little dermal prickles
commonly found only behind the pectoral fin bases. The family is essentially a marine one. Only one large genus, *Cottus*, is importantly
freshwater. Freshwater sculpins are bottom dwellers. Various species
are found in streams and large inland lakes, both about the shores and
at considerable depths. In most of their habitats, the principal situations
selected are those with rocky bottoms, under the stones of which the
sculpins commonly conceal themselves during the daytime. In species
of *Cottus*, egg clusters are as a rule attached in the spring to the under-
sides of stones adjacent to flowing water. The male drives the female
into the nest and then guards the eggs. Stomach contents include algae,
aquatic insects and their larvae, sometimes fish, and rarely fish eggs.
Sculpins are not sought as sport fish but are sometimes used by anglers
as bait.

STICKLEBACK FAMILY—GASTEROSTEIDAE

The sticklebacks are spiny-rayed fishes of North American marine
and fresh waters. Essentially, they are northern species that occur cir-
cumpolar-wise. The few species of inland fresh waters, like their marine
relatives, are distinguished by the separated spines of the dorsal fin,

each of which possesses a tiny membrane behind it making of it a finlet. Typically, sticklebacks are inhabitants of quiet waters of streams and boggy situations. In the spring, the brook stickleback constructs an elaborate nest somewhat resembling that of an oriole. Fewer than a hundred eggs are usually placed in such a nest and are diligently guarded by the male. Sticklebacks appear to have little direct economic significance.

STUDY PROGRAM

Learn the names and natural grouping of the families of freshwater fishes of North America, north of Mexico. Examine specimens and/or illustrations to gain or review impressions of the species included in each family. Then, for desired species in the Appendix F checklist, add regional colloquial names, work out the general range and local distribution, and emend the natural history accounts and the broad economic classification given in Appendix F, to show greater detail for species which occur in your region. Add and complete similar information for any kind of fish of particular importance in your area which is not on the list. Obtain help from references such as those listed and from individuals qualified to be of assistance to you.

REFERENCES

Berg, L. S. 1940. Classification of fishes, both recent and fossil. Trav. Inst. Zool. Acad. Sci. U.R.S.S. Tome 5, Livr. 2: 87-517.

Curtis, Brian. 1949. The life story of the fish his morals and manners. New York, Harcourt, Brace and Company, xii, 284 p., 34 figs., other illus.

Jordan, David Starr, and Barton Warren Evermann. 1902. American food and game fishes . . . New York, Doubleday, Page and Co., 1, 573 p., illus.

Jordan, D. S. 1923. A classification of fishes. Stanford Univ. Pubs., Biol. Sci., 3 (2): 77-243.

Chapter III

Identification of Fishes and Other Aquatic Organisms

Proper identification of fishes is of great importance to management, but it is often difficult to attain. Many fishes, such as the minnows, are not easy to identify even with the aid of carefully prepared keys. Other fishes hybridize freely and the hybrids are not treated in most keys; the sunfishes are notorious in this regard. It behooves the worker in fishery biology, then, to have at least elementary training in ichthyology and to be acquainted with the means for obtaining correct technical designations for his animals.

For identification of fishes there are several useful publications which together more or less cover the United States and Canada. The student will soon recognize, however, that the faunas of certain regions, for example the south-central and south-western parts of the United States, are less well known than others. At least in the early stages of his work, an investigator should have his attempts at classification verified by someone qualified to do so. Sometimes he will take his specimens to museums and compare them with materials previously classified by experts. At other times he will send series to such centers for identification — always with the understanding that only duplicates will be returned to him and that rare materials may be retained by the museum consulted. For eastern and southwestern North America, the Museum of Zoology of the University of Michigan is best able to provide this service. The U. S. National Museum, Washington, D. C., and the Royal Ontario Museum, Toronto, will also be helpful. In western North America, collections at the Natural History Museum of Stanford and the California Academy of Sciences will be useful. Besides these agencies there are certain individual specialists who are willing to cooperate. The same use may be made of cooperative specialists for the identification of other aquatic organisms. The American Society of Limnology and Oceanography periodically publishes a list of such workers in its Special Publication series which will serve as a directory to this service.

Needless to say, scientific work requires the finest identifications. Only by correct procedure in this regard may costly blunders be avoided, confusion in the literature of investigational reports held to a minimum, and your personal reputation maintained. No study in which organisms are mentioned by name attains its maximum value, be it a food study, a bottom fauna analysis, etc., unless all forms are accorded their fullest possible identity.

There follows a geographically analyzed list of certain publications which are useful for identifying American fishes occurring north of Mexico. I have arranged these studies by political areas for ease in finding. Under each state, territory or province are listed authors and dates of the pertinent papers; the full citation is given in the References. Rather than to assign extra-limital values to the many publications included, each is given only under the area of its primary significance. This means that the user should consult the articles listed for surrounding regions as well as those for the zone of his primary interest. Works of continental coverage such as Jordan and Evermann (1896-1900), Jordan, Evermann, and Clark (1930), Schrenkeisen (1938), etc., are included in the References but are not analyzed geographically.

REGIONAL ANALYSIS OF CERTAIN PUBLICATIONS USEFUL IN
THE IDENTIFICATION OF FISHES FOUND IN THE
FRESH WATERS OF NORTH AMERICA

Region	Principal Reference(s) for Fish Identification
Alabama	Bailey, Winn and Smith, 1954; Breder, 1948; Fowler, 1945
Alaska	Evermann and Goldsborough, 1907; Rhode and Barker, 1953; Walford, 1937; Wilimovsky, 1954; Wynne-Edwards, 1952
Alberta	Dymond, 1947; Halkett, 1913
Arizona	Dill, 1944; Evermann and Rutter, 1895; Gilbert and Scofield, 1898; Miller, 1946 and 1952; Mulch and Gamble, 1954; Snyder, 1915; Wallis, 1951; Winn and Miller, 1954
Arkansas	Black, 1940; Hubbs and Ortenburger, 1929b; Moore and Paden, 1950
British Columbia	Carl and Clemens, 1948 and 1953; Clemens and Wilby, 1946; Dymond, 1947; Halkett, 1913
California	Miller, 1946 and 1952; Murphy, 1941; Roedel, 1948; Rutter, 1908; Schultz, 1936; Shapovalov, 1947; Shapovalov and Dill, 1950; Snyder, 1917; Walford, 1931 and 1937
Colorado	Beckman, 1952; Ellis, 1914; Miller, 1946
Connecticut	Bigelow, et al., 1948; Breder, 1948; Webster, 1942
Delaware	Breder, 1948; Harmic, 1952
Florida	Bailey, Winn and Smith, 1954; Breder, 1948; Carr, 1937; Carr and Goin, 1955; Evermann and Kendall, 1899; Fowler, 1945
Georgia	Breder, 1948; Fowler, 1935b and 1945

Idaho	Miller, 1946; Schultz, 1936
Illinois	Forbes and Richardson, 1920; Hubbs and Lagler, 1949a; Koelz, 1929
Indiana	Evermann and Clark, 1920; Gerking, 1945 and 1955; Hubbs and Lagler, 1949a; Koelz, 1929
Iowa	Aitken, 1936; Bailey, 1956
Kansas	Breukelman, 1946; Evermann and Cox, 1896
Kentucky	Evermann, 1918; Kuhne, 1939
Labrador	Bigelow, et al., 1948; Breder, 1948; Dymond, 1947; Halkett, 1913; Kendall, 1909; Scott, 1954.
Louisiana	Breder, 1948; Evermann, 1899; Fowler, 1945; Gowanloch, 1933
Maine	Bigelow, et al., 1948; Bigelow and Welsh, 1953; Breder, 1948; Everhart, 1950
Manitoba	Dymond, 1947; Halkett, 1913; Hinks, 1943
Maryland	Breder, 1948; Elser, 1950; Fowler, 1945; Hildebrand and Schroeder, 1928; Truitt, Bean, and Fowler, 1929
Massachusetts	Bigelow, et al., 1948; Breder, 1948; McCabe, 1943 and 1945
Mexico	Alvarez, 1950; Hubbs, 1936 and 1938; Meek, 1904; Regan, 1906-08
Michigan	Hubbs and Lagler, 1949a and b; Koelz, 1929; Lagler, 1949; Taylor, 1954
Minnesota	Eddy and Surber, 1947; Hubbs and Lagler, 1949a; Koelz, 1929
Mississippi	Breder, 1948; Evermann, 1899; Fowler, 1945; Hildebrand and Towers, 1928
Missouri	Evermann and Cox, 1896; Funk et al., 1953
Montana	Evermann, 1892; Evermann and Cox, 1896; Henshall, 1906; Miller, 1946; Schultz, 1936 and 1941
Nebraska	Evermann and Cox, 1896; Johnson, 1942
Nevada	LaRivers, 1952; LaRivers and Trelease, 1952; Miller, 1951 and 1952; Miller and Alcorn, 1946; Schultz, 1936; Snyder, 1917; Wallis, 1951.
New Brunswick	Bigelow, et al., 1948; Breder, 1948; Dymond, 1947; Halkett, 1913; Scott, 1954
Newfoundland	Bigelow, et al., 1948; Breder, 1948; Dymond, 1947; Halkett, 1913; Scott, 1954
New Hampshire	Bailey, 1938; Bigelow, et al., 1948; Breder, 1948; Carpenter and Siegler, 1947
New Jersey	Breder, 1948; Fowler, 1906 and 1907
New Mexico	Evermann and Kendall, 1894; Miller, 1946

New York	Adams and Hankinson, 1928; Bean, 1903; Bigelow, et al., 1948; Breder, 1948; Greeley, et al., 1926-40; Hubbs and Lagler, 1949a; Koelz, 1929
North Carolina	Breder, 1948; Fowler, 1945; Frey, 1951; King, 1947; Smith, 1907
North Dakota	Evermann and Cox, 1896; Hankinson, 1929; Personius and Eddy, 1955
NW Territories	Dymond, 1947; Halkett, 1913; Rawson, 1951; Wynne-Edwards, 1952
Nova Scotia	Bigelow, et al., 1948; Breder, 1948; Dymond, 1947; Halkett, 1913; Livingstone, 1952; Scott, 1954
Ohio	Hubbs and Lagler, 1949a; Trautman, 1946
Oklahoma	Hubbs, 1946; Hubbs and Ortenburger, 1929 a and b; Moore, 1952; Moore and Paden, 1950
Ontario	Dymond, 1947; Halkett, 1913; Hubbs and Lagler, 1949a; Koelz, 1929; Nash, 1908; Radforth, 1944; Scott, 1954
Oregon	Miller, 1946; Schultz, 1936; Schultz and DeLacy, 1935-36; Walford, 1937
Pennsylvania	Fowler, 1919 and 1940; Hubbs and Lagler, 1949a
Quebec	Bigelow, et al., 1948; Breder, 1948; Dymond, 1947; Halkett, 1913; Legendre, 1954; Scott, 1954; Wynne-Edwards, 1952
Rhode Island	Bigelow, et al., 1948; Breder, 1948
Saskatchewan	Clemens, et al., 1947; Dymond, 1947; Halkett, 1913; Rawson, 1949
South Carolina	Breder, 1948; Fowler, 1935 and 1945
South Dakota	Churchill and Over, 1933; Evermann and Cox, 1896
Tennessee	Evermann, 1918; Kuhne, 1939
Texas	Breder, 1948; Burr, 1932; Evermann, 1899; Evermann and Kendall, 1894; Fowler, 1945; Hubbs, Kuehne and Ball, 1953; Jurgens and Hubbs, 1953; Knapp, 1953
Utah	Miller, 1946 and 1949; Tanner, 1936
Vermont	Evermann and Kendall, 1896
Virginia	Breder, 1948; Fowler, 1945; Hildebrand and Schroeder, 1928; Raney, 1950
Washington	Miller, 1946; Schultz, 1936; Schultz and DeLacy, 1935-36; Walford, 1937
West Virginia	Goldsborough and Clark, 1908; van Meter, 1950
Wisconsin	Green, 1935; Hubbs and Lagler, 1949a; Koelz, 1929
Wyoming	Evermann, 1892; Miller, 1946; Simon, 1946; Simon and Simon, 1939

STUDY PROGRAM

Examine as many as you can of the publications on the following list of references and make notes as to their content, date, quality, and the research center at which the work was done. Verify each citation for accuracy. Keep the list alive and growing by adding other papers which come to your attention. Note that it is composed mostly of faunal studies and does not include revisionary ones. The latter are very important for keeping nomenclature up-to-date, but are the particular subject matter of taxonomic ichthyology.

REFERENCES

General (and a few special) references not included in the foregoing geographical analysis are preceded by an asterisk in the following list.

Adams, Charles C., and T. L. Hankinson. 1928. The ecology and economics of Oneida Lake fish. Roosevelt Wild Life Annals, 1 (3-4): 235-548, figs. 175-244, 4 col. pl.

Aitken, Walter W. 1936. Some common Iowa fishes. Iowa State Coll. Extension Circ., 224, 32 p., 27 figs.

Alvarez, J. 1950. Claves para la determinación de especies en los peces de las aguas continentales mexicanas. Secr. Marina, Dir. Gen. Pesca Ind. Conex., 136 pp., 16 figs.

Backus, R. H. 1951. New and rare records of fishes from Labrador. Copeia, 1951 (4): 288-294.

Bailey, Reeve M. 1938. Key to the fresh-water fishes of New Hampshire. [In] The fishes of the Merrimack watershed. Biol. Surv. of the Merrimack watershed. N. H. Fish and Game Dept. Biol. Surv. Rept., 3, pp. 149-185, 12 text-figs.

Bailey, Reeve M. 1956. A revised list of the fishes of Iowa, with keys for identification. [In] Iowa fish and fishing, 3rd Ed., Des Moines, Iowa St. Cons. Comm., pp. 327-377, 10 figs., 25 text-figs.

Bailey, Reeve M., Howard Elliott Winn, and C. Lavett Smith. 1954. Fishes from the Escambia River, Alabama and Florida, with ecologic and taxonomic notes. Proc. Acad. Nat. Sci. Philadelphia, 106: 109-164, 1 fig.

*Barnhart, Percy Spencer. 1936. Marine fishes of Southern California. Univ. California Press, Berkeley, 209 p., 290 figs.

Bean, Tarleton H. 1903. Catalogue of the fishes of New York. N. Y. St. Mus. Bull., 60, 784 p.

Beckman, William C. 1952. Guide to the fishes of Colorado. Univ. Colo. Mus. Leaflet, 11, 110 p., 14 figs., 106 text-figs.

Bigelow, Henry B., et al. 1948. Fishes of the western North Atlantic Part One (Lancelets, Cyclostomes, Sharks). Mem. Sears Foundat. Marine Res., No. 1, xvii, 576 p., 106 figs.

Bigelow, Henry B., and William W. Welsh. 1953. Fishes of the Gulf of Maine. U. S. Fish and Wildlife Service, Fish. Bull. 74, 577 p., 288 figs.

Black, John D. 1940. The distribution of the fishes of Arkansas. Univ. Mich. (Ph. D. Thesis), 243 p., 69 maps.

Breder, C. M., Jr. 1929. Field book of marine fishes of the Atlantic Coast from Labrador to Texas, being a short description of their characteristics and habits with keys for their identification. N. Y. and London, Putnam, xxxvii, 332 p., 7 col. pl., frontis., 403 other illus. (Rev. ed., 1948)

Breukelman, J. 1946. A review of Kansas ichthyology. Trans. Kans. Acad. Sci., 49 (1): 51-70, 1 fig.

Burr, J. G. 1932. Fishes of Texas, handbook of the more important game and commercial types. Bull. Tex. Game, Fish and Oyster Comm., 5: 41 p., 35 figs.

Carl, G. Clifford, and W. A. Clemens. 1948. The fresh-water fishes of British Columbia. B. C. Prov. Mus. Handbook, 5, 132 p., 6 figs., many half-tones, 7 col. pl.

Carpenter, R. G., and H. R. Siegler. 1947. A sportsman's guide to the fresh-water fishes of New Hampshire. N. H. Fish and Game Dept., 87 p., 70 text-figs.

Carr, A. F., Jr. 1937. A key to the fresh-water fishes of Florida. Proc. Fla. Acad. Sci., 1 (1936): 72-86, 1 fig.

Carr, A., and C. J. Goin. 1955. Guide to the reptiles, amphibians and fresh-water fishes of Florida. Gainesville, Univ. Fla. Press, ix, 341 p., 30 figs., 67 pl.

Churchill, Edward P., and William H. Over. 1933. Fishes of South Dakota. S. D. Dept. Game and Fish, 83 p., 71 figs.

Clemens, W. A., A. H. MacDonald, H. A. McAllister, A. Mansfield, and D. S. Rawson. 1947. The fishes of Saskatchewan [In] Rept. Roy. Comm. on the Fisheries of the Prov. of Sask. Regina, Sask., pp. 15-19.

Clemens, W. A., and G. V. Wilby. 1946. Fishes of the Pacific Coast of Canada. Bull. Fish. Res. Bd. Canada, 68, 368 p., 253 figs. (Extensive bibliography)

Dill, William A. 1944. The fishery of the lower Colorado River. Calif. Fish and Game, 30: 109-211, 82 figs.

Dimick, R. E., and Fred Merryfield. 1945. The fishes of the Willamette River system in relation to pollution. Oregon St. Coll. Eng. Exp. Sta. Bull. Ser., 20, 58 p., 20 figs.

*Dymond, J. R. 1922–. [Various papers on the fishes of Ontario]. Publ. Ont. Fish. Res. Lab. Also, Publ. Roy. Ont. Mus. Zool., etc.

Dymond, J. R. 1947. A list of the freshwater fishes of Canada east of the Rocky Mountains with keys. Misc. Publ. Roy. Ont. Mus. Zool., 1, 36 p., Mimeo.

Eddy, Samuel, and Thaddeus Surber. 1943. Northern fishes, with special reference to the upper Mississippi Valley. Univ. Minnesota Press, Minneapolis, xi, 252 p., 57 figs., frontis. (Rev. ed., 1947)

Ellis, Max M. 1914. Fishes of Colorado. Univ. Colo. Studies, 11 (1): 1-136, 63 figs.

Elser, Harold J. 1950. The common fishes of Maryland how to tell them apart. Publ. Maryland Dept. Res. and Educ., 88, 45 p., 71 text-figs.

Everhart, W. Harry. 1950. Fishes of Maine. Me. Dept. Inland Fish and Game, [ii], 53 p., 65 text-figs., 9 col. pl.

Evermann, B. W. 1892. A reconnaissance of the streams and lakes of western Montana and northwestern Wyoming. Bull. U. S. Fish Comm., 11 (1891): 3-60, pls. 1-27.

Evermann, B. W. 1899. Report on investigations by the U. S. Fish Commission in Mississippi, Louisiana, and Texas, in 1897. Rept. U. S. Fish Comm., 1898: 285-310, pls. 8-36.

Evermann, B. W. 1918. The fishes of Kentucky and Tennessee: a distributional catalogue of the known species. Bull. U. S. Bur. Fish., 35 (1915-16): 295-368.

Evermann, B. W., and Howard Walton Clark. 1920. Lake Maxinkuckee, a physical and biological survey. Ind. St. Dept. Cons., v. 1, 660 p., frontis., text-figs., col. pl. (Fishes pp. 238-451)

Evermann, B. W., and Ulysses O. Cox. 1896. A report upon the fishes of the Missouri River basin. Rept. U. S. Fish Comm., 1894: 325-429.

Evermann, B. W., and Edmund Lee Goldsborough. 1907. The fishes of Alaska. Bull. U. S. Bur. Fish., 26 (1906): 219-360, 144 figs., 20 col. pl.

Evermann, B. W., and William C. Kendall. 1894. The fishes of Texas and the Rio Grande basin, considered chiefly with reference to their geographic distribution. Bull. U. S. Fish Comm., 12 (1892): 57-126, pls. 10-50.

Evermann, B. W., and William C. Kendall. 1896. An annotated catalogue of the fishes known from the State of Vermont. Rept. U. S. Fish Comm., 1894: 579-604.

Evermann, B. W., and William C. Kendall. 1900. Check-list of the fishes of Florida. Rept. U. S. Fish Comm., 1899: 37-103.

Evermann, B. W., and Cloud[sley] Rutter. 1895. The fishes of the Colorado basin. Bull. U. S. Bur. Fish., 14 (1894): 473-486.

Forbes, Stephen Alfred, and Robert Earl Richardson. 1908. The fishes of Illinois. Ill. Nat. Hist. Surv., 3, cxxxi, 357 p., many figs. and col. pls. Atlas, 103 maps. (Rev. ed., 1920)

Fowler, Henry W. 1906. The fishes of New Jersey. Ann. Rept. N. J. St. Mus., 1905, 2, pp. 35-477, frontis., 103 pl. (Also: Supplement, 1907. Ann. Rept. 1906, 3).

Fowler, Henry W. 1919. A list of the fishes of Pennsylvania. Proc. Biol. Soc. Washington, 32: 49-73.

Fowler, Henry W. 1935a. Notes on South Carolina fresh-water fishes. Contr. Charleston Mus., 7, 28 p., 54 figs.

Fowler, Henry W. 1935 b. Notes on Georgia fishes — 1930 to 1933. The Fish Culturist, 15 (4): 72-74.

Fowler, Henry W. 1940. A list of the fishes recorded from Pennsylvania. Bull. Pa. Bd. Fish Comm., 7: 25 p.

Fowler, Henry W. 1945. A study of the fishes of the southern Piedmont and Coastal Plain. Phila. Acad. Nat. Sci., 7, vi, 408 p., 313 figs.

Frey, David C. 1951. The fishes of North Carolina's Bay Lakes and their intraspecific variation. Jour. Elisha Mitchell Sci. Soc., 67 (1): 1-44.

Funk, J. L., et al. 1953. The Black River studies. Univ. Missouri Studies, 26 (2): 1-136, illus.

Gerking, Shelby D. 1945. The distribution of the fishes of Indiana. Invest. Ind. Lakes and Streams, 3 (1): 1-137, 113 maps.

Gerking, Shelby D. 1955. Key to the fishes of Indiana. Invest. Ind. Lakes and Streams, 4: 49-86.

Gilbert, Charles Henry, and Norman Bishop Scofield. 1898. Notes on a collection of fishes from the Colorado basin in Arizona. Proc. U. S. Nat. Mus., 20: 487-499, pls. 36-39.

Goldsborough, E. L., and H. W. Clark. 1908. Fishes of West Virginia. Bull. U. S. Bur. Fish., 27: 31-39, 1 text-fig.

Gowanloch, James Nelson. 1933. Fishes and fishing in Louisiana. Bull. La. Dept. Cons., 23, 638 p., sev. figs., some col., 1 map.

Greeley, J. R., et al. 1926-1940. [Various papers on the fishes of New York.] [In] Biol. Surv. Repts.; Suppl. Ann. Rept. N. Y. St. Cons. Dept.

Greene, C. Willard. 1935. The distribution of Wisconsin fishes. Wis. Cons. Comm., 235 p., 96 maps.

Halkett, Andrew. 1913. Check list of the fishes of the Dominion of Canada and Newfoundland. Ottawa, Parmelee, 138 p., 14 pl.

Hankinson, T. L. 1929. Fishes of North Dakota. Pap. Mich. Acad. Sci., Arts, and Lett., 10 (1928): 439-460, 4 pl.

Harmic, J. L. 1952. A check list of fishes found in Delaware [In] Fresh water fisheries survey. Delaware Bd. Game and Fish Commissioners, Fisheries Publ. 1, 154 p., illus.

Henshall, James A. 1906. A list of the fishes of Montana with notes on the game fishes. Bull. Univ. Mont., 34, 10 p.

Hildebrand, Samuel F., and William C. Schroeder. 1928. Fishes of Chesapeake Bay. Bull. U. S. Bur. Fish., 43 (1) (1927), 366 p., 211 figs.

Hildebrand, Samuel F., and Irving L. Towers. 1928. Annotated list of fishes collected in the vicinity of Greenwood, Miss., with descriptions of three new species. Bull. U. S. Bur. Fish., 43 (1927) (2): 105-136, 9 figs.

Hinks, David. 1943. The fishes of Manitoba. Man. Dept. Mines and Nat. Res., Winnipeg, x, 102 p., illus.

Hubbs, Carl L. 1936. Fishes of the Yucatan Peninsula. Carnegie Inst. Wash., 457 (17): 157-287, 15 pl.

Hubbs, Carl L. 1938. Fishes from the caves of Yucatan. Carnegie Inst. Wash., 491 (21): 261-295, 4 pl.

Hubbs, Carl L. 1946. List of the fishes of Oklahoma. [In] Fish Management Guide for Oklahoma. Okla. St. Fish and Game Comm., pp. 36-39.

Hubbs, Carl L., and Karl F. Lagler. 1941. Guide to the fishes of the Great Lakes and tributary waters. Bull. Cranbrook Inst. Sci., 18, 100 p., 118 figs.

Hubbs, Carl L., and Karl F. Lagler, 1949a. Fishes of the Great Lakes region. Bull. Cranbrook Inst. Sci., 26, xi, 186 p., 38 text-figs., 251 figs., 26 col. pl. (Corrected second printing)

Hubbs, Carl L., and Karl F. Lagler. 1949b. Fishes of Isle Royale, Lake Superior, Michigan. Pap. Mich. Acad. Sci., Arts and Lett., 33 (1947): 73-133, 2 pl., 1 fig.

Hubbs, Carl L., and A. I. Ortenburger. 1929a. Further notes on the fishes of Oklahoma with descriptions of new species of Cyprinidae. Publ. Univ. Okla. Biol. Surv., 1 (2): 15-43, pls. 1-5.

Hubbs, Carl L., and A. I. Ortenburger. 1929b. Fishes collected in Oklahoma and Arkansas in 1927. Publ. Univ. Okla. Biol. Surv., 1 (3): 45-112, pls. 6-13.

Hubbs, Clark, Robert A. Kuehne, and Jack C. Ball. 1953. The fishes of the upper Guadalupe River, Texas. Tex. Jour. Sci., 5 (2): 216-244.

Johnson, Raymond E. 1942. The distribution of Nebraska fishes. Univ. Mich. (Ph. D. thesis), vi, 145 p., 8 pl., 51 maps.

*Jordan, David S. 1929. Manual of the vertebrate animals of the Northeastern United States inclusive of marine species. Yonkers-on-Hudson, World Book Co., 13th ed., xxxi, 446 p.

*Jordan, D. S., and Barton Warren Evermann. 1896-1900. The fishes of North and Middle America; a descriptive catalogue of the species of fish-like vertebrates found in the waters of North America, north of the Isthmus of Panama. Bull. U. S. Nat. Mus., 47: (1), 1896, lx, 1240 p.; (2), 1898, xxx, 1241-2183; (3), 1898, xxiv, 2183a-3136; (4), 1900, ci, 3137-3313, 958 figs.

*Jordan, D. S., B. W. Evermann, and H. W. Clark. 1930. Check list of the fishes and fishlike vertebrates of North and Middle America north of the northern boundary of Venezuela and Colombia. Rept. U. S. Fish Comm., 1928, (2), iv, 670 p. (Reprinted, 1955)

Jurgens, Kenneth C., and Clark Hubbs. 1953. A checklist of Texas freshwater fishes. Tex. Game and Fish, 11 (4): 12-15.

Kendall, William C. 1909. The fishes of Labrador. Proc. Portland Soc. Nat. Hist., 2: 207-243.

King, Willis. 1947. Important food and game fishes of North Carolina. N. C. Dept. Cons. and Dev., 54 p., 32 figs.

Knapp, Frank. 1953. Fishes found in the freshwaters of Texas. Brunswick, Ga., Ragland Studio and Litho Printing Co., 166 p., 190 figs.

Koelz, Walter. 1929. Coregonid fishes of the Great Lakes. Bull. U. S. Bur. Fish., 43 (1927) (2): 297-643, 31 figs.

*Koelz, Walter. 1931. The coregonid fishes of northeastern North America. Pap. Mich. Acad. Sci., Arts and Lett., 13 (1930): 303-432, 1 pl.

Kuhne, Eugene R. 1939. A guide to the fishes of Tennessee and the Mid-South. Tenn. Dept. Cons., 124 p., 81 figs.

Lagler, Karl F. 1949. Fish and fishing in Michigan. Ann Arbor, Folletts, 91 p., 51 text-figs.

*LaMonte, Francesca. 1945. North American game fishes. Garden City, Doubleday, xiv, 202 p., 73 pl. (many in col.).

La Rivers, Ira. 1952. A key to Nevada fishes. Bull. So. Calif. Acad. Sci., 51 (3): 96-102.

La Rivers, Ira, and T. J. Trelease. 1952. An annotated check list of the fishes of Nevada. Calif. Fish and Game, 38 (1): 113-123.

Legendre, Vianney. 1954. Key to game and commercial fishes of the Province of Quebec. Montreal, Soc. Can. d'Ecologie and Que. Game and Fish. Dept., 180 p., many text-figs., 80 figs.

Livingstone, D. A. 1952. The fresh water fishes of Nova Scotia. Proc. N. S. Inst. Sci., 23 (1): 1-90, 36 figs., 43 text-figs.

McCabe, Britton C. 1943. An analysis of the distribution of fishes in the streams of western Massachusetts. Copeia, 1943 (2): 85-89.

McCabe, Britton C. 1945. Fishes. [In] Fisheries Survey Report 1942. Mass. Dept. Cons., pp. 30-68, 5 figs., 7 text-figs.

Meek, Seth E. 1904. The fresh-water fishes of Mexico north of the Isthmus of Tehuantepec. Field Columbian Mus., Publ. 93, Zool. Ser., 5, lxiii, 252 p., 72 figs., 17 pl.

Miller, Robert R. 1946. The need for ichthyological surveys of the major rivers of western North America. Science, 104 (2710): 517-519.

Miller, Robert R. 1949. A list of the fishes of Utah with keys to identification. 13 p. (MS., Mimeo.)

Miller, Robert R. 1952. Bait fishes of the lower Colorado River from Lake Mead, Nevada, to Yuma, Arizona, with a key for their identification. Calif. Fish and Game, 38 (1): 7-42, 32 figs.

Miller, Robert R., and J. R. Alcorn. 1946. The introduced fishes of Nevada, with a history of their introduction. Trans. Amer. Fish. Soc., 73 (1943): 173-193.

Miller, Robert R., and Ralph G. Miller. 1948. The contribution of the Columbia River system to the fish fauna of Nevada: five species unrecorded from the state. Copeia, 1948 (3): 174-187, 1 map.

Moore, George A. 1952. Fishes of Oklahoma. Oklahoma City, Okla. Fish and Game Dept., (11) p., illus.

Moore, George A., and John M. Paden. The fishes of the Illinois River in Oklahoma and Arkansas. Amer. Midland Nat., 44 (1): 76-95, 1 fig.

Mulch, Ernest E., and William C. Gamble. 1954. Game fishes of Arizona. Ariz. Game and Fish Dept., 19 p., 8 col. pl., 2 maps.

Murphy, Garth. 1941. A key to the fishes of the Sacramento-San Joaquin basin. Calif. Fish and Game, 27 (3): 165-171, figs. 46-49.

Nash, C. W. 1908. Check list of the fishes of Ontario. [In] Vertebrates of Ontario. Toronto, Ont. Dept. Educ., 122 p., 8 figs., 32 pl.

*Nichols, John T. 1942. Representative North American fresh-water fishes. New York, Macmillan, 128 p., 60 figs.

Personius, Robert G., and Samuel Eddy. 1955. Fishes of the Little Missouri River. Copeia, 1955 (1): 41-43.

Radforth, Isobel. 1944. Some considerations on the distribution of fishes in Ontario. Contr. Roy. Ont. Mus. Zool., 25, 116 p., 32 figs.

Raney, E. C. 1950. Freshwater fishes. [In] The James River Basin, past, present and future. Richmond, Virginia Acad. Sci., pp. 151-194.

Rawson, D. S. 1949. A check list of the fishes of Saskatchewan.—Regina, Rept. Roy. Comm. on the Fisheries of Saskatchewan, 1947, 8 p., 9 figs.

Rawson, D. S. 1951. Studies of the fish of Great Slave Lake. Jour. Fish. Res. Bd. Canad., 8 (4): 207-240.

Regan, C. Tate. 1906-08. Pisces. [In] Biologica Centrali-Americana, 8, xxxii, 203 p., 26 pl., 2 maps.

Rhode, Clarence J., and Will Barker. 1953. Alaska's fish and wildlife. U. S. Fish and Wildlife Serv., Circ. 17, iv, 60 p., many text-figs.

Roedel, Phil M. 1948. Common marine fishes of California. Calif. Div. Fish and Game Fish Bull., 68, 150 p., 111 figs., col. frontis.

*Roedel, Phil M., and Wm. Ellis Ripley. 1950. California sharks and rays. Calif. Div. Fish and Game Fish Bull., 75, 88 p., 65 figs.

*Rostlund, Erhard. 1952. Freshwater fish and fishing in native North America. Univ. Calif. Publ. Geog., 9, x, 313 p., 47 maps.

Rutter, Cloudsley. 1908. The fishes of the Sacramento-San Joaquin basin, with a study of their distribution and variation. Bull. U. S. Bur. Fish., 27 (1907): 103-152, 4 figs., 1 pl.

*Schrenkeisen, Ray. 1938. Field book of fresh-water fishes of North America north of Mexico. New York, Putnam, xii, 312 p., many text-figs.

Schultz, Leonard P., and Allan C. DeLacy. 1935-1936. Fishes of the American Northwest. A catalogue of the fishes of Washington and Oregon, with distributional records and a bibliography. [5 pts.] Jour. Pan-Pac. Inst. [In] Mid-Pacific Magazine, 48 (4): 365-380; 49 (1): 63-78; 49 (2): 127-142; 49 (3): 211-226; 49 (4): 275-290.

Schultz, Leonard P. 1936. Keys to the fishes of Washington, Oregon and closely adjoining regions. Univ. Washington Publ. Biol., 2 (4): 103-228, 50 figs. (Second printing, 1938)

Schultz, Leonard P. 1941. Fishes of Glacier National Park, Montana. U. S. Dept. Interior Cons. Bull., 22, 42 p., 26 figs.

Scott, W. B. 1954. Freshwater fishes of eastern Canada. Toronto, Univ. Toronto Press, xiv, 128 p., 109 text-figs.

Shapovalov, Leo. 1947. Distinctive characters of the species of anadromous trout and salmon found in California. Calif. Fish and Game, 33 (3): 185-190.

Shapovalov, Leo, and William A. Dill. 1950. A check list of the freshwater and anadromous fishes of California. Calif. Fish and Game, 36 (4): 382-391 .

Simon, James R. 1946. Wyoming fishes. Wyo. Game and Fish Dept. Bull., 4, 129 p., 92 figs., other illus.

Simon, James R., and Felix Simon. 1939. Check list and keys of the fishes of Wyoming. Univ. Wyo. Publ., 6 (4): 47-62.

Smith, Hugh M. 1907. The fishes of North Carolina. N. C. Geol. and Econ. Surv., 2, xi, 453 p., 188 figs., 21 pl.

Snyder, John Otterbein. 1915. Notes on a collection of fishes made by Dr. Edgar A. Mearns from rivers tributary to the Gulf of California. Proc. U. S. Nat. Mus., 49: 573-586, 1 text-fig., pls. 76-77.

Snyder, John Otterbein. 1917. The fishes of the Lahontan system of Nevada and northeastern California. Bull. U. S. Bur. Fish., 35 (1915-16): 33-86, pls. 3-5, figs. 1-9.

Tanner, Vasco M. 1936. A study of the fishes of Utah. Utah Acad. Sci., Arts and Lett., 13: 155-184, pls. 1-3.

Taylor, William R. 1954. Records of fishes in the John N. Lowe collection from the Upper Peninsula of Michigan. Misc. Publ. Univ. Mich. Mus. Zool., 87, 50 p.

Trautman, M. B. 1946. Artificial keys for the identification of the fishes of the state of Ohio. Ohio St. Univ. Franz Theo. Stone Lab., 52 p. Mimeo.

Truitt, Reginald V., Barton A. Bean, and Henry W. Fowler. 1929. The fishes of Maryland. Cons. Bull. Md. Dept. Cons., 3: 120 p., frontis., 62 figs.

van Meter, Harry. 1950. Identifying fifty prominent fishes of West Virginia. Publ. W. Va. Cons. Comm. Div. Fish Mgt., 3, 45 p., 50 figs., 1 text-fig.

Walford, Lionel A. 1931. Handbook of common commercial and game fishes of California. Calif. Div. Fish and Game Fish Bull., 28, 181 p., 137 figs.

Walford, Lionel A. 1937. Marine game fishes of the Pacific Coast from Alaska to the Equator. Berkeley, Univ. Calif. Press, xxix, 205 p., many figs., 69 col. pl.

Wallis, Orthello L. 1951. The status of the fish fauna of the Lake Mead National Recreational Area, Arizona-Nevada. Trans. Amer. Fish. Soc., 80 (1950): 84-92, 1 fig.

Webster, Dwight A. 1942. The life histories of some Connecticut fishes. Bull. Conn. Geol. and Nat. Hist. Surv., 63: 122-227, 60 figs.

Wilimovsky, Norman J. 1954. List of the fishes of Alaska. Stanford Ichthyol. Bull., 4 (5): 279-294.

Winn, Howard E., and Robert R. Miller. 1954. Native postlarval fishes of the lower Colorado River basin, with a key to their identification. Calif. Fish and Game, 40 (3): 273-285, 1 fig., 4 pl.

Wynne-Edwards, V. C. 1952. Freshwater vertebrates of the Arctic and Subarctic. Bull. Fish. Res. Bd. Canad., 94, 28 p.

Chapter IV

The Literature of Fish and Fisheries

When one undertakes the study of a particular fish species, works on a management problem, or engages in almost any phase of fishery research, he finds it advantageous to go through the literature in order to learn what has been done previously on the subject. First access to the literature is through general bibliographies and indices or through the references cited in books or articles. This in turn leads to periodicals and journals of learned societies and other agencies which may then be searched for additional references. A thorough search can be very tedious, because there are many hundreds of such publications, both domestic and foreign, that carry fish papers. Newspapers, sporting magazines, ships' logs, autobiographies, and a host of very obscure sources often yield information of critical value.

A METHOD OF COMPILING A BIBLIOGRAPHY

Since the published sources of information on fish and fisheries are so diffuse, conformance to a basic routine for reasonable coverage of the literature on any particular subject may be of value. If the following suggestions are carefully considered, adopted where pertinent and emended where not, there will be a minimum of inaccuracy and wasted effort. Certain investigational needs will, however, call for the consultation of bibliographic source materials and the employment of methods not listed here.

1. From existing bibliographies and indices such as Dean (1916-1923), the Zoological Record, Biological Abstracts, papers in hand, etc., enter on temporary slips the desired references on a given subject. On each slip indicate the bibliographic source of the information; this simple expedient may save much time in event that an error of transcription has been made.

2. Arrange these slips according to publication source, in order to facilitate the process of finding references and verifying the citations.

3. As the original of each reference is studied, enter its full citation in correct, permanent form under its author as heading. A form such as the following may be used to insure against omissions, or the general style of abbreviated entries employed in the references at the ends of chapters in this book may be followed. One should be consistent in style, as, for example, in the matter of capitalization.

FISH LITERATURE ANALYSIS FORM

File under...

Name used in reference...

Author...Year of publication.......................

Title ....

Reference ....

Ser./Ed. .... Vol. .... Fas./Pt. .... Sec./Art./No. .... Pages...........

Pl. .... Fig. .... Text-Fig. ....Charts, etc.......................

Locality ....

General nature: Morphol. Physiol. Genetics Evol. Taxon. Life Hist. Ecol. Bibliography Conservation Management

Subjects treated: Range Distribution Habitats Associations Anatomy Coloration Sexual dimorphism Reproduction Sex ratio Courtship Breeding Fecundity Survival Embryology Fertilization Hatching Larval development Food Feeding habits Food conversion Food requirements Growth Age-length Age-weight Length-weight Condition Behavior Movements Migrations Schooling Territoriality Learning Populations Rate of mortality Diseases Predators Competitors Relations to man Values Fisheries Fishery methods Fishery yields Conservation Artificial propagation Stocking Laws Environmental surveys Environmental improvement

Notes:

Fig. 8. LITERATURE ANALYSIS. Form for use in preparation of literature citations and analyses in fisheries. For simplicity, ordinary library cards may be used, but for high utility the Keysort or IBM systems have much to offer (e.g., Adams, 1955. Jour. Wildlife Mgt., 19 (4): 472-476).

4. After completing each citation, verify it against the original and ascertain that:

    a. all spellings are exact duplicates of those used in the publication, including author's name and title;

    b. nothing has been abbreviated by you which is not already in abbreviated form in the title;

    c. all punctuation is exactly the same as in the title as published;

    d. italics are indicated where they appeared in the original title;

    e. pagination, etc., are correct and complete, and cited in the following general order: introductory pages in Roman numerals, text-pages, figures, plates, unnumbered text-figures, maps, charts;

    f. journal name, publisher, or other required information are completely spelled out, unless you have the standard abbreviations for the particular item clearly in mind—do not guess (see Appendix C);

g. actual year of publication as well as intended year of publication for the work are recorded in your citation, especially where the two years are not the same.

5. Copy or abstract that information which you desire from the reference. If any portion is transcribed verbatim, indicate this with quotation marks and make sure that the copy is exact. Proof-read it against the original. Record the page on which a quotation was found and if the quotation runs from one page to another, give the number of the succeeding page in brackets between the last word of the earlier page and the first word of the next one.

6. Search for other papers on the subject in each journal to which your attention has been directed by the use of existing bibliographies and indices, and treat any additional references as above.

7. Make note of the location of the publication consulted in order that you may find it again easily should the need arise.

8. In some instances, one is unable to secure an original document for examination and must rely upon another author's statement concerning it or on his quotation from it. If such information must be used, and it is better that it be used than ignored, make it clear that you have not had the original in hand. In your bibliography state that you have not seen the article and thereby disclaim responsibility for the accuracy of the entry. The words "original not seen" will suffice for this purpose.

LITERATURE SOURCES

The literature of fish and fisheries is international and voluminous. On the following pages there is presented a selection of general bibliographies, currently appearing bibliographies and abstracts, indices, and special bibliographies. Emphasis has been placed on American items. Additional foreign sources are cited in the works of Rounsefell and Everhart (1953, Appendix, Fishery Journals) and Scattergood (1954). See also the list of periodicals in Dean's 1916-23 bibliography and in Jul's 1950 "Handbook for World Fishery Abstracts".

GENERAL BIBLIOGRAPHIES ON FISH

"A bibliography is to a subject what an index is to a book."

Artedi, Petri. 1738. Bibliotheca ichthyologica. . . .Ichthyologia, pt. 1, Lugduni Batavorum (Leyden, Holland), 66 p. (The first bibliography of fishes)

Walbaum, Johann Julius. 1788. Bibliotheca ichthyologica. . . .(Greifswald, Germany), vi, 230 p. (A second edition of Artedi's bibliography, with additions and corrections)

Dean, Bashford. 1916-1923. A bibliography of fishes (in 3 vols.). Vol. I: 1916, x, 718 p.; Vol. II: 1917, 702 p., enlarged and edited by C. R. Eastman; Vol. III: 1923, xiii, 707 p., extended and edited by E. W.

Gudger with the co-operation of A. W. Henn. Published by the American Museum of Natural History at the Cambridge University Press, Mass. (One of the outstanding bibliographic works in zoology; contains about 50,000 titles and brings the biblography from the earliest times through 1916. First two volumes contain list of titles arranged by author; third volume contains addenda, corrigenda, titles of pre-Linnaean publications, general bibliographies, voyages and expeditions, list of periodicals, and subject index in 3 sections) (Card catalogue of the Dean Memorial Library in the American Museum of Natural History is being kept up to date as a continuation of the published volumes of Dean's bibliography)

ZOOLOGICAL RECORD. Fish section. London, J. Van Voorst *(etc.)* (Annual, 1864–)

BIOLOGICAL ABSTRACTS. Fish section. Philadelphia. (Monthly, 1930– irregular, 1926–)

CURRENT BIBLIOGRAPHIES AND ABSTRACTS

Conseil Permanent International pour l'Exploration de la Mer.
    CURRENT BIBLIOGRAPHY [In] Journal du Conseil. (Quarterly, 1926–)

United Nations Food and Agricultural Organization.
    WORLD FISHERIES ABSTRACTS. (Bi-monthly, 1950–)

United States Fish and Wildlife Service.
    COMMERCIAL FISHERIES ABSTRACTS. (Monthly, for fishery industries, Jan., 1948–)
    THE PROGRESSIVE FISH-CULTURIST. (Bi-monthly, formerly published by U. S. Bur. Fish.; 1938–, suspended during 1942-46, from 1952 on published by U. S. Govt. Printing Office, Washington)
    WILDLIFE REVIEW. (Monthly, formerly published by U. S. Bur. Biol. Surv., 1935–)
    WILDLIFE ABSTRACTS 1935-51. By Neil Hotchkiss. 1954. 435 p. (An annotated bibliography of the publications abstracted in the Wildlife Review, Nos. 1-66)
    SPORT FISHERY ABSTRACTS. (Irregular, July, 1955–)

INDICES

AGRICULTURAL INDEX. New York, Wilson. (Vols. 1-6, 1919-35; annual and current, 1935–)

ECOLOGY THIRTY YEAR INDEX (Vol. 1-30, 1920-1949). 1952. Ecol. Soc. Amer., 212 p.

ENGINEERING INDEX. New York, Engineering Index, Inc. (Annual, 1884–. Alphabetical subject index and brief abstract for about 1500 periodicals; also available on cards as a weekly service for any particular subject).

FISHERY PUBLICATION INDEX, 1920-54. U. S. Fish and Wildlife Service Circular 36, 1955, x, 254 p. Continues MacDonald (1921) index; treats publications of the Bureau of Fisheries to 1940 and since then the publications of the Fish and Wildlife Service, by authors, subjects, and series. Pages v-x describe the publication series of these agencies with dates of issue, volumes, etc. An invaluable aid because of the irregular nature of many of the series and their systems of distribution.

McDonald, R. E. 1921. AN ANALYTICAL SUBJECT BIBLIOGRAPHY OF THE PUBLICATIONS OF THE BUREAU OF FISHERIES, 1871-1920. Rept. U. S. Fish. Comm., 1920, Appendix 5, 306 p. (All the material of this bibliography presumably is contained in Dean's bibliography of fishes)

INDEX TO PUBLICATIONS BY THE INTERNATIONAL COUNCIL FOR THE EXPLORATION OF THE SEA, 1899-1938. Cons. Perm. Int. pour l'Exploration de la Mer, 1939, 145 p.

INDEX FOR MICHIGAN CONSERVATION MAGAZINE, MARCH, 1935, THROUGH NOVEMBER-DECEMBER, 1952. Lansing, Mich. Cons. Dept., 1953, 74 p.

INDEX OF THE TRANSACTIONS OF THE AMERICAN FISHERIES SOCIETY 1872-1928 VOLUMES 1-58. Baltimore, Amer. Fish. Soc., 1929, 99 p.

Beckman, William C. 1955. INDEX TO THE TRANSACTIONS OF THE AMERICAN FISHERIES SOCIETY 1929-1952 VOLUMES 59-82. Ann Arbor, Amer. Fish. Soc., 112 p.

LIST OF PUBLICATIONS OF THE FISHERIES RESEARCH BOARD OF CANADA, 1901-1949. Fish. Res. Bd. Canad. Bull., 87: 1-96.

PUBLICATIONS OF THE CALIFORNIA FISH AND GAME COMMISSION. Calif. Fish and Game, 33: 35-51.

PUBLICATIONS OF THE INSTITUTE FOR FISHERIES RESEARCH, 1930-1949. Lansing, Mich. Cons. Dept., 20 p. (Also later editions).

Petrides, George A.. Charles A. Dambach, and Daniel L. Leedy. 1950. TEN YEAR INDEX TO THE JOURNAL OF WILDLIFE MANAGEMENT. Wildlife Society, 53 p.

Reed, Clyde F. 1955. INDEX TO COPEIA 1913-1954. PART I. AUTHOR INDEX. Lancaster, Pa., The Science Press, 106 p. 1956. PART II. SUBJECT INDEX, 332 p.

Yeager, Lee E., et al. 1947. CUMULATIVE INDEX TO THE TRANSACTIONS OF THE NORTH AMERICAN WILDLIFE CONFERENCE VOLUMES 1-12, 1937-1947 and AMERICAN GAME CONFERENCE VOLUMES 15-21, 1928-1935. Trans. 12th N. Amer. Wildlife Conf., pp. 541-632. (Also published separately by Wildlife Management Institute, Washington, D. C., 92 p.)

SPECIAL BIBLIOGRAPHIES

In addition to the bibliographies on special subjects listed below, others of value will be found in the references at the end of each chapter in this book.

Allen, E. J. 1926. A selected bibliography of marine bionomics and fishery investigations. Journal du Conseil, 1: 77-96 (473 titles arranged by subjects)

Baughman, J. L. 1947. An annotated bibliography for the student of Texas fishes and fisheries, with material on the Gulf of Mexico and the Caribbean Sea. Texas Game, Fish and Oyster Comm., 240 p., mimeo.

Baughman, J. L. 1948. An annotated bibliography of oysters with pertinent material on mussels and other shellfish and an appendix on pollution. College Station, Texas A. and M. Res. Foundat., 794 p.

Beard, H. R. 1921. Selected bibliography of chemical literature pertaining to the fish industry. Calif. Fish and Game, 7 (4): 256-260. (Gives 95 titles on examination of fish, preservation of fish, oil from fish, meal from fish, and miscellaneous)

Borodin, N. A. 1933. Abstracts on foreign fishery literature. Trans. Amer. Fish. Soc., 62 (1932): 391-398. (Information on six foreign periodicals that contain literature on fisheries)

Bryant, Harold C. 1921. Publications of the California Fish and Game Commission, 1870-1920. Calif. Fish and Game, 7 (2): 87-98. (Subject index, pp. 94-98)

Carbine, William F. 1952. Doctoral dissertations on the management and ecology of fisheries. Additional listings—1952. U. S. Fish and Wildlife Serv., Spec. Sci. Rept.: Fish., 87: 1-44

Carlander, Kenneth D. 1953. Handbook of freshwater fishery biology with the first supplement. Dubuque, Iowa, Wm. C. Brown Company, 429 p. (Bibliography of more than 1500 titles, mostly on age and growth)

Carter, Neal M. 1935. Publications from the Pacific Fisheries Experimental Station on technology of fisheries products other than fish oils. Prog. Rept. Pac. Biol. Sta. and Pac. Fish. Exp. Sta., 24: 11-14. (44 titles on bacteriology, preservation of fish, refrigeration, fish glue, fish meals, canning, etc.)

Corwin, Genevieve. 1930. A bibliography of the tunas. Calif. Div. Fish and Game, Fish. Bull. 22, 104 p. (Titles listed by author, pp. 7-64; abbreviation list, pp. 65-72; subject index, pp. 73-103)

Demol, R., and H. N. Maier. 1924-1936. Handbuch der Binnenfischerei Mitteleuropas. Six vols. Stuttgart, Schweizerbart. (The various volumes contain the following articles of particular interest, with bibliographies; titles translated): Vol. I — Fish food organisms by A. Willer; Enemies of fishes by O. Hämpel; Fish diseases by M. Plehn. Vol. IIB — Physiology of freshwater fishes by W. Wunder. Vol. V — Fisheries of inland waters by A. Seligo)

Elliott, R. Paul. 1950. Information sources for students of commercial fisheries. U. S. Fish and Wildlife Service, Fish. Leaflet, 362, 20 p.

Freund, L. 1923. Bibliographia pathologiae piscium collegit atque edidit auxilio ministerii pro agricultura czechoslovakiae. Prague, Hopfer, pp. 187-263.

Goode, G. Brown, et al. 1884-1887. The fisheries and fishery industries of the United States. U. S. Comm. Fish and Fisheries, 5 sects. (Bound in 7 vols.)

> Section I. 1884. Natural history of useful aquatic animals, 2 vols., 277 pl. (Mammals, reptiles, amphibians, fishes, molluscs, and crustaceans)
> Section II. 1887. A geographical review of the fisheries industries and fishing communities for the year 1880.
> Section III. 1887. The fishing grounds of North America.
> Section IV. 1887. The fishermen of the United States. (Bound with Section III)
> Section V. 1887. History and methods of the fisheries. (2 vols. of text and 1 vol. of 255 pl.)

Green, Charles. 1908. Index to the scientific publications of the fisheries of the Dept. of Agriculture and Technical Instruction for Ireland. Dept. Agric. and Tech. Instr. Ireland, Fish. Branch, Scientific Invest., 6, (1906), 27 p. (63 references, pp. 1-6; subject index, pp. 7-27)

Hubbs, Carl L., and R. W. Eschmeyer. 1938. The improvement of lakes for fishing — a method of fish management. Bull. Inst. Fish. Res. 2, 233 p., 74 figs. (Selected annotated bibliography, pp. 211-228, with 218 references)

Hubbs, Carl L., and Karl F. Lagler. 1947. Fishes of the Great Lakes region. Bull. Cranbrook Inst. Sci., 26, xi, 186 p., 26 col. pl., 251 figs., 38 text-figs., endpaper map. (Contains list of 167 references arranged by author with important titles on the distribution and natural history of American fishes) (Corrected printing, 1949)

International Board of Inquiry for the Great Lakes. 1943. Report and Supplement. U. S. Fish and Wildlife Service, Washington, D. C., iii, 213 p. (Appendix C is a selected bibliography on the Great Lakes, their fishes, and fisheries, with 309 references)

Jul, Mogens. 1950. Handbook for World Fisheries Abstracts. Washington, United Nations Food and Agricultural Organization, iii, 155 p. (Includes list of serials abstracted)

Karrick, Neva. 1948. The nutrition of fish in hatcheries. A literature review. U. S. Fish and Wildlife Serv., Fish. Leaflet, 325: 1-23, mimeo.

Mohr, Erna W. 1927. Bibliographie der Alters- und Wachstums-Bestimmung bei Fischen. Journal du Conseil, 2: 236-258. (437 titles listed by author; subject index, pp. 254-258)

Nemenyi, Paul. 1941. An annotated bibliography of fishways (covering also related aspects of fish migration, fish protection, and water utilization). Iowa St. Univ. Eng. Bull., 16, (n.s., 389), 64 p. (101 titles)

Robb, James. 1946. Notable angling literature. London, Herbert Jenkins, Ltd., 229 p.

Russell, E. S. 1942. The overfishing problem. Cambridge, Univ. Press, viii, 130 p. (At the end of each chapter there is a selected bibliography with a total of 56 references)

Russell, E. S., and H. O. Bull. 1932. A selected bibliography of fish behaviour. Journal du Conseil, 7: 255-276. (671 titles)

Spiers, J. Murray, J. M. Johnston, and Ruth Kingsmill. 1950. Bibliography of Canadian biological publications for 1948. Toronto, Research Council of Ontario, 126 p.

Spiers, J. Murray, Ruth Kingsmill, and George W. North. 1953. (?). Bibliography of Canadian biological publications for 1949. Quebec Biological Bureau and University of Toronto, 192 p.

Tressler, D. K. 1923. Marine products of commerce. New York, Chemical Catalog Co., 762 p., illus. (Rev. ed., 1951, New York, Reinhold)

U. S. Department of Defense. 1953-1954. Arctic bibliography. Washington, U. S. Govt. Print. Office, Vol. 1, 1498 p.; Vol. 2, pp. 1499-2967; Vol. 3, pp. 2968-4478; Vol. 4, x, 1591 p.

U. S. Department of the Navy, Bureau of Aeronautics. 1951. Antarctic bibliography. 6-147 pp.

U. S. Fish and Wildlife Service. 1950. Doctoral dissertations on the management and ecology of fisheries. Spec. Sci. Rept.: Fish., 31: 1-35.

Westwood, Thomas, and Thomas Satchell. 1883. Bibliotheca piscatoria. A catalogue of books on angling, the fisheries, and fish culture, with bibliographical notes and an appendix of citations, touching angling and fishing from old English authors. London, W. Satchell, 1883, xxiv, 397 p. (All the material of this bibliography presumably is contained in Dean's bibliography)

Wheeler, G. C. 1931. A bibliography of the sardines. Calif. Div. Fish and Game Fish Bull., 36, 135 p. (List of titles arranged by authors, pp. 7-96; list of abbreviations used, pp. 97-104; subject index, pp. 105-133)

AMERICAN PERIODICALS CONTAINING FISH PAPERS

American Fisheries Society
TRANSACTIONS OF THE AMERICAN FISHERIES SOCIETY.
(Annual, 1872–; see cumulative indices for volumes to 1952)

American Society of Ichthyologists and Herpetologists
COPEIA. (Quarterly, 1913–)

American Society of Limnology and Oceanography
SPECIAL PUBLICATIONS. (Irregular, May, 1939–; formerly Amer. Limnological Soc. to 1948)
LIMNOLOGY AND OCEANOGRAPHY. (Quarterly, Jan. 1956–)

California Division of Fish and Game
FISH BULLETIN. (Irregular, 1913–)
CALIFORNIA FISH AND GAME. (Quarterly, 1914–)

Canada, Department of Fisheries
THE CANADIAN FISH CULTURIST. (Irregular, 1946–)

Canada, Fisheries Research Board (formerly Biological Board of Canada)
BULLETIN OF THE FISHERIES RESEARCH BOARD OF CANADA. (1918–)
PROGRESS REPORTS OF ATLANTIC COAST STATIONS. (Irregular, 1931–)
PROGRESS REPORTS OF PACIFIC COAST STATIONS. (Irregular, 1929–)
CONTRIBUTIONS TO CANADIAN BIOLOGY AND FISHERIES. (Publication started in 1901, 9 vols., until 1921; from 1922 on it began to be numbered, 8 vols. being published from then to 1933, ending with vol. 8; it was replaced by the next journal)
JOURNAL OF THE BIOLOGICAL BOARD OF CANADA. (3 vols. which then became the next journal listed)
JOURNAL OF THE FISHERIES RESEARCH BOARD OF CANADA. (Irregular, 1934–)

Indiana Department of Conservation
INVESTIGATIONS OF INDIANA LAKES AND STREAMS. (Irregular, 1928–)

Michigan Department of Conservation Institute for Fisheries Research
BULLETIN OF THE INSTITUTE FOR FISHERIES RESEARCH. (Irregular, 1932–)
MISCELLANEOUS PUBLICATIONS OF THE INSTITUTE OF FISHERIES RESEARCH. (Irregular, 1944–)

Ontario Fisheries Research Laboratory
PUBLICATIONS OF THE ONTARIO FISHERIES RESEARCH LABORATORY. (Irregular, 1922–, in University of Toronto Studies, Biol. Ser.; starting as Publ. 1 in the Univ. Toronto Biol. Ser. No. 20, 1922)

Sport Fishing Institute
BULLETIN (Monthly, Dec., 1951–)

Stanford University Natural History Museum
STANFORD ICHTHYOLOGICAL BULLETIN. (Irregular, 1938–)

United Nations Food and Agricultural Organization
FISHERIES BULLETIN (Bi-monthly, 1948–1958)

U. S. Fish and Wildlife Service
CIRCULARS (Irregular, 1941–)
COMMERCIAL FISHERIES REVIEW (formerly FISHERY MAR-
KET NEWS) (Monthly, 1939–)
CONSERVATION BULLETIN (Irregular, 1940–)
CURRENT FISHERY STATISTICS (Irregular, 1941–)
FISHERY BULLETIN (formerly BULL. U. S. BUR. FISH.) (Irregu-
lar, 1882–; vol. 1 was for the year 1881; mostly annual volumes
to 1930; volumes irregular since 1930)
FISHERY LEAFLETS (1941–)
INVESTIGATIONAL REPORTS (Irregular, 1931–)
MARKET DEVELOPMENT LEAFLETS (1949–)
REGULATORY ANNOUNCEMENTS (Irregular, 1941–)
REPORTS OF THE COMMISSIONER (Annual, 1871-1903, Comm.
Fish and Fisheries; 1904-1937, Bur. Fish.)
RESEARCH REPORTS (Irregular, 1941–)
SPECIAL SCIENTIFIC REPORTS (Irregular, 1940-1949)
SPECIAL SCIENTIFIC REPORTS: FISHERIES (Irregular, 1949–)
STATISTICAL DIGEST (1942–)
THE PROGRESSIVE FISH-CULTURIST. U. S. Bur. Fish. (Month-
ly until Oct., 1938, No. 41) and later by the U. S. Fish and Wildlife
Service (Bi-monthly from 51, 1940 to 56, Dec., 1941, No. 56; dis-
continued during war; reestablished bi-monthly Jan., 1947–)

Wildlife Management Institute (formerly American Wildlife Institute)
TRANSACTIONS OF THE NORTH AMERICAN WILDLIFE CON-
FERENCES (Annual, 1937–)

Wildlife Society
JOURNAL OF WILDLIFE MANAGEMENT (Quarterly, 1937–)

STUDY PROGRAM

Prepare a bibliography on a species of fish or on a fishery problem
of your choice, following the routine described at the beginning of this
Chapter. In so doing, become acquainted with the principal bibliographies, indices, books, papers, and journals which are in the foregoing
lists. Study their contents and methods of indexing. Keep a record of

the names of publications in which you find fish articles but which are not included in the preceding lists.

REFERENCES

Jul, Mogens. (Editor). 1950. Handbook for world fisheries abstracts. Washington, United Nations Food and Agriculture Organization, iii, 155 p.

Rounsefell, George A., and W. Harry Everhart. 1953. Fishery science its methods and applications. New York, John Wiley and Sons, Inc., xii, 444 p., illus.

Scattergood, Leslie W. 1954. Bibliographic sources for fishery students and biologists. Trans. Amer. Fish. Soc., 83 (1953): 20-37.

Chapter V

Fish Anatomy

A fishery biologist needs to have an acquaintance at least with the gross features of fish anatomy, both for technical purposes such as identifying and sexing fish and performing autopsies, and for public relations such as answering the queries of fishermen.

Like other vertebrates, a fish is composed of ten systems of organs. The organs are composed of various combinations of six tissue types: epithelial, contractile, nervous, circulatory, supporting, and reproductive. The structural and functional units of these tissues are cells which, as in other animals, are each characterized by nucleus, cytoplasm, and cell membrane.

The anatomical systems and basic functions of each system of organs in a fish follow:

1. Integumentary — covers the body and affords protection by skin, pigmentation, mucus, and usually also by some form of squamation.

2. Digestive — renders food substances soluble in order that they may be absorbed for use in production of energy, growth, and repair.

3. Circulatory — transports nutrient materials, blood cells, fluids, dissolved gases, and wastes about the body.

4. Respiratory — functions in external respiration to absorb oxygen from the surrounding medium and void carbon dioxide to it; participates in regulation of chemical balance between fish and surrounding medium by exchange principally through surface of the gills.

5. Skeletal — frames the body, supports it, and thereby has much to do with its form; also provides attachment and lever systems for muscles and thus acts in locomotion, biting, and swallowing, and has many other functions; major components are bone, cartilage, and connective tissue.

6. Muscular — functions, in its three basic kinds of cells, to produce natatory, skeletal, eye, and other movements (skeletal, striated muscle), to pump the blood (cardiac muscle), and to move food along the digestive tract and give other involuntary movements (smooth muscle); also figures importantly in giving form to the body.

7. Excretory — by way of kidney function, rids the body of certain wastes; important in maintaining chemical balance (osmoregulation) between fish and surrounding water.

8. Nervous—integrates operation of other systems, and relates and adjusts fish to environmental conditions by means of organs of special sense, cranial and spinal nerves, and brain.

9. Endocrine — by hormones produced in the various glands of internal secretion, shares functional integration of other systems with nervous system and is a controlling factor in growth (e.g., thyroid gland) and in reproduction (e.g., pituitary gland).

10. Reproductive — perpetuates species by production of eggs and sperms.

The inter-relationships of these systems are best understood by studying the anatomy of a whole fish. For this purpose a representative of either of the two most common types of American freshwater fishes may be used. These two types are soft-rayed and spiny-rayed. The former are exemplified by such fish as trout, minnows, and suckers and have only soft, minutely segmented rays in their fins. The latter include the basses, sunfishes, perch, and others and typically have one or more unsegmented, hardened spines in their dorsal, anal, and pelvic fins.

ANATOMY OF A SOFT-RAYED FISH
WITH SPECIAL REFERENCE TO A BROOK TROUT

External Characters

The body is elongated, compressed, thickest near the middle, and tapering to both head and tail. It is somewhat fusiform. The mouth is terminal. The upper jaw is supported by two freely movable bones, the premaxilla at the front and the maxilla behind. Both of these bones bear teeth typically in a single row. When the mouth is opened a row of palatine teeth is seen internally and parallel to those of the maxilla; in the middle of the roof of the mouth there are vomerine teeth. The lower jaw or mandible in front is made up of a dentary bone bearing teeth, and two small bones in back, on each side. The dentaries meet at a symphysis in front at the midline. This symphysis becomes swollen and curved upward into a hook in breeding males.

The large eyes have no eyelids; the cornea is transparent. A short distance in front of the eye is the double nostril which ends blindly. There is no external indication of the auditory organ.

On each side of the posterior region of the head is the operculum or gill cover with three bones: the opercular, subopercular, and interopercular. The last is attached to the angle of the mandible. The preopercular is one of the cheek bones following the outline of the hyomandibular. The ventral portion of the opercular region is produced into a thin membranous extension, the branchiostegal membrane supported by thin, flattened bones, the branchiostegal rays. The narrow area on the ventral surface of the throat which separates the two gill openings from one another is called the isthmus.

On the ventral surface of the body at the anterior base of the anal fin is the anus or vent.

The head extends from the snout to the hindmost limit of the opercular membrane; the trunk is from operculum to anus; the postanal region is the tail.

There are two **dorsal fins**. The anterior one is supported by **soft, fin rays**. The posterior one has no rays; it is a small, thick **adipose fin**. Other fins are the quite **homocercal caudal**, the **anal**, and the **paired pectorals** and **pelvics**; all of these are soft-rayed. In the salmonids there is gristly **pelvic axillary process** in the angle between pelvic fin and body wall.

The body is covered with small **scales**, but these are absent from the head and fins. A well-marked **lateral line** is present and is sensory in function.

Skin and Exoskeleton

The **epidermis** contains **mucus glands** and **pigment cells**. The **scales** are in pouches in the **dermis**. Each scale is a thin bony plate with surface markings. The scales are imbricated like the shingles on a roof. They are called **cycloid** since the exposed margin of each is smooth (Figs. 36 and 38). If they bore teeth, as in many spiny-rayed fishes, they would be called **ctenoid** (Figs. 37 and 39).

The following features are most easily seen in a midsagittal section (Fig. 9).

Endoskeleton

The **vertebral column** supports the body axially and is made up of two kinds of **vertebrae** — **trunk** and **tail** or **caudal**. The **first caudal vertebra** is identified as the first one to have a **hemal spine**. The parts of a typical trunk vertebra are **neural spine**, **neural arch**, **centrum**, **zygapophyses**, and **parapophyses**. The last named bear ribs in the trunk vertebrae, but in the tail vertebrae they are presumably extended ventrally to fuse into a **hemal arch** and hemal spine.

The posterior part of the caudal region is modified to support the tail fin. The last vertebrae have their centra deflected dorsally. Neural and hemal spines of the last several vertebra are directed caudally, are broadened and flattened, lie close to one another, and support the caudal fin rays.

The skull is very complex and is composed of mingled bone and cartilage. Its parts are the **cranium, hyoid apparatus, jaws** and **suspensorium, opercular apparatus,** and **branchial arches.**

Dorsal and anal fins are supported by **interneural** and **interhemal bones** respectively. Pectoral fins are supported by **cleithrum, supracleithrum, postemporal, scapula,** and **coracoid.** Pelvic fins are placed in the belly musculature on **basipterygia** which compose the "pelvic girdle."

Skeletal Muscle

The **trunk muscles** are arranged in zigzag **myomeres.** Special muscles of segmental origin operate the fins, jaws, eyes, and other movable parts.

Body Cavities

The **body cavity** is partitioned into an **abdominal cavity** and a **pericardial cavity.**

The **air bladder** lies above the viscera and opens into the esophagus by way of the **pneumatic duct**; the condition is referred to as physostomous.

Digestive Organs

The **mouth** leads into the **pharynx** from which the **gill slits** lead to the exterior and from which the **esophagus** leads to the tubular **stomach.** A **pyloric valve** separates the stomach from the **small intestine** which continues caudally into the **large intestine.** Opening into the fore part of the small intestine are several blind tubes, **pyloric caeca,** which are absent in many freshwater fishes such as the minnows and suckers. **Liver** with a **gall bladder,** and **spleen** are present.

Respiratory Organs

Four pairs of **gills,** each with a double row of **filaments,** are present. The fifth gill arch bears no filaments. A hyoidean **pseudobranch** is present on each side anteriorly under the operculum. The extent of the respiratory surface of each filament is greatly enhanced by the numerous **lamellae** of which it is composed.

Inspiration is effected by gill covers being moved outward about the middle of their length but sealed against the body posteriorly. During this process the mouth is open and water flows into it since it cannot enter from behind because of the closure of the operculum and branchiostegal membranes there. **Expiration** is brought about by the gill covers moving inward. The mouth closes and **oral valves** seal the spaces behind the teeth of the jaws so that the water must exit over the gills and out through the space between the operculum and body.

Circulatory Organs

The **heart** consists of a **sinus venosus, atrium,** and **ventricle.** The ventricle leads into a **bulbus arteriosus** from which the blood passes into the gills by way of a branching **ventral aorta.** The blood is oxygenated in the gills and passes into the forward part of the body and into the caudal part; it goes anteriorly via the **carotid arteries** and caudally via the **aorta.** The blood supplies the various systems and returns to the **sinus venosus.** The **red blood corpuscles** are microscopic, nucleated discs.

Nervous System

A more or less typical fish **brain** with ten pairs of **cranial nerves** arising from it is housed in the cranium. The **olfactory sac** is a blind cavity into which the nostrils open. The **eye** has a flat **cornea** and globular **lens;** the lens may be seen through the **pupil** (opening) in the **iris.** The **ear** has only middle and inner parts. Three **semi-circular canals** are developed on each side and **otoliths** are present.

Urogenital Organs

The **kidneys** (mesonephric type) are of considerable size and run the length of the trunk dorsal to the swim bladder. Caudally the kidneys

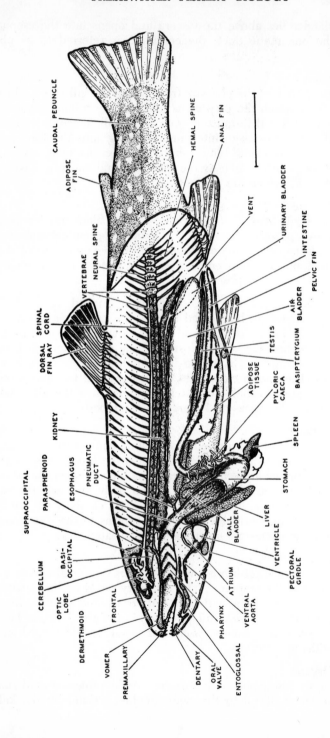

Fig. 9. ANATOMY OF A SOFT-RAYED FISH. Anatomical features of the brook trout. The scale bar equals 1 inch.

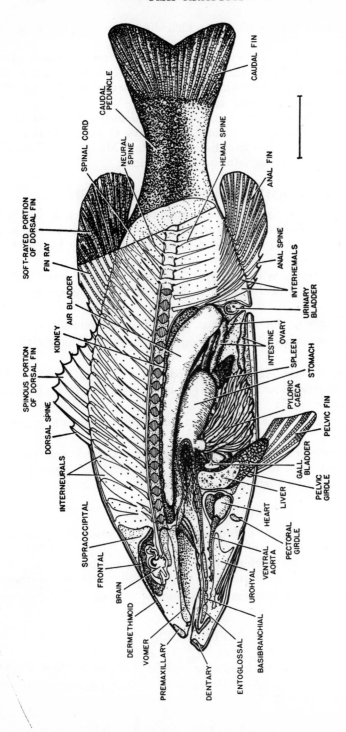

Fig. 10. ANATOMY OF A SPINY-RAYED FISH. Anatomical features of the largemouth bass. The scale bar equals 1 inch.

drain into a small **urinary bladder** which discharges into the **urogenital sinus.**

The **testes** of males are long, smooth, whitish organs which extend throughout most of the length of the abdominal cavity. Each is continued posteriorly into a duct which opens into the urogenital sinus. They lie just beneath the air (swim) bladder.

The **ovaries** also run the length of the abdominal cavity and contain numerous **ova;** oviducts are lacking. They have at least a granular appearance in contrast to the smoothness of testes. Mature eggs find their way to the exterior through the urogenital sinus.

ANATOMY OF A SPINY-RAYED FISH

Fundamentally, the anatomy of a spiny-rayed fish such as the largemouth bass (Fig. 10) is the same as that of a soft-rayed one such as the brook trout (Fig. 9). Among the differences which may be noted between these two species, however, are the following:

1. Spines—present in dorsal, anal, and pelvic fins of bass, and differing from most soft-rays of trout in being stiffened, unsegmented, and unbranched.

2. Scales—mostly ctenoid in bass, rather than all cycloid as in trout.

3. Pelvic fins — thoracic in position in bass and lacking pelvic axillary process.

4. Ovaries — confined to posterior part of abdominal cavity in bass rather than elongated anteriorly as in trout; oviducts present in bass, absent in trout.

5. Pneumatic duct — absent in bass (physoclistous condition); present in trout.

6. Tooth rows on jaw bones—numerous on mandible and premaxillary, but absent from maxillary which is excluded from gape of mouth in bass; typically in a single row on all three bones in trout.

STUDY PROGRAM

Using actual specimens of representative forms, study the gross anatomy of both a soft-rayed and a spiny-rayed fish. Supplement the information thus gained by making further dissections and by preparing cross-sections. Make free use of standard textbooks of vertebrate anatomy.

Sketch contrasting features of anatomical difference between soft-rayed and spiny-rayed fishes.

REFERENCES

Parker, T. Jeffery, and William A. Haswell. 1947. A text-book of zoology. Vol. 1. London, Macmillan and Co., Ltd., xxxii, 770 p., 733 figs.

Young, J. Z. 1950. The life of vertebrates. Oxford, Clarendon Press, xv, 767 p., 497 figs.

Chapter VI

Fish Embryology

A knowledge of the developmental process is important to a fishery biologist because of its part in life history studies and in fish cultural practice. Besides, embryology unfolds many features of evolutionary relationships, heredity, mechanics of development, and environmental influences on ultimate structure and form. Unfortunately, much of the detail of fish embryology remains yet to be learned in spite of the fact that no other class of vertebrates offers a better opportunity to follow the development of organs and systems. General lack of pigment, transparency, and convenient size facilitate observation of changes in organs and tissues even long after hatching.

The following general accounts of embryonic development in fish are based largely on the works of Battle (1944) and Carr (1942), and thus use the Atlantic salmon and largemouth bass as types. These species were chosen as examples because of the general availability of salmonid and/or centrarchid materials at fish hatcheries in the United States and Canada, and because of the relatively advanced stage of the information concerning the two forms.

SEX CELLS

The first steps of embryonic development are best understood by a consideration of the male and female sex cells before they unite in the process of fertilization.

Spermatozoa

Spermatozoa or sperms develop in the male gonads, the testes. When they are mature, each is characterized by a head, a neck, a midpiece, and a long, flagellate tail (Fig. 11). At spawning, the spermatozoa typically pass out of the male fish in a liquid plasma; this combination of sex cells and fluid medium is termed milt. In most of our freshwater fishes, the milt is shed directly into the water, and through whipping movements of their flagellum tails, the sperms reach the eggs and unite with them. This is external fertilization. However in the mosquitofish (Poeciliidae) and in the live-bearing perch (Embiotocidae), the sperms are placed inside the body of the female fish and fertilization and gestation are completed internally (ovoviviparity). Many egg-laying (oviparous) fishes lend themselves to stripping of eggs for artificial fertilization and hatching in fish cultural practice; this is not so far the ovoviviparous ones.

Ova

Eggs or ova (also collectively called roe) develop in the ovaries of female fish. The process of maturation of sex cells in the female gonads entails changes in the structure and constitution of the nucleus and cytoplasm of the cell, and further involves functional or physiological ripening. One of the most noticeable changes is the synthesis by the egg cytoplasm of stored food material in the form of yolk and oil droplets for the nutrition of the future embryo. Fats, carbohydrates, and protein substances thus stored eventually constitute the bulk of the mature eggs, so that at maturity the cytoplasm itself is reduced to a thin layer covering the yolk and oil droplets. This cytoplasm is somewhat more abundant in the region of the nuclear material (egg blastodisk, Fig. 11).

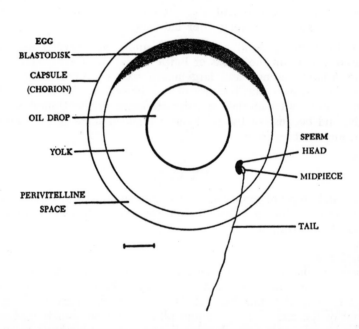

Fig. 11. SPERMATOZOAN AND UNFERTILIZED EGG. Diagrams of egg and sperm of yellow walleye; scale bar equals 0.1 mm. (Adapted from Reighard, 1893).

While an egg cell is maturing, a capsule is formed around it. This structure will later afford protection to the delicate embryo, and be of great importance in the proper exchanges between the embryo and its environment. The capsule may be derived exclusively from the egg cytoplasm (e.g., mummichog, *Fundulus heteroclitus*), in which case it is a true vitelline membrane. In other fishes (e.g., yellow perch, *Perca flavescens*) there is added to it a second membrane derived from the surrounding follicular cells in the ovary; this second, outer one is a true chorion. In many fishes it is possible to distinguish two layers in the vitelline membranes. The innermost one has a radiate appearance and is then usually termed zona radiata. Another feature of the egg membrane in many species is a pore-like opening, the micropyle, for the admission of the sperm.

The developments just described, together with nuclear and physiological ones, make an egg ready for fertilization by the sperm. An ovary replete with such ready eggs is called ripe (sometimes the eggs themselves are termed ripe). In some females (salmon, trout, and walleye), eggs may be pressed easily from the body of a ripe female; in others, the eggs will run out without manual pressure when such a fish is picked from the water (carp, perch). Eggs not ready for fertilization are harder than mature ones, and are called green by fish culturists—or the ovaries are called green.

Newly deposited eggs of freshwater fishes are characteristically more or less adhesive and soft. They rapidly take on water, and in most forms, become more firm. In this condition they are called water-hardened.

Fish eggs vary in shape, size, color, number, and specific gravity, according to species. These characters are useful in the identification of eggs, and in studies of productivity and survival.

FERTILIZATION

Spawning in oviparous fishes varies from a close contact between male and female to mere swimming of the male above or near the female. In all instances the sperm reaches and penetrates the egg with the help of its flagellum as an organ of locomotion; eventually, the sperm nucleus unites with that of the egg. This union is fertilization. As the sperm crosses the egg capsule and reaches the egg cytoplasm, the latter emits a fluid and shrinks. These events, together with the swelling of the capsule, leave a fluid-filled space (the perivitelline space) between the egg surface and the capsule. The space allows the egg cell to move freely, cushioned and bathed by the perivitelline fluid.

The initial phase of the union of sperm and egg is impregnation or penetration. The resultant events are: (1) barring of entry of additional sperms by changes within the egg; (2) uniting of nuclear materials of sperm and egg to form a zygote; (3) cleaving or dividing of the one-celled zygote into an embryo of very many cells; (4) and organizing of the many cells into tissues, organs, and systems giving form and function to the embryo as the process proceeds. Impregnation is thus the entry of sperm into an egg. Fertilization is the union of the nuclear material of the sperm with that of the egg. And a zygote is a fertilized egg prior to cleavage (Fig. 12).

The life of deposited eggs, prior to fertilization, is relatively short. This fact must be kept in mind by fish culturists. Even with the most rapid techniques of artificial spawning one cannot expect fertilization of all eggs. Fortunately, unfertilized eggs are easy to recognize, for they soon lose their transparency, become whitish and opaque, and are called ringers. These must be removed from cultured lots promptly, for as they degenerate they lower the oxygen content of the water, change its general chemical content, and provide a good field for bacterial or fungus infestation.

Under normal conditions, fertilization initiates a series of structural and and physiological changes which eventually result in an adult similar in appearance and genetic constitution to its parents.

EARLY DEVELOPMENT

After fertilization is completed, the blastodisk assumes more definite shape (Fig. 12) and soon begins to undergo cleavage (Figs. 13-15). Since cleavage in most fish eggs is confined to the blastodisk (the yolk does not cleave except in the lampreys), the segmentation process is classified as meroblastic and discoidal.

The first cleavage divides the blastodisk in half (Fig. 13). Subsequent divisions follow to give 4-, 8- (Fig. 14), 16-, and 32-celled stages in the series. Additional subdivisions of these cells yield a many-celled blastoderm (Fig. 15) — first one cell layer thick, then two, then more. Each of the cells resulting from cleavage may be called a blastomere. As the number of blastomeres increases, the individual ones become smaller and smaller and increasingly difficult to see on the surface of the blastoderm (Fig. 15). The space which appears between blastoderm and yolk is the segmentation cavity. When the segmentation cavity has appeared, the embryo may be thought of as being a blastula.

As cell divisions and resultant spread of the blastoderm progress further, the blastoderm becomes concave (first like a cap over part of the yolk, later more concave and covering more of the yolk), and finally proceeds to enclose the yolk mass (Figs. 16-21). During this process the segmentation cavity (also known as the blastocoel or subgerminal cavity) between cap or blastula and the yolk enlarges. In addition, a thick band of cells comes into being around the margin of the blastoderm, enclosing a lighter central area. This rim of cells is called the germ ring (Fig. 16). If the embryo should perish at this stage, this dense ring becomes lighter, its central area darker, giving rise to the term "ringer" for such a dead individual and rendering its identification among a batch of living embryos very easy. This characteristic is useful in hatcheries for sorting dead embryos at this stage from ones still viable. An embryonic shield next appears at one side of the germ ring (Figs. 16 and 17). A transitory, syncytial layer, the periblast (Fig. 27), spreads over the yolk more or less in conjunction with the spread of the blastoderm and is destined to become part of the covering of the yolk mass.

ORGANOGENY

Organogeny in the Atlantic Salmon

The first indication of the definitive salmon embryo is the appearance of the so-called embryonic or primordial shield on one side of the germ ring (Fig. 16). Here there occurs a heavy concentration of undifferentiated cells, the posterior margin of which constitutes the dorsal lip of the blastopore (Fig. 17). At gastrulation, an inner cell layer (the hypoblast) forms by involution of the blastoderm at the blastopore. The remaining outer cells of the blastoderm become known as the epiblast and give rise to the ectoderm. The ectoderm then thickens medially to form the neural plate from which the nervous system will come. Soon the hypoblast produces the antecedent of the axial notochord. The mesoderm arises laterally to the notochord, and the remaining cells of the hypoblast become the entoderm.

As overgrowth (epiboly) of the yolk by the blastoderm runs along (Figs. 18-21), various embryonic features become externally visible. When epiboly is about half completed in the Atlantic salmon, a few pairs of body segments (somites) are already visible, and eye and brain fundaments (anlage) are also apparent (Figs. 18 and 23; 19 and 24). Later more pairs of somites are present, the optic vesicles are more discrete, and olfactory and lens placodes are in evidence (Figs. 20 and 25).

At thirty somites in the Atlantic salmon, the germ ring of the blastoderm has overgrown more than three-quarters of the yolk mass (Figs. 20 and 25). The three primary brain regions are visible — forebrain, midbrain, and hindbrain. The optic vesicles are cup-like, and the lens placode is becoming better formed in the ectoderm which overlies the vesicles.

At forty somites, epiboly is complete and the blastopore has closed (Figs. 21 and 26). The embryo is now evidently discrete above the yolk mass, and lies in a straight line upon it, extending about one-third of the way around the mass. The olfactory pit has formed at the site of the olfactory placode, the lens of the eye is fully formed and is free from the overlying ectoderm. Cerebrum and infundibulum (from forebrain), optic lobes (from midbrain), and cerebellum and medulla oblongata (from hindbrain) are now defined.

At the time of closure of the blastopore, the dorsal finfold has appeared as the precursor of the dorsal and caudal fins (Fig. 21). The

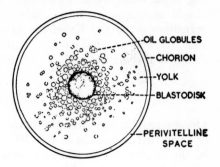

Fig. 12.   FERTILIZED EGG.   Polar view of a recently fertilized egg of Atlantic salmon; diameter of blastodisk, 1.2 mm.; 7 hrs.; 44.6°F.

OIL GLOBULES
CHORION
YOLK
BLASTODISK
PERIVITELLINE SPACE

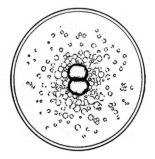

Fig. 13.   TWO-CELLED STAGE.   Embryo of Atlantic salmon resulting from first cleavage; diameter of each cell, 1.0 mm.; 15 hrs.; 46.4°F.

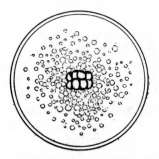

Fig. 14.   EIGHT-CELLED   STAGE. Embryo of Atlantic salmon at 23 hrs.; 46.4°F.

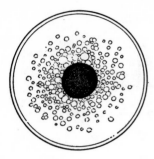

Fig. 15. EARLY BLASTODERM. Many-celled, early blastoderm of Atlantic salmon; 5 days; 47.1°F.

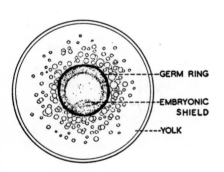

GERM RING

EMBRYONIC SHIELD

YOLK

Fig. 16. GERM RING. Beginning of germ ring and embryonic shield in Atlantic salmon embryo; 12 days; 39.2°F.

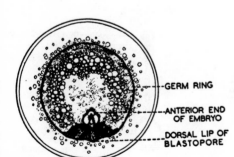

GERM RING

ANTERIOR END OF EMBRYO

DORSAL LIP OF BLASTOPORE

Fig. 17. EMBRYONIC SHIELD. Initial differentiation of embryonic shield and further growth of blastoderm over yolk in Atlantic salmon; 12 days; 44.6°F.

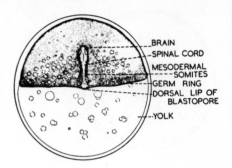

Fig. 18. FIVE SOMITES. Structures in evidence when blastoderm has overgrown about half of yolk in Atlantic salmon; 5 somites; 22 days; 38.1°F.

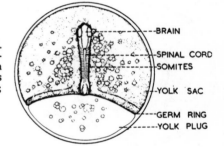

Fig. 19. SEVENTEEN SOMITES. Elongation of embryo to 3.3 mm. and appearance of additional somites when blastoderm has covered about two-thirds of yolk in Atlantic salmon; 17 somites; 68 days; 34.7°F.

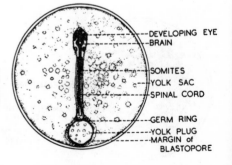

Fig. 20. THIRTY-FIVE SOMITES. Dorsal aspect of embryo of Atlantic salmon when blastoderm has overgrown almost all of yolk (yolk-plug stage); 35 somites; 83 days; 34.3°F.

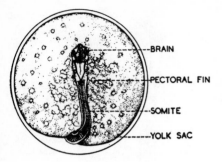

—BRAIN

—PECTORAL FIN

—SOMITE

—YOLK SAC

Fig. 21. FIFTY-EIGHT SOMITES. Soon after closure of blastopore in Atlantic salmon showing dorsal finfold as a white band on middorsal line of embryo (unlabelled); 58 somites; 43 days; 36.5°F.

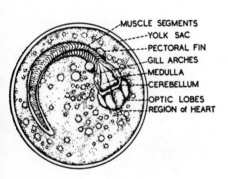

—MUSCLE SEGMENTS
—YOLK SAC
—PECTORAL FIN
—GILL ARCHES
—MEDULLA
—CEREBELLUM
—OPTIC LOBES
—REGION of HEART

Fig. 22. ADVANCED EMBRYO. Atlantic salmon embryo of 10.5 mm. in length; 86 days; 35.1°F.

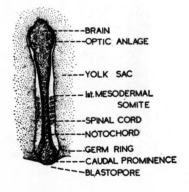

—BRAIN
—OPTIC ANLAGE

—YOLK SAC

—Ist. MESODERMAL
    SOMITE

—SPINAL CORD
—NOTOCHORD
—GERM RING
—CAUDAL PROMINENCE
—BLASTOPORE

Fig. 23. DETAIL OF 5-SOMITE STAGE. Dorsal aspect of Atlantic salmon embryo of 2.1 mm.; 5 somites; 22 days; 38.1°F.

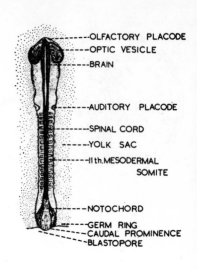

Fig. 24.   DETAIL   OF   17-SOMITE
STAGE.   Dorsum of Atlantic salmon
embryo of 3.3 mm.; 17 somites; 68 days;
34.7°F.

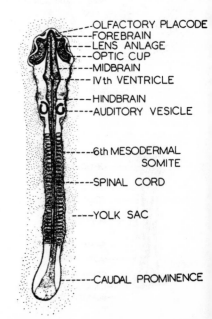

Fig. 25.   DETAIL   OF   30-SOMITE
STAGE.   Dorsum of Atlantic salmon
embryo of 4.2 mm.; 30 somites; 80 days;
34.3°F.

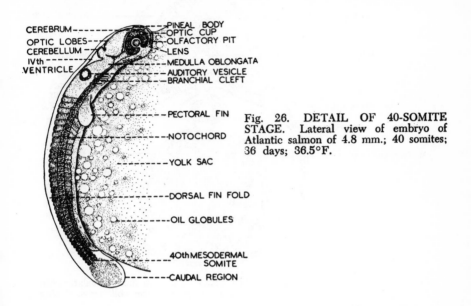

CEREBRUM
OPTIC LOBES
CEREBELLUM
IVth
VENTRICLE

PINEAL BODY
OPTIC CUP
OLFACTORY PIT
LENS
MEDULLA OBLONGATA
AUDITORY VESICLE
BRANCHIAL CLEFT

PECTORAL FIN

NOTOCHORD

YOLK SAC

DORSAL FIN FOLD

OIL GLOBULES

40th MESODERMAL
SOMITE
CAUDAL REGION

Fig. 26. DETAIL OF 40-SOMITE STAGE. Lateral view of embryo of Atlantic salmon of 4.8 mm.; 40 somites; 36 days; 36.5°F.

pectoral fins are at the first somites in the form of small buds. The notochord is well established anteriorly, although it still disappears caudally into a yet undifferentiated cell mass. The yolk is completely covered by ectoderm outwardly, two layers of mesoderm intermediately, and cells of periblast origin internally (Fig. 27). The yolk sac is thus fundamentally established. Toward the head the pharynx has made its appearance, and ventrally the heart has come into being as a tube enclosed in the pericardial cavity.

After the yolk sac (Fig. 27) is fully formed, the body of the embryo appears to develop fast and begins to look more and more like a fish (Figs. 22 and 28). The tail is seen free from the yolk sac; fins, gut, central nervous system, sense organs, notochord, and somites attain greater and greater detail. In the last three-fourths of the incubation period, the principal externally evident involvements are increase in size, appearance of gill arches, definition of brain regions, decrease in volume of the yolk sac, and pigment formation in the eye and finally elsewhere. When the eyes are darkly pigmented, the Atlantic salmon embryo extends about three-fourths of the way around the remainder of the yolk mass. Embryos which have attained this coloration of the eyes are termed "eyed" by the practical fish culturist. Prior to hatching, the

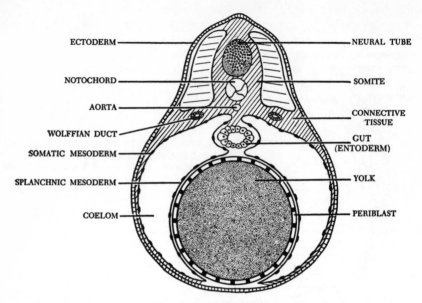

Fig. 27. SCHEMATIC CROSS SECTION. Diagram showing relationship of parts, with special reference to the covering of the yolk mass, during somite stages.

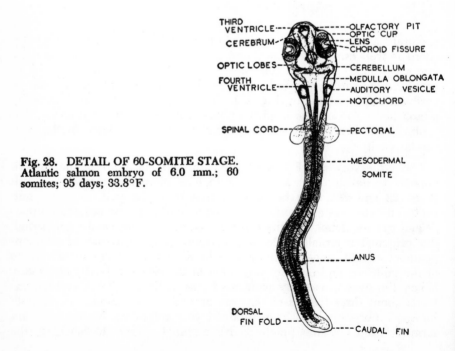

Fig. 28. DETAIL OF 60-SOMITE STAGE. Atlantic salmon embryo of 6.0 mm.; 60 somites; 95 days; 33.8°F.

embryo is larger than the greatest circumference of the yolk sac, and the pelvic fins have appeared near the posterior juncture of the yolk sac with the ventral muscles of the trunk.

A newly hatched Atlantic salmon larva (Fig. 29) still carries a heavy yolk sac which is characteristically pear-shaped, as it also is in several other salmonids. In the dorsal finfold there are appearances of regional differentiation into the dorsal and adipose fins. The ventral continuation of this fold beneath the tail is forming the anal fin. The pelvic or ventral fins are in evidence, and the full compliment of myotomes (sixty pairs) is extant.

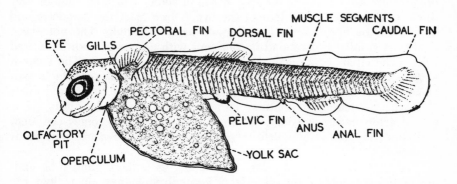

Fig. 29. NEWLY HATCHED LARVA. Young Atlantic salmon of 22 mm. total length and 60 somites; 178-184 days; 34.9°F.

Organogeny in the Largemouth Bass

The events here described are based on the developmental rate for temperatures between 73.4° and 78.8° F. (23° and 26° C.) and largely follow Carr (1942). The whole developmental process is faster in this warmwater fish than in the salmonids.

As in the Atlantic salmon, the blastopore forms at the posterior pole of concentration of blastodermal cells. Involution of cells at the blastopore establishes the hypoblast at the 8-hour stage. Notochord, mesoderm, and entoderm subsequently arise from this hypoblast. The germ ring and the start of the embryonic shield are also visible.

By 16 hours the blastopore is verly nearly closed, but a small yolk plug is still discernible. The neural plate has formed in the ectoderm and has become thickened medially. The entoderm has spread to the limits of the embryo, and the ectoderm has grown over the extra-embryonic region. Mesodermal plates extend laterad from the level of the neural tube and have formed four somites.

About half way through the developmental period, at 24 hours, the olfactory placodes are evident, and optic vesicles and otic capsules have begun to take shape. Ten pairs of somites are established, the noto-chord and neural tube are defined, and differentiation of the brain has begun.

At 32 hours, about two-thirds through the embryonic period, the tip of the tail is free from the yolk. The three primitive brain regions are delineated (forebrain, midbrain, and hindbrain). The otocysts are formed. The olfactory pits are still poorly differentiated but the optic vesicles have become cupped. Lens placodes are well established. More than sixteen somites are present, and the ectoderm is several cell layers thick.

At hatching, about 47 hours, the optic stalks still communicate with the third brain ventricle. The optic lobes are barely developed and the beginnings of the cerebellum are just distinguishable from the medulla oblongata. Among the sense organs, the olfactory placodes, though very discrete, lack a pit. The lens of the eye is free from the ectoderm and housed in the optic cup. The otocysts have enlarged. The notochord is distinct craniad but caudad is confluent with a mass of undifferentiated cells. The circulatory organs form a simple closed system. The heart is a mere tube located anterior to the head over the yolk. A single pair of aortic arches extends from heart to aorta, passes by the paired ducts of Cuvier, ultimately to continue into the tail as the caudal artery. The caudal artery returns craniad as the caudal vein and becomes confluent with the vitelline vein which in turn drains into the sinus venosus at the heart.

The digestive system appears at hatching as a short blind tube end-ing anteriorly behind the otocysts. Pronephric kidney ducts join the gut tube near the anus to make a cloaca. Both mouth and anus are still closed by the oral and anal plates respectively.

STUDY PROGRAM

Embryonic Development

With the foregoing descriptions as a guide, study the embryonic de-velopment of a fish. If possible, use living embryos, whole-mounts and sections. Identify all principal structures and gain an understanding of the developmental processes involved in their formation.

Enumeration of Fish Eggs

In life history studies, in practical fish culture, and in actual fish man-agement it is often very desirable to know the number of eggs, fry and young produced. For example, the number of eggs must be known if survival is to be estimated (Carbine, 1939, 1944)—an important factor in fish production when related to fishing pressure, and one that is inade-quately investigated up to the present. The number of eggs produced is also of obvious significance in fish cultural procedures, since the size of brood stock, amount of rearing facilities, and extent of other equipment which must be on hand are dependent on it.

The most accurate enumeration of fish eggs is probably by actual count but this can be very tedious and time-consuming. When the actual counting of eggs is impracticable, approximate numbers may be obtained by methods described below. Test each method of approximation on a lot of fish eggs, then count the lot and determine which means is most accurate. Repeated tests based on random sampling may be used to ascertain confidence limits.

Complete the following table using the routines given below for each method. If possible, repeat each method several times and evaluate the results statistically.

COMPARISON OF RESULTS OF VARIOUS METHODS FOR DETERMINING NUMBER OF FISH EGGS

Kind of eggs (species):...

Average diameter of eggs in sample: ....

Approximate number per quart (from von Bayer's table): ....

Actual count of total lot of eggs:...

Method	Estimated number of eggs (Mean)	Percentage error (of Mean)	Fiducial limits— Range at 5% level
Volumetric			
Gravimetric			
von Bayer			
Actual count			

Volumetric method. Take a convenient sample (or samples) of the unknown lot of eggs. Blot or dry excess moisture from each sample and then obtain volume of each sample in a finely graduated cylinder or burette by water displacement. Similarly dry the entire lot of eggs, including all samples, and obtain the total volume. Then estimate the total number of eggs in the unknown by

$$X{:}n = V{:}v$$

where X is the unknown total number of eggs in the lot, n is the number counted in sample, V is total displaced volume of all eggs and v, volume of sample.

A somewhat different volumetric procedure may also be tested. Count out 100 eggs and measure the volume of water displaced by them. Then measure the total displacement of the entire lot of eggs including the sample and calculate as above—n will now be equal to 100. A rapid way to count eggs is to have a piece of bakelite or other suitable material countersunk with a known number of holes of proper size to accommodate the eggs in question.

Gravimetric method. Weigh a known number of eggs following removal of excess moisture. Then find the total weight of the entire lot similarly dried and compute the total number by proportion.

von Bayer method (modified slightly). Find the average diameter of the eggs by means of a small metal trough graduated in tenths of inches (Fig. 30); remove excess moisture from between eggs. Make at least three determinations based on as many eggs as ruler in trough will permit, and obtain average diameter.

Consult the von Bayer table giving the number per quart for eggs of various diameters. These values may be changed to number per cc., by dividing number per quart by 946.4 (the number of cc. in a quart).

Find the number of cc. in unknown lot by displacement and calculate number.

Actual count method. Using a tally-whacker and/or other mechanical aid for counting (see previous mention of perforated plate), carefully ascertain the actual number of eggs in the lot to which the estimating methods have been applied.

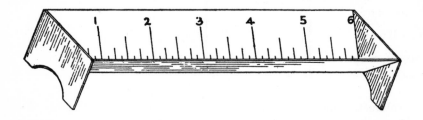

Fig. 30. EGG MEASURING TROUGH. Metal trough for use in determining diameters of fish eggs. Preferred construction has ruler graduated in tenths of inches. (From von Bayer, 1910).

In the experiments of Burrows (1951), using preserved salmon eggs, the volumetric or displacement method gave more accurate results than the von Bayer or weight methods. However, it took about twice as long as the gravimetric one, while the von Bayer technique took about three times as long as the gravimetric one. How does this compare with your experience?

VON BAYER'S (1910) TABLE FOR APPROXIMATING NUMBER OF FISH EGGS OF GIVEN DIAMETER PER LIQUID QUART

Diameter.	Number.	Diameter.	Number.	Diameter.	Number.	Diameter.	Number.
Inch.		Inch.		Inch.		Inch.	
0.300	2,506	0.230	5,562	0.160	16,521	0.090	92,826
	2,531		5,635		16,835		95,990
	2,557		5,709		17,157		99,297
	2,583		5,785		17,487		102,762
	2,609		5,862		17,825		106,390
0.295	2,636	0.225	5,941	0.155	18,172	0.085	110,190
	2,663		6,021		18,528		114,172
	2,690		6,102		18,894		118,346
	2,718		6,185		19,270		122,730
	2,746		6,269	0.151	19,655		127,333
0.290	2,775	0.220	6,355	0.150	20,050	0.080	132,170
	2,804		6,442		20,456		137,251
	2,833		6,531		20,874		142,600
	2,863		6,622		21,303		148,220
	2,893		6,715		21,744		154,155
0.285	2,923	0.215	6,809	0.145	22,197	0.075	160,400
	2,954		6,905		22,662		166,995
	2,985		7,002		23,140		173,950
	3,017		7,102		23,633		181,300
	3,050		7,204		24,140		189,070
0.280	3,083	0.210	7,307	0.140	24,661	0.070	197,290
	3,116		7,412		25,197		205,992
	3,150		7,520		25,748		215,204
	3,184		7,629		26,316		224,995
	3,219		7,741		26,901		235,377
0.275	3,254	0.205	7,855	0.135	27,504	0.065	246,410
	3,290		7,971		28,125		258,141
	3,326		8,089		28,764		270,631
	3,363		8,210		29,422		283,936
	3,400	0.201	8,333		30,101		298,132
0.270	3,438	0.200	8,459	0.130	30,801	0.060	313,289
	3,476		8,587		31,523		329,490
	3,515		8,717		32,268		346,828
	3,555		8,851		33,036		365,405
	3,595		8,987		33,829		385,331
0.265	3,636	0.195	9,126	0.125	34,647	0.055	406,733
	3,677		9,268		35,492		429,750
	3,719		9,413		36,364		454,539
	3,762		9,561		37,265		481,270
	3,806		9,712		38,198		510,139
0.260	3,850	0.190	9,866	0.120	39,161	0.050	541,362
	3,895		10,023		40,156		575,173
	3,940		10,184		41,186		611,893
	3,986		10,348		42,251		651,776
	4,033		10,516		43,354		695,223
0.255	4,081	0.185	10,688	0.115	44,494	0.045	742,613
	4,129		10,863		45,676		794,400
	4,178		11,042		46,899		851,128
	4,228		11,225		48,166		913,380
0.251	4,279		11,412		49,480		981,852
0.250	4,331	0.180	11,603	0.110	50,841	0.040	1,057,350
	4,383		11,799		52,254		1,140,780
	4,436		11,999		53,720		1,233,250
	4,490		12,203		55,239		1,335,960
	4,545		12,412		56,817		1,450,406
0.245	4,601	0.175	12,627	0.105	58,456	0.035	1,578,320
	4,658		12,846		60,159		1,721,630
	4,716		13,069		61,925		1,883,020
	4,776		13,298		63,766		2,065,130
	4,835		13,533	0.101	65,680		2,271,500
0.240	4,895	0.170	13,774	0.100	67,670	0.030	2,506,310
	4,956		14,020		69,741		
	5,019		14,272		71,899		
	5,083		14,529		74,146		
	5,148		14,793		76,486		
0.235	5,214	0.165	15,064	0.095	78,927		
	5,281		15,341		81,473		
	5,350		15,625		84,130		
	5,419		15,916		86,904		
	5,490		16,215		89,800		

CONVERSIONS

1 inch	= 25.4 mm.	1 liter	= 61.0234 cubic in.
1 millimeter	= 0.03937 in.	1 liter	= 1.0567 quarts.
1 quart	= 57.75 cubic in.	1 pound	= 0.4536 kilogram.
1 quart	= 0.9464 liter.	1 kilogram	= 2.2046 pounds.

OVARIAN EGG COUNTS

Sometimes it is necessary to make ovarian egg counts. To do this one must have entire ovaries, well-preserved (in 20% formalin to harden the eggs), and preferably taken just prior to spawning. If time and available materials permit, study a mature ovary. Measure its total volume in cc. by water displacement and then obtain volumes of each of three or more well-spaced segments from it, each approximating one cc. Then separate out and count the mature eggs in each of the sample sections, segregating them from the other eggs and fibrous ovarian materials. Take volumes of the latter remains and subtract from the volumes of the corresponding segments to get volume of mature eggs counted. Average the results for the three or more assays, compute number of fully developed eggs per cc., and then compute total number in the ovary.

Discuss the probable sources of error in this method.

Propose a plan of sampling subject to statistical evaluation and carry it out if possible.

REFERENCES ON EMBRYOLOGY

Battle, Helen I. 1940. The embryology and larval development of the goldfish (Carassius auratus L.) from Lake Erie. Ohio Jour. Sci., 40 (2): 82-93, 21 figs., 1 graph.

Battle, Helen I. 1944. The embryology of the Atlantic salmon (Salmo salar Linnaeus). Canad. Jour. Res., 22 (D, 5): 105-125, 39 figs. (Contains a useful list of references of papers on fish embryology)

Carr, Marjorie H. 1942. The breeding habits, embryology and larval development of the large-mouthed black bass in Florida. Proc. New England Zool. Club, 20: 43-77, 38 figs., 5 pl.

Hayes, Frederick R. 1949. The growth, general chemistry, and temperature relations of salmonid eggs. Quart. Rev. Biol., 24 (4): 281-308.

Henneguy, L. F. 1889. Recherches sur le développement des poissons osseux: embryogénie de la truite. Jour. Anat. Physiol. (Paris), 24 (1888): 1-183.

Kuntz, Albert. 1914. The embryology and larval development of Bairdiella chrysura and Anchovia mitchilli. Bull. U. S. Bur. Fish., 33 (1913): 3-19, 46 figs.

Mansueti, Romeo. 1954. A partial bibliography of fish eggs, larvae and juveniles. Md. Dept. Res. and Education, 55 p., mimeo.

McEwen, Robert S. 1949. Vertebrate embryology. New York, Henry Holt and Company, xv, 699 p., 343 figs.

Morgan, T. H. 1896. The formation of the fish embryo. Jour. Morphol., 10: 419-472.

Nelson, Olin E. 1953. Comparative embryology of the vertebrates. New York, Blakiston, xxxiii, 982 p., 380 figs.

Oppenheimer, Jane M. 1937. The normal stages of *Fundulus hetero-clitus.* Anat. Rec., 68: 1-16.

Reighard, Jacob. 1890. The development of the wall-eyed pike. Bull. Mich. Fish. Comm., 1: 1-66, 78 figs.

Reighard, Jacob. 1893. The ripe eggs and the spermatozoa of the wall-eyed pike and their history until segmentation begins. Tenth Bienn. Rept. Mich. St. Bd. Fish Comm., 89-166, 48 figs.

Riddle, Mathew C. 1917. Early development of the chinook salmon. Publ. Puget Sound Marine Sta., 1: 319-339, 5 pl.

Rugh, Roberts. 1948. Experimental embryology. Minneapolis, Burgess Publ., vii, 480 p., illus.

Solberg, A. N. 1938. The development of a bony fish. Prog. Fish-Cult., 40: 1-19, 44 figs.

Stewart, Norman H. 1926. Development, growth, and food habits of the white sucker, *Catostomus commersonii* LeSueur. Bull. U. S. Bur. Fish., 42 (1926): 147-184, 55 figs.

Sumner, F. B. 1903. A study of early fish development, experimental and morphological. Archiv für Entwick. der Organismen, 17: 92-149, 35 figs., 5 pl.

Tavogla, W. M., and Roberts Rugh. 1947. Development of the platyfish, *Platypoecilus maculatus.* Zoologica, 32: 1-15, 25 figs.

Wilson, Henry V. 1891. The embryology of the sea bass (Serranus atrarius). Bull. U. S. Fish Comm., 9 (1889): 209-278, 20 pl.

REFERENCES ON ENUMERATION ON FISH EGGS

Burrows, Roger E. 1951. An evaluation of methods of egg enumeration. Prog. Fish-Cult., 13 (2): 79-85.

Carbine, W. F. 1939. Observations on the spawning habits of centrarchid fishes in Deep Lake, Oakland County, Michigan. Trans. Fourth N. Amer. Wildlife Conf., pp. 275-287, 5 figs.

Carbine, W. F. 1944. Egg production of the northern pike, *Esox lucius* L., and the percentage survival of eggs and young on the spawning grounds. Pap. Mich. Acad. Sci., Arts and Lett., 29 (1943): 123-137, 4 figs.

Rodd, James A. 1947. Standard terms and methods of measurement in fish culture. Trans. Amer. Fish. Soc., 74 (1944): 19-20.

von Bayer, H. 1910. A method of measuring fish eggs. Bull. U. S. Bur. Fish., 28 (1908) (2): 1011-1014.

Chapter VII

Life History Stages Following Hatching

In most fishes an important and large portion of the developmental process takes place after hatching or birth. The early part of the post-hatching period frequently finds the hatchling or larva in many ways still in an embryonic condition. Furthermore, the state of development of both structure and form at emergence and at successive intervals thereafter differs from one species to another. It also varies slightly among the individuals within a species.

CHANGING FEATURES

In order to systematize a beginning study of fish development after hatching, one may focus attention on features such as those which follow. These are not all of the things which may be observed, but they are among the important items which should not be missed in making records of changes.

Length

Length at hatching or birth is variable and is related to size of egg, which in turn reflects kind of fish and size of female parent. Length at scale formation is of particular concern to students of age and growth. This measurement of larvae is perhaps best made by overall length (total length), at least until the tail elements are fully formed.

Finfold

At hatching a median finfold usually extends down the middle of the back, around the tail, and forward ventrally to the anus or beyond. It is variously interrupted and developed, and, depending on the species, may or may not show the beginnings of fin rays at the time of larval emergence (Fig. 29).

Median Fins

As described in the preceding chapter, the median fins (dorsal, caudal, and anal) typically form from the median finfold. Indications of the boundaries of the individual fins are sometimes discernible in very young fish, as are the rudiments of the fin rays.

Pectoral Fins

The pectoral fins are ordinarily evident at hatching, but their size varies among species. The length from base to tip of fin may be recorded as a measure of growth in successive stages.

Fin Rays

The fin rays are sometimes not in evidence until after hatching. All of the rays in any one fin do not appear simultaneously, nor do they appear at the same time in all fins. The fin rays, if distinguishable, may be counted as they form at fin sites. Their numbers are a basis for identifying developmental stages and for making comparisons among different species.

Yolk Sac

Not only are the size of the yolk sac at hatching and its changes in succeeding periods of larval growth observable features, but the shape and position of the sac are of value for distinguishing species from one another. The size of the fish (and the time) when the yolk sac disappears is also worthy of note. The oil globule or globules within the yolk sac also progressively disappear.

Mouth

Larval development and the beginning of oral feeding involve significant changes in the mouth. In some fishes the mouth is still closed when the young emerge.

Pigmentation

Dark pigmentation of the eyes in early developmental stages occurs in several kinds of fishes. Black or brown chromatophores, generally called melanophores, have patterns of distribution on the body and yolk sac which are distinctive of developmental stages within species. The location of melanophores on key areas is also characteristic in certain species and is useful for their identification (as illustrated in the larval fish key of Winn and Miller, 1954, q. v.).

Myomeres

The total number of myomeres or muscle segments appears to be fixed for each fish species within reasonably narrow limits. Counts of the numbers which have appeared at various stages of development may serve to identify the stage better than records of time or body length. Myomere counts are also useful in species identifications.

Relative Growth of Parts

Changing proportions of head, trunk, tail and other body parts mark the early growth stages of fish. Records of the proportional relationships of parts are critical when identification of unknown larvae is to be attempted. Often the head is relatively larger in the larva stage than in succeeding stages. Changes in position of the anus and in gut length have been observed in some forms. That the proportional relationships of body parts are poorly known for very many species is attested by the fact that most keys for the identification of fish kinds do not include workable information for early life history stages; the key of Winn and Miller (1954) is exceptional in this regard.

LARVAL DEVELOPMENT OF LARGEMOUTH BASS

Data from living specimens. Measurements in millimeters. (Adapted from Carr, 1942)

Feature	1 Day	4 Days	8 Days	10 Days	15 Days
Total length	4.10	6.20	7.2		
Standard length	4.00	6.00	7.0		
Length to vent	2.12	2.70	3.5		
Greatest depth before vent	1.40	1.40	1.3		
Diameter of eye	.28	.40	.60		
Number of myomeres before and behind vent	11-23 or 24 (3 or 4 in tail tip)	11-19, as in adult			
Choroid fissure	almost closed	closed but line of juncture evident		line of juncture obscured by iridescence	
Pigmentation	none	eye iridescent; melanophores on head and body more numerous	stellate melanophores enlarging and becoming rounded	yellow pigment cells above lateral line; abdominal wall iridescent	
Yolk sac	1.45 × 1.00	1.40 × 1.00	much smaller	disappearing	completely absorbed
Oil globule	latero-dorsal in position	becoming smaller			completely absorbed
Air bladder	not evident	rudiment discernable	filled with gas		

Dorsal fin	broadly continuous with caudal and anal; no mesenchyme evident		no mesenchyme evident	thickened mesenchyme present	9 rays formed
Caudal fin		no mesenchyme evident	rays forming in ventral portion	rays forming	distal part of vertebral column clevated
Anal fin		no mesenchyme evident	mesenchyme evident	rays forming	9 rays formed
Pectoral fin	rounded and enlarging ridge	rapidly fanning; no rays evident	rays present and increasing in size		
Pelvic fin	no trace	no trace			still no trace
Otocysts	.15 × .09	.25 × .21 otoliths evident	.40 × .50		
Heart beat	75 per min. at 15° C.				
Upper jaw	no sign of development	no sign of development	mouth functional		
Lower jaw	no sign of development	developed, movable	extends to tip of snout		
Opercle	no sign of development	rudiment evident; does not cover rudimentary gills	covers gills		
Larval movements	on side, active	leaves bottom for short intervals; rests on ventral surface	schooling begins; capable of suspended swimming; feeding has begun		

The manner in which structural and functional features change has been measured and recorded by Carr (1942) for the largemouth bass. The accompanying selections from Carr's summary illustrate both a good method of study and items which may be observed by a student of early life history stages in fish.

Comparison of larvae of different species may be made on the basis of equal size, of equal age, or of equal developmental stage. Often comparisons based on identical developmental stage (Oppenheimer, 1937; Balinsky, 1948) will be most useful, particularly in working out diagnostic, recognition characteristics among species. For this purpose "normal" stages of development have been proposed; for minnows these stages follow (as adapted by Winn and Miller, 1954, from Balinsky, 1948):

Stage 1. Unfertilized egg.

Stages 2-27. Development of fertilized egg. Hatching occurs at about stage 27.

Stages 28-32. Prolarval stage with yolk sac.

Stage 33. Yolk is assimilated; no caudal fin rays present; postlarval stage begins.

Stage 34. End of notochord straight; caudal fin with 3-4 rays; no trace of dorsal or anal fin.

Stage 35. End of notochord upturned; caudal fin with 7-9 rays; elevated fin membrane at site of future dorsal and anal fins.

Stage 36. Dorsal and anal with rudimentary, cartilaginous rays; caudal fin rounded, nearly complete, with 15-17 rays. Air bladder subdividing.

Stage 37. Rays of dorsal and anal fins partly ossified; caudal emarginate, with 19 principal rays; rudiments of pelvics appear. Air bladder subdivided into two parts.

Stage 38. Pelvic fins in the form of crescentic folds.

Stage 39. Pelvic fins in the form of paddles, with no trace of rays.

Stage 40. Pelvic fins with rudimentary, unossified rays; postlarval stage ends.

Stage 41. Pelvic rays partly ossified; continuous finfold reduced.

Stages 42-46. Finfold lost, scales develop, and lateral-line canal forms.

In the foregoing, stages 2 to 27 are embryonic, unless the embryo hatches before 27; the prolarval period is from stages 28 to 32, the postlarval from 33 to 40. Ossification of the pelvic fin rays is held to mark passage out of the postlarval stage in this group of fishes.

METAMORPHOSIS

Metamorphosis is transformation; it involves the loss of the features which mark an individual as a larva, and the attainment of those which characterize it as an adult. Usually the characters involved are structural, their alteration is gradual, and the actual change is relatively small. In such conditions, metamorphosis is not a well defined stage in the developmental process because it may even involve the whole post-hatching period. In a few fishes, however, metamorphosis is relatively sudden and involves great changes. Striking illustrations of the latter exist in the lampreys (Petromyzontidae), the freshwater eel (Anguillidae), herrings and relatives (clupeoids), and smelts (Osmeridae). In the sea lamprey the oral hood of the larvae is lost, horny teeth develop, the free feeding habit is forsaken and the parasitic one assumed. In the fresh-water eel, the compressed, transparent pelagic larva metamorphoses into an elver which is in form and opacity like an adult of the species (e.g., Plate IV, J. R. Norman, 1931, History of Fishes, London, Benn). For fishes such as these some particular treatment of the subject of meta-morphosis seems to be desirable.

TERMINOLOGY FOR LIFE HISTORY STAGES

The need for the application of precise terminology to life history stages has been enunciated by Hubbs (1944). He also defined the major stages according to generally acceptable standards; with minor emenda-tions, they and their definitions follow:

1. **Larva.** Developmental stages well differentiated from the later young and juvenile stages and intervening between the time of hatching and time of transformation (loss of larval characters); the following two stages of larvae are commonly, but not universally, recognizable.

   a. **Prolarva.** Larva still bearing yolk, are often called **sac fry** or **fry** by fish culturists. (Fig. 29).

   b. **Postlarva.** Larva after the time of absorption of yolk, but applied only when the structure and form continue to be strikingly different from the later stages, hence largely subjective.

   The postlarval period extends from yolk sac absorption to a stage when the fish resembles a young or juvenile individual. Thus a post-larva is characterized by absence of yolk sac, presence of a continu-ous finfold, and pigment characters different from the next stages (Winn and Miller, 1954). On this basis, postlarvae are recognizable in the following fish families: mooneye, whitefish, pike, sucker, min-now, troutperch, sunfish, perch and sculpin. In salmonids and North American freshwater catfishes the prolarvae transform directly into young fish with the essential form and structure of adults, and are called **alevins** or **advanced fry** by fish culturists.

2. **Young.** Usually taken to mean **young-of-the-year** or a member of age-group O, and extending from hatching until January 1 in the Northern Hemisphere or July 1 in the Southern Hemisphere.

3. **Juvenile.** Fish neither young nor adult but in the stages between; in fishes with very short life cycles the terms juvenile and young will be synonymous.

4. **Adult.** Mature fish about to spawn, spawning, spent, or living to spawn again. In distinction, that stage of maturity or adulthood which

is characterized by breeding condition of the gonads is called **ripe; spent** fish have just spawned.

5. Half-grown. A term to be loosely applied; because any precise distinction involves age determination, after which the following terminology of the life-history workers becomes applicable. In their practice the age-groups are numbered O, I, II, etc. There is discrepancy as to time when one group changes into the next one, but a convenient division is at January 1 in the Northern Hemisphere. Age-groups are not year classes; a year class is the group of fish spawned and hatched in any one calendar year. For some species the term half-grown will apply to juveniles, for others to small adults.

6. Yearling. Member of age-group I, thus in second calendar year of life.

7. Two-year-old. Member of age-group II, etc.

In practical fish culture, the following general terminology is still in use (Titcomb, 1910):

(1) **Fry.** Fish up to the time when the yolk sac has been absorbed.

(2) **Advanced fry.** Fish from the termination of the fry stage until a length of 1 inch has been attained.

(3) **Fingerlings.** A classification entirely based on length, with the various sizes designated as No. 1 for lengths from 1.0 to 1.9 inches; No. 2, 2.0 to 2.9 inches; No. 3, 3.0 to 3.9 inches; No. 4, 4.0 to 4.9 inches; etc.

STUDY PROGRAM

Where possible, use series of whole specimens and describe the changes in each of the items of the foregoing list which take place from hatching until the definitive body form and structure are reached. Preferably this series should run from sac fry to adult and should show the major stages previously named. Sketch representative stages to illustrate your account. Supplement your observations with study of published figures and text materials (see References).

REFERENCES

Balinsky, B. I. 1948. On the development of specific characters in cyprinid fishes. Proc. Zool. Soc. London, 118 (2): 335-344, 12 figs.

Battle, Helen I. 1940. The embryology and larval development of the goldfish (Carassius auratus L.) from Lake Erie. Ohio Jour. Sci., 40 (2): 82-93, 21 figs., 1 graph.

Carr, Marjorie H. 1942. The breeding habits, embryology and larval development of the large-mouthed black bass in Florida. Proc. New England Zool. Club, 20: 43-77, 38 figs.

Fish, Marie Poland. 1932. Contributions to the early life histories of sixty-two species of fishes from Lake Erie and its tributary waters. Bull. U. S. Bur. Fish., 47: 293-398, 144 figs.

Hubbs, Carl L. 1944. Terminology of early life history stages of fishes. Copeia, 1943 (4): 260.

Kuntz, Albert, and Lewis Radcliffe. 1917. Notes on the embryology and larval development of twelve teleostean fishes. Bull. U. S. Bur. Fish., 35 (1915-16): 87-134, 126 figs.

Rawles, Mary E. 1948. Origin of melanophores and their role in development of color pattern in vertebrates. Physiol. Rev., 28 (4): 383-408.

Rodd, James A. 1947. Standard terms and methods of measurement in fish culture. Trans. Amer. Fish. Soc., 74 (1944): 19-20.

Titcomb, John W. 1910. Fish-cultural practices in the United States. Bureau of Fisheries. Bull. U. S. Bur. Fish., 28 (1908) (2): 697-757, 26 figs., 13 text-figs.

Winn, Howard Elliott, and Robert Rush Miller. 1954. Native postlarval fishes of the Lower Colorado River Basin, with a key to their identification. Calif. Fish. and Game, 40 (3): 273-285, 4 pl.

Chapter VIII

Food

The natural food of fishes comes from the many groups of plants and animals that inhabit waters, as well as from others that do not. Certain chemical elements, such as calcium, in addition, are absorbed from the water itself. The classes of food substances represented include proteins, carbohydrates, fats, lipids, and vitamins—the materials are animal, vegetable, and mineral.

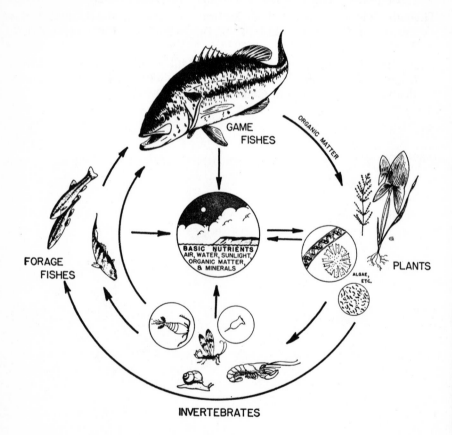

Fig. 31. FOOD RELATIONSHIPS. Some aspects of food chains leading to fish production.

First feeding of most fishes in nature may be presumed to be upon bacteria, desmids, diatoms and other microscopic plankters, both plant and animal. Open-water, pelagic organisms eaten include algae, protozoans, and microcrustaceans. Periphyton and associated tiny animals, forming more or less of a slimy coating on bottom materials, on debris, and on plant stems and leaves, are also browsed upon.

It may be safely assumed that most fish are omnivorous even in early life, eating and digesting both plant and animal tissue. As fish grow toward adulthood, however, feeding adaptations develop and the diets of some kinds become highly restricted. Many remain more or less omnivorous throughout life (bluegill and other sunfishes, carp). A few become plankton feeders at an early stage and remain so (gizzard shad, paddlefish, some ciscoes). Some become highly herbivorous (stoneroller minnow, redbelly dace), others carnivorous (pike, gars—largely piscivorous; trouts—quite insectivorous). Some species are cannibalistic (pike, largemouth bass). Certain lampreys (sea, chestnut, silver) assume a parasitic feeding habit as adults. The freshwater drum and shellcracker sunfish become quite malacophagous, utilizing snails and clams; the bullheads turn into efficient scavengers; and black basses eat quantities of crayfishes (carcinophagy).

The staple equivalents of meat and potatoes for most fishes, including many of the foregoing kinds with specialized habits, are insects in their aquatic stages, and other aquatic invertebrates. Occasionally amphibians, reptiles, birds, and mammals fall prey to predacious fishes such as pike, muskellunge, gars, and the black basses.

Aquatic invertebrates of greatest importance to fish as food are: (1) annelid worms (earth worms, sludge worms, and leeches); (2) the molluscs (snails and clams); and (3) the arthropods which include crustaceans (crayfish, sowbugs, fairy shrimp, and scuds) and the insects.

Some of the insects upon which fish feed live on or in the water for all or parts of their lives and are thus readily captured and eaten. Others are terrestial or aerial and are consumed only when they fall or are washed or blown into the water (e.g., grasshoppers, bees). Insect orders with members important as fish food which are aquatic or which pass one or more stages of their life cycle in water are: Ephemeroptera (mayflies); Plecoptera (stoneflies); Odonata (dragonflies and damselflies); Hemiptera (waterbugs, water striders, backswimmers); Megaloptera (alder flies, dobson flies, fish flies, hellgrammites); Trichoptera (caddisflies); Coleoptera (whirligig beetles, diving beetles); Diptera (midges, mosquitoes, blackflies, and other true flies). In addition a few moths (Lepidoptera) have aquatic larvae, and larval spongillids (Neuroptera) live in freshwater sponges.

Immature stages of most aquatic insects are of outstanding importance in the food chains of fresh waters leading to fish production, because of the great extent to which they convert plant material into animal tissue that is utilizable by carnivorous food and games fishes. The aquatic stages of some groups, however, are predatory upon small fish (all Odonata, most Hemiptera and Megaloptera, many Coleoptera, and few Trichoptera, Diptera, and Plecoptera).

The situations inhabited by the numerous kinds of organisms upon which fish feed are many and varied. Major zones, however, are: (1) bottom or benthic zone, on or in the substrate, debris, or rooted aquatic plants (most immature stages of insects, worms, molluscs, sowbugs, crayfish); (2) the open-water, pelagic zone (plankton and plankton feeders, including larvae of some fishes); (3) just beneath the surface film (mosquito wigglers); (4) the water's surface (water striders, fallen terrestial insects, birds, and frogs); (5) just above the water's surface (adults of many aquatic insects, such as mayflies, caddisflies and mosquitoes, and other insects). Fish with particular adaptations of gill rakers, mouth, dentition, and vision feed in all of these zones, some by day and others in the same places at night.

In order to express simply the relationship between the relative abundance of an organism in the environment and the degree to which it is used as food by a fish, a forage ratio has been proposed. This ratio is the quotient of the percentage which a given kind of organism makes up of the total stomach contents, divided by tht percentage which this same organism makes up of the total population of food organisms in the fish's environment. These percentages may be calculated from number, volume, or weight (Hess and Swartz, 1940:160). The values obtained give a simple index of interaction between a fish and its environment.

Until recently, the manner in which food is converted into fish flesh has been reported in simple food conversion indices. An index of this kind is obtained by dividing the weight of food consumed by the gain in weight of the consumer during the corresponding interval of time. Reported values have ranged broadly between 2.0 and 5.0 for both "natural" and artificial foods. Limitations of this index are now seen, due largely to the work of Gerking and others, because important sources of variation such as the following have been largely ignored; (1) conditioning of fish for the experiments; (2) relation of experimental period to natural growing seasons and environmental factors of growth; (3) differences among individuals, species, and diets in assimilation into fats, carbohydrates, and proteins; (4) differences in tissue water content of experimental fish; and (5) genetic heterogeneity of experimental animals. Improved approaches to the study of food conversion deal in terms of protein utilization for growth (Gerking, 1952) or of energy transfer in the food chain (Ivlev, 1945) rather than in crude total-weight gain.

The basic productivity of waters, turnover of fish food organisms, and fish populations are related in very fundamental though extremely complex ways. The results of integrated studies of both forage and fish populations hold much of interest for the future of fish management.

FOOD HABITS

Food relationships do at least in part determine population levels, rates of growth, and condition of fish. They serve as a partial basis for determining the status of various predatory or competing forms. For any species, food habits change with the seasons, with life history stages, and with the kinds of food available. A distinction is made between food habits, or food eaten, and feeding habits; the latter are the behavioristic aspects of feeding.

Since food studies may show details of the ecological relationships among organisms (Fig. 31), complete identifications of food items are requisite; this entails good working facilities and collections of comparative materials. It is obviously impossible for one person to accord detailed treatment to all of the remains that he finds; it is only with practice and by much comparison with reference collections that one may become proficient even for a few groups of organisms. The aid of other specialists must be used for identification in order to attain the highest quality of food analyses (see Chapter III on identification).

Food studies based on contents of digestive tracts or of droppings merely show what an animal will eat (Fig. 32). However, such facts, related to feeding habits and accompanied by ecological studies, may constitute an important base for resource management. A study of feeding habits may be of great help in reducing limitations imposed on food analyses by the differential rates of digestion of various food items. If it is first determined when an animal feeds, for example, specimens may be collected close to or during that time and thus they will have been taken when they contain relatively whole, undigested materials, whether the organisms eaten are soft- or hard-bodied.

METHODS OF STUDYING FOOD HABITS

Numerical Method

In the numerical method, a count is made of the individuals of each kind of food item occurring in a food sample (such as the contents of a stomach). When all of the samples have been analyzed, the total number of individuals of each kind of food organism is obtained. By comparing the totals one can draw limited conclusions as to the relative significance of the different items. The greatest limitation of the method lies in the obvious fact that the organism occurring in largest numbers need not necessarily constitute the most important food item. A large number of flying ants, for example, might have considerably less food value to a small predatory fish than a few forage minnows would have.

Frequency of Occurrence Method

In order to determine frequency of occurrence, one records the number of individual food samples in which he finds each kind of food item. The results are usually expressed as percentage of the total number analyzed of specimens containing food. Unfortunately, the findings are often biased by the accumulation within individuals of remains of certain food organisms which are resistant to digestion. This tends to make the apparent frequency of such organisms greater than the actual frequency with which they are taken during successive feeding periods. When relied upon exclusively, this method fails to disclose the numbers of forage individuals involved. It also does not show the bulk relationships of the various categories of food items.

Method of Estimating Percentage by Bulk

If possible, one first measures by water displacement the total volume of the food in the sample. He next sorts the kinds of food items from one another and then estimates the percentage which each item composes of the entire mass of the sample. The estimated percentages for each item in a sample may then be converted into a corresponding volumetric value by multiplying the volume of the sample by the decimal equivalent of the original estimated percentage. The summation of the volumetric values for each item in a series may be converted into percentages again by first dividing each sum by the total food volume of all of the samples and then by multiplying the quotient obtained by 100. If the total volume of each sample was not taken, the average percentage of the bulk composed by each food item must be computed. In either event the results will give a picture of the relative volumetric importance of each food item. The impressions gained are hardly as accurate as a complete set of measured volumes, and fail entirely to disclose the important features of number of individuals in each of the items. Furthermore, they may be distorted by the exceptional occurrence of a food item of large volume.

Gravimetric Method

In applying the gravimetric method, one first carefully sorts the kinds of organisms in a sample from one another. He next obtains the weight (dry or with a consistent degree of moistness) of each item involved. Summation by kinds of items is then made for a series of samples and the results expressed as percentages of the weight of the total mass of food for all samples in the series. When the weight method is used alone, the real meaning may be much distorted by the stray or occasional occurrence of a food item of exceptionally great weight.

Volumetric Method

The procedure in the volumetric method is essentially the same as in the gravimetric one; but instead of weighing the different food items encountered, their volumes are obtained by water displacement. For each item in the series, the volume is then totalled and finally expressed as percentage of the total volume of food in the whole series. The volumetric method, when it is used alone, is subject to the same criticisms as the gravimetric one. In addition, some error may be introduced into both methods by the differential rate of digestion of hard-bodied and soft-bodied food organisms. The tendency of certain remains which resist digestion to accumulate from several feedings may also influence the results.

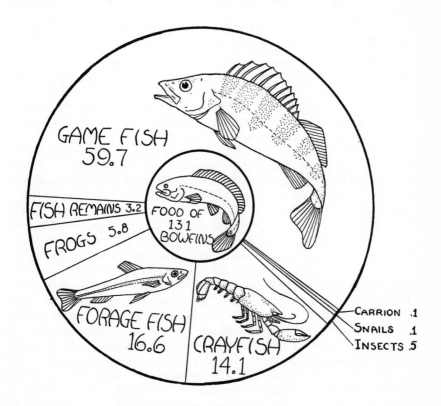

Fig. 32. FOOD CHART. Graphic method of presenting food habits data to show percentage composition of food by volume.

Method of Restoration of Original Properties of Food Items

In order to overcome bias due to differences in rates of digestion of food items, the original weight or volume of individuals of the various items may be restored. Take for example a stomach containing the much-digested remains of an identifiable minnow and a whole, hard-bodied crayfish. One may obtain an approximate volume-when-alive value for the minnow to afford a fairer comparison with the undigested crayfish by measuring an entire specimen of the same species and size from a preserved collection. The original volumetric relationships of other items in a similar condition may be recreated likewise and summarized in their restored condition. This is a cumbersome and tedious procedure and, even if executed successfully, will not alone disclose all of the facts which may be gleaned from the analysis of contents of digestive tracts or droppings. Obviously, in order to apply this method one must be able to identify and substitute proper values for all of the organisms encountered.

It must now be clear indeed that food studies employing the methods described may be relied upon only to show what an animal will eat in a given circumstance. It must also be evident that complete conclusions cannot be drawn from the results of any one method. In order partly to overcome the objections to any single practice, several of the procedures are often combined. The most frequently used combination is numerical, frequency, and volumetric (or gravimetric). From this aggregate one obtains a reasonable appraisal of the kinds of foods eaten, the number of individuals of each kind of food item, the frequency with which each category of food is taken, and the part of all of the food comprised by each kind. When such information is related to observations or experiments on the availability of and preference for the different foods, frequency of feeding, daily food requirements, nutritional value of the different kinds of food items, and efficiency of conversion of each food organism into fish flesh, one is approaching the ideal in food habits work.

Food habit studies should never form the sole basis for appraising the economic or ecological role of any organism. Furthermore, comparisons among species or within species should always be made on analyses of the same kinds of samples. Data from stomachs should not be compared with those from intestines or droppings except when such a comparison is desired per se. Results are best when a large number of samples and a substantial volume of food are analyzed. In cases of doubt, the worker in the field should secure more specimens than he thinks may be needed in order to compensate for those which will be empty or void of worthwhile information. Preferably, no analysis of food habits should be made without good information on the kinds, amount, and availability of food in the habitat. And finally, the biological evidence should be tested statistically before claims as to its nature and significance are made.

COMPARISON OF METHODS OF STUDYING FOOD HABITS

Basic Steps in Procedure	METHOD					
	Numerical	Frequency	% By Bulk	Gravimetric	Volumetric	Restoration
Measure total volume of food in sample			X			
Weigh total mass of food in sample				X		
Sort sample to kind of food item using species or subspecies wherever possible	X	X	X	X	X	X
Count the individuals of each food item in the sample	X					
Total the number of samples in which each food item occurred and convert to percentage frequency		X				
Estimate percentage of total mass in sample which is composed by each food item			X			
Weigh each food item in sample				X		
Calculate percentage which each kind of food composes of total weight of food in the series				X		
Obtain volume of each food item in the sample					X	
Calculate percentage which each kind of food item composes of total volume of food in the series				X	X	
Restore volume (or weight) of each food item in sample						X
Calculate percentage which each kind of food item composes of total restored volume (or weight) of all food in the series of samples						X

STUDY PROGRAM

Analyze the contents of the stomachs of as many fish of one species as possible. Employ the numerical, frequency, and volumetric methods. An appropriately designed blank form will be of assistance both in original tabulation and in summarization (Figs. 33 and 34).

Insofar as possible, work out the food chains of the organisms encountered in the study and prepare a composite diagram of them (as in Fig. 31).

Consult as many published accounts of food habit studies as possible and try to judge their quality and limitations.

SPECIES:..........
SL..........TL..........Wt..........Sex..........
Date..........Time..........
Gear:..........
Collector:

INSTITUTE FOR FISHERIES RESEARCH
DIVISION OF FISHERIES
MICHIGAN DEPARTMENT OF CONSERVATION
COOPERATING WITH THE
UNIVERSITY OF MICHIGAN

FISH STOMACH ANALYSIS RECORD
Lake or Stream:..........
County:..........
T..........R..........S..........
Determination by:

ORGANISM	No. of Species	No. of Individ.	Vol. in cc.	% of Tot. Vol.	ORGANISM	No. of Species	No. of Individ.	Vol. in cc.	% of Tot. Vol.	ORGANISM	No. of Species	No. of Individ.	Vol. in cc.	% of Tot. Vol.
ANNELIDA					Trichoptera					Coleoptera				
MOLLUSCA														
ENTOMOSTRACA					Diptera									
										Lepidoptera				
MALACOSTRACA										Diptera				
AQUATIC INSECTS					ARACHNIDA									
Ephemeroptera					Hydracarina									
					Araneae (Terrest.)									
										Hymenoptera				
					Others									
Odonata														
										Others				
					Total volume									
Plecoptera					TERRESTRIAL INSECTS									
					Collembola					Total volume				
					Orthoptera					FISH				
Hemiptera														
					Psocoptera									
					Homoptera					ALGAE				
Coleoptera										DEBRIS				
					Hemiptera					Inorganic				
										Plant				
										Animal				
										GRAND TOTAL				

L=Larva; P=Pupa; N=Nymph; A=Adult.
Form 5473 2-16-48—2M

For Remarks, see reverse side.

Fig. 33. DETAILED FOOD RECORD CARD.

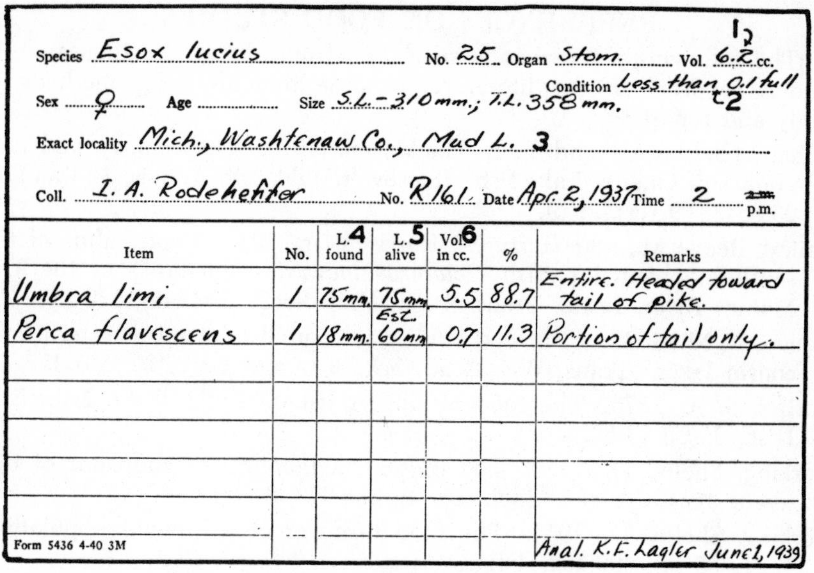

Species Esox lucius No. 25 Organ Stom. Vol. 6.2 cc. 1

Condition Less than 0.1 full 2

Sex ♀ Age ...... Size S.L.-310 mm.; T.L. 358 mm.

Exact locality Mich., Washtenaw Co., Mud L. 3

Coll. I. A. Rodehefer No. R161. Date Apr. 2, 1937 Time 2 p.m.

Item	No.	L. found 4	L. alive 5	Vol. in cc. 6	%	Remarks
Umbra limi	1	75 mm.	75 mm.	5.5	88.7	Entire. Headed toward tail of pike.
Perca flavescens	1	18 mm.	Est. 60 mm.	0.7	11.3	Portion of tail only.

Form 5436 4-40 3M

Anal. K.F. Lagler June 1, 1939

Fig. 34. FOOD RECORD. Simple record card for food analysis: (1) total volume of *food* in organ; (2) degree of organ's relative fullness; (3) exact locality where specimen was collected; (4) size of remains of food organism found in organ; (5) size of food organism when alive; (6) volume of food item by water displacement.

GENERAL REFERENCES

Collinge, W. E. 1927. The food of some British wild birds. York (England), publ. by author, xxii, 427 p.

Cottam, C. 1936. Economic ornithology and the correlation of laboratory and field methods. U.S.B.S. Wildlife Res. and Mgt. Leaflet, BS-30, 13 p. Mimeo.

McAtee, W. L. 1912. Methods of estimating the contents of bird stomachs. Auk, 29: 449-464.

Hess, A. D., and J. H. Rainwater. 1939. A method for measuring the food preference of trout. Copeia, 1939 (3): 154-157.

Hess, A. D., and A. Swartz. 1940. The forage ratio and its use in determining the food grade of streams. Trans. 5th N. Amer. Wildlife Conf., pp. 162-164.

Salyer, J. Clark, II, and Karl F. Lagler. 1940. The food and habits of the American Merganser during winter in Michigan, considered in relation to fish management. Jour. Wildlife Mgt., 4 (2): 186-219. (Contains description of methods)

Wight, H. M. 1938. Field and laboratory technic in wildlife management. Ann Arbor, Univ. Mich. Press, 107 p., 37 figs.

REFERENCES ON FOOD STUDIES

The following references were chosen from among the thousands of studies reported in the literature, because they illustrate methods of study and reporting.

Adams, Charles C., and T. L. Hankinson. 1928. The ecology and economics of Oneida Lake fish. Roosevelt Wild Life Annals, 1 (3 and 4): 235-548, 69 figs., 4 pl.

Bailey, Reeve M., and Harry M. Harrison, Jr. 1948. Food habits of the southern channel catfish (*Ictalurus lacustris punctatus*) in the Des Moines River, Iowa. Trans. Amer. Fish. Soc., 75 (1945): 110-138.

Couey, F. M. 1935. Fish food studies in a number of northeastern Wisconsin lakes. Trans. Wis. Acad. Sci., Arts and Lett., 29: 131-172.

Forbes, S. A. 1878. The food of Illinois fishes. Bull. Ill. St. Lab. Nat. Hist., 1 (2): 71-86.

Gerking, Shelby D. 1952. The protein metabolism of sunfishes of different ages. Physiol. Zool., 25 (4): 358-372, 3 figs.

Gerking, Shelby D. 1954. The food turnover of a bluegill population. Ecol., 35 (4): 490-498, 4 figs.

Ivlev, V. S. 1945. The biological productivity of waters. (Translated by W. E. Ricker.) Adv. Mod. Biol., 19: 98-120.

REFERENCES ON FOOD ORGANISMS

Morgan, A. H. 1930. Field book on ponds and streams. New York, G. P. Putnam's Sons, 448 p., 23 pl.

Needham, James G., and Paul R. Needham. 1951. A guide to the study of fresh-water biology with special reference to aquatic insects and other invertebrate animals and phyto-plancton. Ithaca, Comstock Publishing Company, Inc., 89 p., many figs. 4th ed., rev.

Needham, James G., and Minter J. Westfall, Jr. 1955. A manual of the dragonflies of North America (Anisoptera). Berkeley, Univ. California Press, xii, 615 p., 341 figs., col. frontis.

Pennak, Robert W. 1953. Fresh-water invertebrates of the United States. New York, The Ronald Press, ix, 769 p., 470 figs.

Peterson, Alvah. Larvae of insects, an introduction to Nearctic species. Columbus, Ohio, publ. by author, Pt. I, 315 p., Pt. II, v, 416 p.

Prescott, G. W. 1951. Algae of the western Great Lakes area exclusive of desmids and diatoms. Bull. Cranbrook Inst. Sci., 31, xiii, 946 p., 136 pl.

Smith, Gilbert M. 1950. The fresh-water algae of the United States. New York, McGraw-Hill Book Company, Inc., 719 p., 449 figs. Rev. ed.

Wright, Anna Allen, and Albert Hazen Wright. 1949. Handbook of Frogs and Toads. Ithaca, The Comstock Publishing Co., Inc., xii, 640 p., 126 pl., 37 maps.

Chapter IX

Age and Growth

A knowledge of the age and rate of growth of a fish is extremely useful in management, and of great biological interest. Although the actual processes of assessing age and of determining growth rates are different, they are very closely related and are usually conducted together; the question in most instances is: "How long does it take a fish to attain a certain length (or weight)?" Thus the analyses are most often called "age and growth studies."

Age and growth work has its practical applications in dealing with the following problems:

(1) At what age does a fish attain sexual maturity? How long must it be held to reach breeding age? How soon will a fresh stock of young reproduce?

(2) At what age will a given species reach catchable size? This is important for fishery regulations.

(3) Determination of the age reached in a given environment may help to discover environmental unsuitabilities.

(4) A comparison of the rate of fish growth in different bodies of water may partly identify good or bad environmental conditions and point the way for future action.

(5) Relation of age and growth in any one body of water to a regional average, as in (4), is a measure of environmental suitability for the species in question.

(6) A partial test of attempts at environmental improvement is afforded by the effect of the changes made on growth rate.

(7) Age and growth studies, may also show suitability of stocking, used as a follow-up measure, (subsidiary to point 6).

(8) Continuing studies of age and growth in particular bodies of water will show the normal fluctuations from year to year and over periods of years—necessary for the proper interpretation of deviations which single samples may show from a regional average (such long-range studies are currently much needed; characteristics of samples from one single year have in general been too much relied upon as indicative of the growth characteristics of fishes in a given body of water).

GENERAL METHODS IN AGE AND GROWTH STUDIES

There are several methods which have been used in age and growth studies in fishes: (1) known age method; (2) length-frequency method; (3) otolith and bone methods; (4) scale method. In the following pages we shall deal with each of these in turn.

Known Age Method

If one takes young-of-the-year fish, places them in a rearing pond, holds them through one or more seasons, and takes periodic samples to determine growth, he is applying the known age method. One may also release tagged, fin-clipped, or otherwise marked fish (Fig. 52) of known age in natural waters and recapture them at intervals for study. Such procedures are of particular value in determining growth potential and in providing verification of other methods. They may serve, for example, as a means for identifying year marks on scale or other bony structures.

Length-Frequency Method

This method is based on the expectancy that frequency analysis of the individuals of a species of any one age-group collected on the same date will show variation around the mean length according to normal distribution (normal bell curve when graphed); it is based further on the expectation that when data for a sample of the entire population are plotted, there will be clumping of fish of successive ages about successive given lengths, making possible a separation by age-groups. Petersen (1891) is said to have made the original statement of this method.

Basic prerequisites for good results with the length-frequency method are the following characteristics of the sample: it must be (1) composed of a large number of individuals, (2) collected in a restricted period of time (in a single day, preferably), and (3) made up of good representation of all of the size- and age-groups in the population. These conditions are seldom met all together; the most common failing is due to selectivity of the method or gear used in collecting. Even when sampling conditions are nearly ideal, as in complete draining or poisoning of waters and recovery of most of the fish, the method normally fails to give reliable estimates of length at various ages beyond those attained by the end of the second or third growing season. As a result, the length-frequency method of age assessment is largely limited in its use to: (1) estimation of mean lengths in younger age-groups; (2) validation of other methods of age assessment described below.

Otolith and Bone Methods

Otoliths (ear stones) and various bones such as ones in the opercular series (Le Cren, 1947), vertebral centra (Fig. 35) (Hooper, 1949), fin rays (Classen, 1944), etc., show zones of differential deposition of bony material. They often exhibit their growth zones best on one of their surfaces which has been polished on a fine abrasive wheel or stone. When these marks can be correlated with annual growth, they are usable for aging fish. Both transmitted and reflected light have been employed to facilitate study of these structures.

The otolith method has been used successfully (with limitations in older age-groups where the lines tend to merge) for sturgeon (Harkness, 1923; Greeley, 1937), for shad (Barney, 1925), plaice (Reibisch, 1899; re-

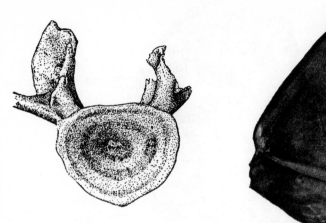

Fig. 35. ANNUAL GROWTH MARKS ON BONE. At left: Enlarged drawing of vertebra of a madtom catfish showing two annual rings darkened circles on centrum). At right: photo-enlargement of opercle of yellow perch showing five annual marks.

ported first use), etc. Lagler and Obrecht were unable to achieve satisfactory results on gars perhaps because of a too great and variable growth potential of these forms (unpublished). Otolith weight has been used successfully for age determination.

Scale Method

Scales, like other bony structures, show seasonal changes in rate of growth. This is particularly true in those waters which become cold enough to interrupt growth for a part of each year. The scale method is the most widely used of all routines in age and growth studies. Because of the way in which they have been demonstrated faithfully to reflect changes in rate of growth for some species, scales also yield other valuable life history information. For example, the time when young salmon or steelheads enter the sea may be told by the sharp increase in spacing of annuli on the scales (as in Fig. 38).

The remainder of this chapter is devoted largely to the scale method because of its general utility.

SCALES OF FRESHWATER FISHES
(See Appendix A)

In order to use scales in age and growth studies, it is necessary to know something of their structure and the special terminology applied to them.

The principal types of scales of freshwater fishes are: **ganoid, bony plates** of sturgeon; **rhombic, ganoid plates** of gars; **cycloid scales** of trout,

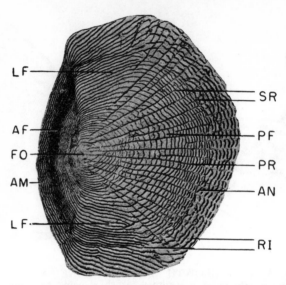

Fig. 36. STRUCTURE OF CYCLOID SCALE. Cycloid scale of common shiner, *Notropis cornutus*, enlarged; LF, lateral field; AF, anterior field; FO, focus; AM, anterior margin; SR, secondary radii; PF, posterior field; PR, primary radius; AN, annulus; RI, ridges (circuli).

minnows, and most other soft-rayed fishes; and **ctenoid scales** of perch, bass, sunfish and most other spiny-rayed fishes. Examine a specimen or a good photograph of each type. With reference to cycloid scales (Figs. 36 and 38), note the **focus, radii,** and the more or less concentric **circuli** (perhaps better called **ridges** on those scales where they are more or less longitudinal or transverse rather than concentric). Distinguish between **anterior** and **posterior margins**; identify the **exposed portion** of the scale. In addition on ctenoid scales (Figs. 37 and 39) note the teeth (**ctenii**) on the posterior margin. A synonymy and definition of scale parts is given in Lagler, 1947.

The structure of ordinary scales is admirably described by Creaser (1926). You are referred to his account for an expansion of the following material.

Scales may lie in a mosaic pattern (eel, burbot) or be imbricated (i.e., overlapping like shingles, most fishes) and are variously shaped depending upon differences in direction of growth. A part of the focus is the first part of the scale to be developed. It is often located at the center, but in the case of widely overlapping scales its position becomes decentralized due to unequal growth of the anterior and posterior areas of the scale.

Ridges or circuli are produced on the first-formed stratum of the outer layer of the scale and are composed of a transparent homogeneous substance called hyalodentine. They are not the peripheral rims of superimposed laminae, as has often been held, and in fact are not de-

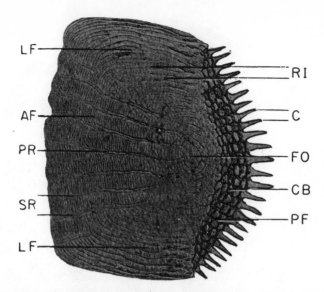

Fig. 37. STRUCTURE OF CTENOID SCALE. Ctenoid scale of green-
side darter, *Etheostoma blennioides,* enlarged; LF, lateral field; AF, anterior
field; PR, primary radius; SR, secondary radii; RI, ridges (circuli); C, ctenii;
FO, focus; CB, basal portions of previous ctenii; PF, posterior field.

posited in any relation to them. According to Creaser, "a ridge is not
built up simultaneously in all its parts. Various detached portions of its
length may be under construction at the same time." These parts may
eventually unite to form a more or less continuous circulus.

Seasonal cessation of growth or other factors may result in one or
more discontinuous ridges on the scale located between two continuous
ones. This is one of the criteria which identifies an annulus or year
mark. Examine such an annual mark on a trout scale (Fig. 38 shows
three distinct annuli identifiable by this characteristic).

Scales of such fishes as the sunfishes and minnows show some of the
circuli ending at different places along the lateral margin at the time of
annulus formation. On the resumption of growth, new ridges parallel
the entire scale margin and hence cut across the unfinished ends of the
outcurved ridges. This feature of "cutting over" is a second aid in the
identification of annuli in some fishes. The one annulus on Fig 39 shows
this cutting over of previous circuli very well.

A third character very useful in the recognition of the annuli of certain fishes is the relative approximation of the circuli. Circuli are often
closer together just inside the line which marks the annulus and farther
apart just outside of it. This character shows well on Fig. 36.

Sometimes the annulus is marked by a clear, narrow streak encircling
the focus, but more often it is not so easily identified. This clear zone,
along with the foregoing criteria, may aid in determining the approximate

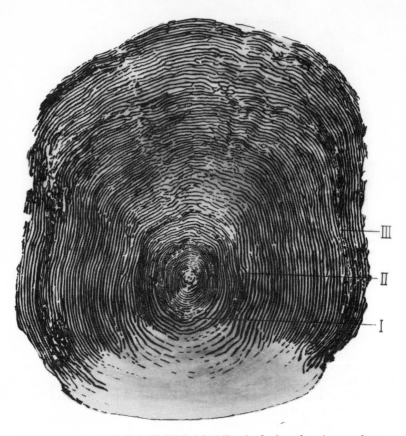

Fig. 38. ANNULI ON TROUT SCALE. Cycloid scale of a rainbow
trout 25 inches long and 5.5 pounds in weight. Enlarged. Three
annuli show (I, II, II).

location of the annulus. All of these characteristics, however, are usually
not in evidence on the scales of any one fish species.

Some scales will be found to have an abnormally large focus; these
are replacement or regenerated scales. The enlarged focus represents the
size of the scale lost by the fish. Replacement scales are hardly usable
for age and growth work. Other scales will be useless because of confusion arising over the presence of supernumerary checks that are not
true annuli. Still other species have annual growth characteristics that
are not reflected in scale structure. The scale worker must take great
care to be highly objective throughout the application of this method.

VALIDITY OF ANNULI ON SCALES AS YEAR MARKS

In general, the use of scales, once it has proven applicable to a species, has shown itself to be the simplest and most accurate means of study-

Fig. 39. ANNULUS ON SUNFISH SCALE. Ctenoid scale of blue-gill, 4.3 inches long. Enlarged. One annulus is in evidence (I).

ing age and growth. After the investigator has gained some experience, annuli on scales of many fishes are easily determined, and have been successfully used both in aging fish and in reconstructing their past growth history. The validity of annuli as year-marks has been established for many species. The evidence used has been summarized by Hile (1941) on whose account the following comments are based.

Annuli may be regarded as year marks if:

1. There is a proper correlation between the presumable age of a fish and its size.

    (a) Regularity in increase in the number of annuli should be accompanied by increase in size of fish, to prove that occurrence of annuli on scales is not haphazard, but that annuli are added systematically as growth proceeds.

    (b) Modes in the length-frequency distribution of small fish should coincide with the modal lengths of corresponding age-groups based on scale readings.

2. There are agreements among calculated growth histories.
   (a) Lengths at the end of various years of life calculated from scale measurements should agree well with the corresponding empirical lengths of younger age-groups whose ages were determined by the examination of scales.
   (b) There should be good agreement among data
      (1) on calculated growth (method for calculating growth described later in this book) of fish of the same age-groups in different years' collections;
      (2) for different age-groups of the same or different years' collections;
      (3) on growth histories of the different age-groups (yearlings, two-year-olds, etc.) of the same year-class (a year-class is composed of the fish spawned in any one calendar year).
   (c) There should be good agreement among different year-classes as to the goodness or poorness of growth in certain calendar years.
3. There is persistent abundance or scarcity of certain year-classes in collections over several years.

The foregoing arguments are fundamental and should be thoroughly understood. They may be applied to determine whether or not evident growth marks are annuli. Validity of annulus-like markings should not be assumed for species where their worth has not been proven. The worker should avoid being misled by "spawning checks," "false annuli," or other annulus-like marks which may be due to any one of several causes such as resorption, interruption of growth by bodily injury, disease, or spawning.

SCALE SAMPLES FOR AGE AND GROWTH STUDIES

A standard procedure is essential in the collection of scale samples for age and growth determination. The utmost care should be exercised to gather complete data on all specimens and to be uniform in methods of handling. The following is an outline of general methods, which may be modified to suit particular investigational needs.

Scale Envelopes
Coin envelopes are frequently used for holding scales and for recording field data (Fig. 40). It is best to print on the envelope headings with blank spaces for data to cover all needs of an ordinary investigation, leaving space for additional notes.

To facilitate subsequent removal of scale samples, each envelope may be loaded with a folded slip of paper into which the scales are placed.

Before removing scales from the fish, it is well to complete the information called for on the envelope.

Species. Give common name of the fish if this will identify the species with certainty. Otherwise give the technical name. Care must be

```
┌─────────────────────────────────────────────────────────┐
│                 DEPARTMENT OF FISHERIES                   │
│    SCHOOL OF NATURAL RESOURCES—UNIVERSITY OF MICHIGAN     │
│  Species ................................................ │
│  Locality .............................................. │
│  How taken ............................ Time ...... a.m.  │
│                                               p.m.        │
│  Collector ................................ Date .......  │
│  ─────────────────────────────────────────────────────── │
│  S.L. .................. T.L. ................. Wt. ..... │
│  Sex ............. Maturity and state of organs ........  │
│  Annuli ......................... Cond. ................  │
└─────────────────────────────────────────────────────────┘
```

Fig. 40.   IMPRINT ON SCALE SAMPLE ENVELOPE.

taken to classify the fish correctly, since erroneous identifications will destroy the worth of the sample and perhaps the whole study. Hybrids demand particular care for their identification.

Locality. Give as a minimum the name of the lake or stream and the county in which it is located. Investigational needs may require more specific information.

How taken. Give method of capture; this information is useful in establishing the degree of freedom from bias which is possessed by the sample.

Time. Useful for determining periods of greatest activity and movement, and also useful in the study of feeding habits and food. The number assigned to the scale sample and written on the envelope may be repeated on a small piece of paper and slipped under the opercle or into the mouth of a specimen subsequently to be preserved whole for other use.

Collector. Name of collector.

Date. Give date on which collection was made.

Length. Ordinarily, the lengths should be given to the nearest millimeter or 0.1 of an inch, as desired, and should be taken when the fish is fresh and not bent in rigor mortis. The measurement of length is made in a straight line, not over the curvature of the body (Fig. 41).

Standard length. The most commonly used "standard length "measurement in fishery operations does not always coincide with the standard length used by ichthyologists. The employment of a measuring board (Fig. 42) is responsible for this; note the difference when snout is ter-

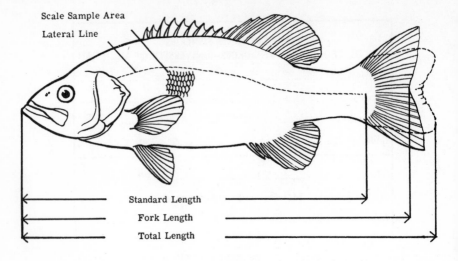

Scale Sample Area

Lateral Line

Standard Length

Fork Length

Total Length

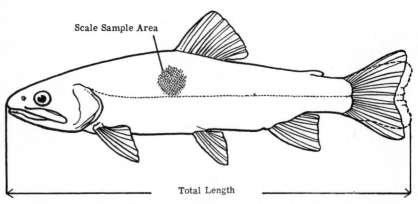

Scale Sample Area

Total Length

Fig. 41. FISH MEASUREMENTS. Measurements commonly used (when a measuring board is employed), and scale sampling areas often employed in fishery research. Other sample areas sometimes provide more readable scales. Spiny-rayed fish, above; soft-rayed fish below. Note that total length measurement requires compressed tail to give niaximum elongation.

minal and when the lower jaw is terminal (Fig. 41). Measure to the hidden bases of the caudal fin rays, where a groove forms naturally when the tail is bent from side to side.

Total length. This is the greatest possible length of the fish with mouth closed and caudal rays squeezed together to give the maximum over-all measurement (Fig. 41).

Fork length. Fork length is advocated by some fishery workers; it is measured from anteriormost extremity to the notch in the tail fin of fork-tailed fishes (or to center of fin when tail is not forked).

Fig. 42. MEASURING. Measuring fish on a
conventional, fishery measuring board.

Weight. Give the total weight to the nearest 0.1 ounce, gram, or to
the nearest 0.1 gram, as equipment permits or investigational needs dictate (Fig. 43). Be consistent in usage as well as degree of wetness for
any one study.

Sex. The sex should be determined whenever possible. With some
practice this can be done even on immature fish. It should be executed
to the smallest possible sizes so that any shifts in sex ratio with age may
be noted, and so that differences in rates of growth of the sexes may be
determined. Sex should be determined by inspection of the gonads
and not by observation of secondary sexual characters which often fails.

Maturity and state of sexual organs. One should determine whether
the fish is sexually immature, mature, ripe, or spent. These factors bear
on the coefficient of condition of the fish which may be calculated in the
laboratory, and on determinations of the length-weight relationship, and
should therefore be recorded at the time of capture.

To standardize the classification of stages of maturity of the sex organs in age and growth studies, the following proposals of W. C. Beckman (unpublished) may be adopted. **During the spawning season** of any
particular species, classify the organs as **immature, ripe,** or **spent.** Immature means that there are no grossly visible eggs or milt. Ripe means
that the fish contain evident eggs or sperms, and spent indicates that
the fish has spawned. **During the remainder of the year** classify fish as
immature (no eggs or milt evident as such by gross inspection) and **mature** (eggs or milt grossly apparent). In the northern United States and
southern Canada, the spawning period of warmwater fishes (bass, bluegills, sunfish, etc.) may for convenience in reckoning be set as May 1
to July 15; for pike and perch, April 1 to May 15; for rainbow trout,

Fig. 43. WEIGHING. Method of weighing large fish in the field on spring balance.

April 1 to May 15; for brook or brown trout, Oct. 1 to Dec. 15. If fish are found to be shedding eggs or milt at times other than these, a statement to this effect should be placed on the scale envelope. A similar definition of spawning period may be made for other species and for other regions.

Taking the Scale Sample

In order to be comparable, scale samples must be removed from the same region of the body of each fish. For some studies "key scales" are taken; these are identical scales or the same scale on each fish of the series, as determined by count along the lateral line, and then again by count above or below it.

In general investigations, about 20 scales are taken from the fish. When fish are to be returned to the water after being scale-sampled, fewer scales should be taken; 10 or less might suffice. If it is a spiny-rayed form, they are often taken from the side of the body below the origin of the dorsal fin and just below the lateral line (Fig. 41). In soft-rayed fishes, the sample is frequently taken from the side of the body just above the lateral line and below the origin of the dorsal fin (Fig. 41). In special investigations, of course, various other regions may be chosen. Where detailed analyses are intended, it is best to study the structure of scales from different parts of the body and to choose the area for sampling in which the scale markings are clearest and most faithful.

The scales may be removed with a knife or with a forceps, that is cleaned between samples. Scraping the epidermis and mucous from the scales before removing them reduces subsequent labor required for cleaning at the time of mounting or making other preparation for study.

PREPARATION OF SCALES FOR STUDY

Several methods have been used for preparing scales for study. Since magnification is necessary for reading scales, remains of soft integument, chromatophores, etc., are best removed and more or less permanent mounts prepared.

Cleaning Scales

Scales may be cleaned in water by scrubbing them with a small, hard-bristled brush or with a sharpened skewer or other stick. Soaking for an hour or more makes the cleaning easier. Care must be taken not to break the margins of the scales and not to disrupt the softer, inner surface.

Temporary Mounts

Wet or dry temporary mounts of cleaned scales may be made. Dry mounts are best when held between microscope slides; if the weight of the slide does not keep the scales flat, the ends of the slide may be pressed down with rubber bands or with cellophane or adhesive tape.

Permanent Mounts

Such mounts are of two principal sorts: (1) celluloid or plastic impressions; (2) permanent mounts of whole scales.

Impression methods. Dry scales may be impressed with strong pressure on untreated cellulose acetate, or with light pressure following surface softening of the plastic with acetone. A practical roller press (Fig. 44) which improves older methods by eliminating the need for heat has been described by Smith (1954). Impression methods are particularly useful in preparing for study scales on which markings are obscured by opaqueness (Greenbank and O'Donnell, 1950). Since one may not secure an imprint of the entire margin of a scale, great care should be taken in using pressed images for measurement in calculated growth studies. Scale proportions are not distorted in the press described by Smith (1954) when properly used.

Mounting media methods. Easily obtained mounting media that have been used for whole-mounts of fish scales are: waterglass (sodium silicate); glycerin-waterglass mixture; karo syrup (clear, white); euparol; balsam; gum arabic; polyvinyl alcohol (PVA); and glycerin-gelatin mixture. The latter mixture is at present most widely used because it is easily prepared, inexpensive, and relatively permanent. It further has a reasonably suitable index of refraction, and scales may be mounted directly from water. The slides, cover slips, and other equipment are easily cleaned with water for re-use.

Fig. 44. ROLLER PRESS. Used for making impressions of surface markings of fish scales on plastic. (From Smith, 1954)

The following formula (Van Oosten, 1929) gives good results: Dissolve 8 ounces of gelatin (sheet gelatin, white preferred, cut into bits) in 850 cc. of water and add 250 cc. of glycerin; warm the mixture to dissolve gelatin, taking care to avoid water loss; place in small jars and add a few drops or crystals of phenol to each to keep molds from growing in them. Use hot (not boiling) for mounting.

STUDY PROGRAMS AND REFERENCES

Study Program on General References

Bibliographies and reviews of literature on the age and growth of fishes are to be found in the publications listed below. As a minimum requirement, it is expected that the student acquaint himself with the nature of the contents of all papers published in this country. With the exception of Mohr, 1927, the arrangement of this list is chronological.

Dahl, Knut. 1909. The assessment of age and growth in fish. Internationale Revue der gesamten Hydrobiologie und Hydrographie, 2 (4-5); 758-769, 6 text-figs. (Leipzig) (Historical resumé)

Taylor, Harden F. 1916. The structure and growth of the scales of the squeteague and the pigfish as indicative of life history. Bull. U. S. Bur. Fish., 34 (1914): 285-330, 8 text-figs., 10 pl.

Lee, Rosa M. [Mrs. T. L. Williams]. 1920. A review of the methods of age and growth determination in fishes by means of scales. Min. Agric. and Fish., Fish. Invest., ser. 2, 4 (2): 1-32, 8 diag., 1 pl. (London)

Hutton, J. Arthur. 1921. The literature of fish scales. Salmon and Trout Magazine, 26: 203-217. (London)

Creaser, Charles W. 1926. The structure and growth of the scales of fishes in relation to the interpretation of their life-history, with special reference to the sunfish Eupomotis gibbosus. Misc. Publ. Univ. Mich. Mus. Zool., 17, 82 p., 12 figs., 1 pl.

Van Oosten, John. 1929. Life history of the lake herring (*Leucichthys artedi* LeSueur) of Lake Huron as revealed by its scales, with a critique of the scale method. Bull. U. S. Bur. Fish., 44 (1928): 265-428, 43 figs.

Graham, Michael. 1929. Studies of age-determination in fish. Part II. A survey of the literature. Min. Agric. and Fish., Fish. Invest., ser. 2, 11 (3) (1928): 5-50. (Abstracts some 70 papers) (London)

Mohr, Erna W. 1927. Bibliographie der Alters- und Wachstums-Bestimmung bei Fischen. Jour. du Conseil, 2 (2): 236-258. (Copenhagen)

Mohr, Erna W. 1930. Bibliographie der Alters- und Wachstums-Bestimmung bei Fischen, II. Nachträge und Fortsetzung. Jour. du Conseil, 5 (1): 88-100. (Copenhagen)

Mohr, Erna W. 1934. Bibliographie der Alters- und Wachstums-Bestimmung bei Fischen, III. Nachträge und Fortsetzung. Jour. du Conseil, 9 (3): 377-391. (Copenhagen)

Hile, Ralph. 1936. Age and growth of the cisco, *Leucichthys artedi* (Le Sueur), in the lakes of the northeastern highlands, Wisconsin. Bull. U. S. Bur. Fish., 48 (1935): 211-317, 11 figs.

Carlander, Kenneth D. 1953. Handbook . . . (see p. 80)

Study Program on Length-Frequency Method

Complete the following exercise:

1. Secure a large (200 or more specimens) sample of one species of fish from a population as nearly on one date as possible and as randomly representative of all lengths as possible.

2. Make the same length measurement on all (preferably do this prior to preservation and also obtain fresh weight, sex, and a scale sample, following procedures given earlier in this chapter).

3. Group the data in small intervals of size, if desired, and construct a frequency polygon of the lengths.

4. Estimate average lengths of various age-groups insofar as possible from the peaks of the polygon.

5. If the scales of these fishes are used in subsequent exercises for age determination, re-evaluate your estimates made in (4) above, in the light of lengths at various ages learned from scale reading.

6. Discuss briefly the utility and limitations of the method as applied by you, with particular reference to biases imposed by various characteristics of your sample.

References on Length-Frequency Method

Applegate, Vernon C. 1943. Partial analysis of growth in a population of mudminnows, *Umbra limi* (Kirtland). Copeia, 1943 (2): 92-96.

Creaser, Charles W. 1926. The structure and growth of the scales of fishes in relation to the interpretation of their life-history, with special reference to the sunfish Eupomotis gibbosus. Misc. Publ. Univ. Mich. Mus. Zool., 17, 82 p.

Lagler, Karl F., and Vernon C. Applegate. 1943. Age and growth of the gizzard shad, Dorosoma cepedianum (LeSuer), with a discussion of its value as a buffer and as forage of game fishes. Invest. Ind. Lakes and Streams, 2 (1942): 99-110.

Petersen, C. G. J. 1891. Eine Methode zur Bestimmung des Alters und Wuchses der Fische. Mitth. Deutsch. Seefischerei Ver., 11: 226-235.

References on Known Age Method

Applegate, Vernon C. 1947. Growth of some lake trout, *Cristivomer n. namaycush*, of known age in inland Michigan lakes. Copeia, 1947 (4): 237-241.

Van Oosten, John. 1923. A study of the scales of whitefishes of known ages. Zoologica, 2 (17): 380-412.

References on Otolith and Bone Methods

Barney, R. L. 1925. A confirmation of Borodin's scale method of age determination of Connecticut River shad. Pt. 3 [In] A report of investigations concerning shad in the rivers of Connecticut. Conn. St. Bd. Fish. and Game, pp. 52-60, 4 figs. (Otoliths used)

Classen, T. E. A. 1944. Estudio bio-estadístico del esturión o sollo del Guadalquivir (*Acipenser sturio* L.). Inst. Espanol de Oceanografia, Trab. 19, pp. 52-70, 3 figs., 17 pl. (Fin rays for age assessment)

Greeley, J. R. 1937. Fishes of the area with annotated list. Pt. 2 [In] A biological survey of the lower Hudson watershed. N. Y. St. Cons. Dept., Suppl. 26th Ann. Rept., (1936), pp. 45-103, (Otoliths of sturgeon), 13 text-figs., 4 col. pl.

Harkness, W. J. K. 1923. The rate of growth and the food of the lake sturgeon (*Acipenser rubicundus* LeSueur). Publ. Ont. Fish. Res. Lab., 18: 15-42, 6 figs.

Hooper, Frank F. 1949. Age analysis of a population of the ameiurid fish *Schilbeodes mollis* (Hermann). Copeia, 1949 (1): 34-38, 3 figs. (Vertebrae for age assessment)

Le Cren, E. D. 1947. The determination of the age and growth of the perch (*Perca fluviatilis*) from opercular bone. Jour. Animal Ecol., 16 (2): 188-204. 6 figs., 1 pl.

Reibisch, J. 1899. Ueber die Eizahl bei *Pleuronectes platessa* und die Alterbestimmung dieser Form aus den Otolithen. Wiss. Meeresuntersuch., (Kiel), n.s. 4: 233-248.

Tenaglia, G. 1925. Structure of otoliths by dark-ground illumination. Atti. Soc., Lomb. Soc. Med. Biol., 14: 186-194.

References on Scales

Creaser, Charles W. 1926. The structure and growth of the scales of fishes in relation to the interpretation of their life-history, with special reference to the sunfish Eupomotis gibbosus. Misc. Publ. Univ. Mich. Mus. Zool., 17, 82 pp.

Lagler, Karl F. 1947. Lepidological studies 1. Scale characters of the families of Great Lakes fishes. Trans. Amer. Microscop. Soc., 66 (2): 149-171, 42 figs.

References on Validity of Annuli

Hile, Ralph. 1941. Age and growth of the rock bass, *Ambloplites rupestris* (Rafinesque), in Nebish Lake, Wisconsin. Trans. Wis. Acad. Sci., Arts and Lett., 33: 189-337, 14 figs.

Cooper, Edwin L. 1951. Validation of the use of scales of brook trout, *Salvelinus fontinalis,* for age determination. Copeia, 1951 (2): 141-148, 2 pl.

Study Program on Taking Scale Samples

To complete his training in this section of age and growth work the student should:

(1) Thoroughly understand the procedures described for taking scale samples.
(2) Learn how to use a measuring board.
(3) Learn how to sex fish without unduly mutilating them and how to estimate maturity and condition of sexual organs.
(4) Take scale samples from several species of fishes for subsequent preparation for study.

References on Taking Scale Samples

Carlander, Kenneth D., and Lloyd L. Smith, Jr. 1945. Some factors to consider in the choice between standard, fork, or total lengths in fishery investigations. Copeia, 1945 (1): 7-12.

Hile, Ralph. 1948. Standardization of methods of expressing lengths and weights of fish. Trans. Amer. Fish. Soc., 75 (1945): 157-164.

Ricker, William E., and Daniel Merriman. 1945. On the methods of measuring fish. Copeia, 1945 (4): 185-191.

Scattergood, Leslie W. 1950. Fish and shellfish measuring devices. Jour. Wildlife Mgt., 14 (2): 147-151.

Study Program on Preparation of Scales for Study

See demonstrations of as many methods of preparing scales for study as you can. Examine critically the products of each of these methods. Prepare a brief statement covering the advantages and/or disadvantages of each method. For the mounting media methods consider each medium separately, particularly from the point of view of ease in handling, relative permanence, and optical properties (especially index of refraction) in relation to those of fish scales.

Make a number of preparations using the available facilities. Practice until you gain acceptable proficiency. Label your preparations to indicate species, scale sample number, body of water, date of collection, sex, and length. Most of these facts are needed for the accurate interpretation of scale marks and annuli, and it is convenient to have them on each preparation.

References on Preparation of Scales for Study

Campbell, Robert S., and Arthur Witt, Jr. 1953. Impressions of fish scales in plastic. Jour. Wildlife Mgt., 17 (2): 218-219, 1 fig.

Greenbank, John, and D. John O'Donnell. 1950. Hydraulic presses for making impressions of fish scales. Trans. Amer. Fish. Soc., 78 (1948); 32-33, 2 figs.

Smith, Stanford H. 1954. Method of producing plastic impressions of fish scales without using heat. Prog. Fish-Cult., 16 (2): 75-78, 2 figs.

Van Oosten, John. 1929. Life history of the lake herring (*Leucichthys artedi* LeSueur) of Lake Huron as revealed by its scales, with a critique of the scale method. U. S. Bur. Fish. Bull., 44 (1928): 265-428, 43 figs.

Chapter X

Age and Growth (Continued)[1]

DETERMINATION OF AGE AND RATE OF GROWTH

As indicated in the preceding chapter, the assessment of age by read-ing annuli or year marks on scales requires certain preliminary steps. The exact nature of the annuli and their identity as true year marks must first be established. This may be accomplished by the tests previously de-scribed. It may also be done in part by applying the Petersen (length-frequency) method to a large series of specimens to determine age-groups, and comparing the results with those based on marks on scales. Or, it may be achieved simply by checking annuli on scales from fish of known age.

It is not a foregone conclusion that even the clearest growth marks are annuli. It is imperative that the validity of this method for aging fish be tested for each species for which it has not been ascertained pre-viously. The possibility of error in this regard is particularly evident in fishes from southern waters which may have many or no checks on their scales for each year of life, but may have no true annuli. Further-more, one must be able to distinguish spawning marks (as on scales of salmon) and other checks from annuli.

Accurate assignment of age is often made difficult or impossible by lack of knowledge of time of annulus formation. Unless this time is known it may be hard to tell whether the marginal area outside the last evident annulus represents the increment for the entire previous sea-son's growth, or whether it constitutes growth during the new growing season. This is particularly true for fish collected in spring and early summer in northern waters. Study of scale samples taken systematically through the first six months of each year will answer the question for most species (see Beckman, 1943).

For age determinations, fish scales must be enlarged; the following methods are in use for this purpose.

Photographic Method

Scales may be used as photographic negatives and as such be pro-jected onto enlarging paper (such as Kodabromide; glossy, white, con-trast) and studied in this way. Although providing a fine record of the scales, this method is time consuming and costly—but not nearly as ex-pensive as if large pieces of film are exposed.

---

[1]Bibliographic entries for some of the literature citations in this chapter are to be found in the lists of references at the end of Chapter IX.

Microscopic Method

An ordinary compound or binocular microscope may be employed for assessing age of scales, but measurements are rather precluded by this method; an ocular micrometer may, however, be used. For small scales (such as those of brook trout), a camera lucida may be engaged to obtain the measurements needed for growth calculation or determination of body-scale relationship.

Projection Method

Various types of microprojection apparatuses are suited for scale study, including some of very simple design such as that described by Mosher (1950). The basic type of machine is that of Van Oosten-Deason-Jobes (1934) as shown in Figs. 45 and 46, a modification of which is now produced commercially (Bausch and Lomb). In the construction of a scale machine any good microprojector may be used, provided that it

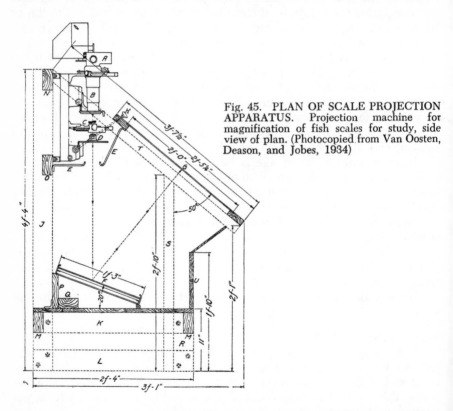

Fig. 45. PLAN OF SCALE PROJECTION APPARATUS. Projection machine for magnification of fish scales for study, side view of plan. (Photocopied from Van Oosten, Deason, and Jobes, 1934)

will accommodate the required objectives. Some workers have claimed advantages in the use of polarized light in such machines for the identification of annuli (e.g., Savage, 1919, and Schoffman, 1939), but it is not generally employed and not really necessary.

Descriptive legend for Figure 45. A, light housing of microprojector. B, condenser (need not be of tube-type shown). As shown, C is the stage on which the prepared scale is placed and D is the lens; here the lens is movable and the stage is fixed but moving the lens for focusing may change the magnfication of successive images; this difficulty may be overcome by having the lens fixed and the stage movable for focusing. For general use, at least a 32 mm. (for larger scales) microtessar lens and a 16 mm. lens (for smaller scales) are required at D. J, vertical upright 4″ x 4″ stock; M, N, O, 2″ x 4″ cross braces. K and L are end braces of 2″ x 4″ stock. The front posts, R, are 4″ x 4″ material. G is the projection screen and may be opal glass, white coated glass, or sheet rubber, Translite film, or tracing cloth secured between two pieces of plate glass. The screen frame has slanting braces, T, and uprights S. The screen is set at 40° with the horizontal whereas the mirror (G) below is set at 20°; these angles may be varied if this ratio is exactly maintained. A shield, E, of galvanized iron with a 4″ aperture is beneath the projector. Plywood may be used to cover the frame, and may largely replace the frame if 5-ply is used for the whole box. U is the front partition. H is the remote control of gears (from a small speed drill) and flexible cable attached to the focusing device of the original microprojection unit. The unit may be adapted for map tracing (by substituting plate glass for the screen) and for photomicrography (by substituting a plywood panel with a central hole and interchangeable focusing glass and negative holder).

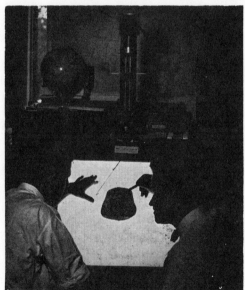

Fig. 46. COMPLETED SCALE PROJECTOR IN USE. A photographic enlargement of a trout scale has been pasted on viewing glass to show appearance of a projected scale when studied.

BODY-SCALE RELATIONSHIP AND THE CALCULATION OF GROWTH HISTORY

As summarized by Van Oosten (1929: 272), one may determine from scales: (1) the age of a fish in years; (2) the approximate length attained by it at the end of each year of life; and (3) its rate of growth for each year of life. We have seen how age is determined. The length at each year of life may be estimated by averaging the lengths of fish of the same age in the sample. The length of a fish at the end of each year of its life may also be computed from a series of measurements of a scale when the length of the fish at time of capture is known (the scale method).

The soundness of the scale method for determining the lengths of a fish at previous, successive years of its life depends on the validity of the following assumptions or propositions (Van Oosten, 1929: 278):

(1) That the scales remain constant in number and retain their identity throughout the life of the fish;

(2) That the annual increment in the length (or some other dimension which must then be used) of the scale maintains, throughout the life of the fish, a predictable ratio to the annual increment in body length; and

(3) That the annuli are formed yearly and at the same time each year (or that some other discoverable relation exists between their formation and increment of time).

The excellent published reviews of ways of calculating growth of fishes from the scale measurements (Taylor, 1916; Van Oosten, 1929; Graham, 1929; Creaser, 1926; Mohr, 1927, 1930, 1934; and others; see References, Chapter IX and X) render any detailed historical discussion of the subject entirely unnecessary. Consequently the historical treatment of the question of the calculation of growth will be limited here to a listing of methods that have been employed. In the presentation of these methods emphasis will be placed on the assumed body-scale relationship rather than on the actual procedure used in calculation. The following summaries have been prepared for me by Ralph Hile and are included here because of their importance and the general inaccesssibility in this country of the original papers.

Dahl-Lea Direct-proportion Method

This method assumes that the mathematical relationship between body length and scale length is expressed by the equation:

$$L = cS$$

Where L = body length, S = scale length,[1] and c is a constant. The Dahl-Lea method of growth calculation therefore holds that the ratio of body length to scale length is constant for all lengths of the fish beyond that at which the first annulus is laid down.

Lee Method

This method assumes that the mathematical relationship between

---

[1] In this discussion scale length may be taken to refer to the particular dimension of the scale actually measured in the study of the growth of a species. The anterior radius is most frequently measured, but some investigators have employed the posterior radius and some have used the diameters of the different growth areas.

body length and scale length is expressed by the equation
$$L = a + cS$$
L, S, and c have been defined previously; a is also a constant. Here the body-scale ratio (L/S) varies between the limits of infinity as L approaches a, and c as L increases without limit, but the ratio of the corresponding increments of body length and scale length is constant. Frequently attempts have been made to interpret the length of the intercept, a, as the body length at which scales first appear on the fish. In some species this interpretation may be approximately correct, but it cannot be accepted as a generalization, since the intercept is negative in certain species (Monastyrsky).

Lea (1933) and later Weese (1949) calculated regressions by the Lee method for each age-group separately. They found that values for a increased successively with age. Thus age and length distribution of the sample must influence estimation of the constant.

Sherriff Method

This method assumes that the mathematical relationship between body length and scale length is expressed by the equation
$$L = a + bS + cS^2$$
where a, b, and c are empirically determined constants. On purely mathematical grounds it is apparent that Sherriff's equation must fit a mass of empirical data on body length and scale length better than Lee's linear equation. This method has been little used. Monastyrsky applied the Sherriff equation to several species of fish and held that the method is open to the same general criticisms as the Lee method, particularly in the interpretation of the constant a as the length of fish at which the scale first appears.

Järvi Method of Arbitrary Correction

An arbitrary correction is made by adding a given quantity (determined empirically) to the calculated length for each year that intervened between the time of capture and the year of life for which the length calculation was made. For example: 5, 10, 15 or 20 millimeters would be added if 1, 2, 3, or 4 years, respectively, intervened.

Monastyrsky Logarithmic Method

This method holds that the logarithms of fish length and scale length exhibit a straight-line relationship, or that
$$\log L = \log c + n \log S.$$
Monastyrsky applied the method to several species of fish and found the calculated growths to agree well with the observed growths. He held that the results obtained from his logarithmic method were far superior to those obtained on the same species by the Lee or Sherriff methods. Monastyrsky made his calculations by means of a logarithmic nomograph.

Segerstråle Empirical Body-Scale Relationship Method

In this method the average scale lengths corresponding to different body lengths are determined through an extensive series of measurements of key scales or "Normalschuppen" taken from a selected area of the body. The resultant body-scale relationship expressed in tabular form, or as a curve, then serves as the basis for the calculation of the growth histories of individual fish. In his publication Segerstråle described a mechanical device for the calculation of growth from the curve of the empirical body-scale relationship.

Fry's Modification of the Monastyrsky Method

Fry added a constant to the Monastyrsky equation to give it the following form:

$$\log (L - a) = \log c + n \log S.$$

Fry's belief that the constant a corresponds to the length at scale formation is of course subject to the same criticism outlined previously. The introduction of the additional constant creates the difficulty that a mathematical fitting of the equation is impractical. In practice, different values of a must be tried, the one giving the closest fit being determined by inspection, and the values of n and c must be estimated from the graph. Fry described a nomograph for the solution of his equation. Although the nomograph is satisfactory, it should not be used as directed.

Carlander's Third-Degree Polynomial Method

Because of the sigmoid character of his graphical representation of his empirical data, Carlander employed a cubic of the following type:

$$L = a + bS + cS^2 + dS^3$$

Carrying Sheriff's method one step further, he calculated growth histories of individual fish from a table following the same general procedure used by Segerstråle.

On purely theoretical grounds the Segerstråle method appears to be the most satisfactory of those just listed, first because it is based on a detailed examination of the actual size of the scale at different body lengths, and second because it involves no assumptions of a fixed mathematical relationship between body length and scale length. The method is faced, however, with the practical difficulty of determining a completely reliable empirical body-scale relationship for the complete range of body lengths over which growth calculations are to be made. The length distribution of a fish population is ordinarily of such a nature that it is difficult or even impossible to obtain adequate representation of certain lengths. This difficulty is particularly great for those species in which the young fish cannot readily be located and captured. Weaknesses in the empirical body-scale curve resulting from inadequate sampling at certain lengths must inevitably be reflected in inaccuracies in growth calculation.

The later methods of growth calculation may all be considered as attempts to improve on the Dahl-Lea method. Each has led to more accurate growth calculations for the species to which it was applied. However, the fact that different authors, working with apparently reliable material, have arrived at such a diversity of conclusions concerning the nature of methods of calculating growth suggests that the question of the body-scale relationship may not be subject to generalization. The body-scale relationship and growth-calculation problems should be considered specific rather than general. Almost certainly the nature of the body-scale relationship varies from one species to another, and it is not improbable that the relationship may vary between races and populations of the same species. For clarity, all reports should specify the manner of computation and the value of a if the Lee method is employed.

Equations given above are descriptive of the general body-scale relation but should not be used as prediction equations. Actual computations can be made by formulas derived from the equations by the normalization of scale measurements and the reading of corresponding fish lengths from tables of solutions or by use of nomographs. With the Dahl-Lea method it is easy to eliminate the constant c to arrive at the formula

$$L_n = (L_T/S_n)\, S_n$$

in which n refers to the nth year of life and T to length of fish (L) or length of scale (S) at time of capture. The corresponding formula with the Lee method is

$$L_n = a + (L_T - a/S_T)\, S_n$$

Use of formulas is not recommended for other relations.

STUDY PROGRAM ON DETERMINATION OF AGE AND RATE OF GROWTH

Growth Rate as Shown by Averages of Actual Length at Various Ages

1. Make age determinations on a series of scale preparations for one species of fish.

2. Obtain average length for each age-group:
   a. for each sex separately,
   b. for both sexes together.

3. Plot the results on graph paper to find growth curves for each of the three series of figures. Use age in years for the abscissa and length for the ordinate.

4. Discuss results, limitations, and requirements concerning time and size of sample needed for best results by this method. Was sexual dimorphism exhibited in growth?

5. Calculate conversion factors for changing standard length to fork length and/or to total length, or vice versa if needed.

Growth Rate as Shown by Calculation of Lengths at Previous Annuli

For the series of scales which you have just aged and analyzed in growth curves based on average empirical lengths of each age-group:

1. Measure the distance from the estimated center of the focus of the scale to the outer edge of each annulus with a ruler, or mark the distance off on a strip of paper. Measurement is customarily along the median, real or imaginary, anterior radius of the scale; other measurements have also been used in certain studies. Also record length to margin of scale along this radius.

2. Compute by the Dahl-Lea direct-proportion procedure, using either a nomograph or the formula, the length of the fish at each annulus for all specimens in your series and record in a table. For ideas on nomographs see Segerstråle (1933), Hile (1941), Carlander and Smith (1944), or Carlander (1953). Good tabular models for age-length calculations are in Hile (1941) and Carlander (1953).

3. Examine the calculated lengths of the different age-groups to see if they exhibit systematic discrepancies (for example, frequently the calculated length at a particular annulus appears to decrease with increase in age of the fish from which the calculation was made—"Lee's Phenomenon"). If such a discrepancy exists, what limitations does it place on the statements you can make about the growth of fish in this population?

4. Derive two "general" curves, one based on average calculated lengths at each annulus and the other based on the summation of the weighted increments of growth for individual age-groups. How do they compare?

5. Add to the graphs in 4, above, a plot of the growth history of each year-class represented in your sample. Discuss differences among year-classes and from general curve for the population.

6. Determine whether or not the ratio of scale length to body length is indeed constant throughout the size range of your material. If not, what effect has your assumption of the constancy had on your calculation of growth? If the calculated regression line of body-scale relationship according to the Dahl-Lea equation does not match a regression line based on the empirical data for your species of fish, the next step would be to determine the actual body-scale relationship empirically or by one of the other methods given on the previous pages.

REFERENCES ON DETERMINATION OF AGE AND RATE OF GROWTH

Beckman, William C. 1943. Annulus formation on the scales of certain Michigan game fishes. Pap. Mich. Acad. Sci., Arts, and Lett., 28 (1942): 281-312, 2 figs., 4 pl. (Method for determining time of annulus formation)

Mosher, Kenneth H. 1950. Description of a projection device for use in age determination from fish scales. Fish. Bull. U. S. Fish and Wildlife Service, 51 (54): 405-407, 4 figs.

Savage, R. E. 1919. Report on age determination from scales of young herrings, with special reference to the use of polarized light. Bd. of Agric. and Fish., Fishery Invest. ser. 2, 4 (1): 1-31, 17 figs. (Use of polarized light)

Schoffman, Robert J. 1939. Age and growth of the red-eared sunfish in Reelfoot Lake. Rept. Reelfoot Lake Biol. Sta., 3: 61-71, 4 figs. (Describes a simple projector and use of polarized light)

Van Oosten, J., H. J. Deason, and F. W. Jobes. 1934. A microprojection machine designed for the study of fish scales. Jour. du Conseil, 9 (2): 241-248, 2 figs.

REFERENCES ON BODY-SCALE RELATIONSHIP AND THE CALCULATION OF GROWTH HISTORY

Carlander, Kenneth D., and Lloyd L. Smith, Jr. 1944. Some uses of nomographs in fish growth studies. Copeia, 1944 (3): 157-162, 2 figs.

Carlander, Kenneth D. 1945. Age, growth, sexual maturity, and populations of the yellow pike-perch, Stizostedion vitreum vitreum (Mitchill), with reference to the commercial fisheries, Lake of the Woods, Minnesota. Trans. Amer. Fish. Soc., 73 (1943): 90-107, 2 figs.

Carlander, Kenneth D. 1945. Growth, length-weight relationship and population fluctuations of the tullibee, Leucichthys artedi tullibee (Richardson), with reference to the commercial fisheries, Lake of the Woods, Minnesota. Trans. Amer. Fish. Soc., 73 (1943): 125-136.

Carlander, Kenneth D. 1953. Handbook of freshwater fishery biology with the first supplement. Dubuque, Iowa, Wm. C. Brown Company, 429 p.

Dahl, Knut. 1909. The assessment of age and growth in fish. Internationale Revue der gesamten Hydrobiologie und Hydrographie, 2 (4-5): 758-769, 6 text-figs.

Dahl, Knut. 1910. The age and growth of salmon and trout in Norway as shown by their scales. (Translated from Norwegian by Ian Baillee) London, The Salmon and Trout Assoc. (1911), 144 p., 32 figs., 10 pl.

Fry, F. E. J. 1943. A method for the calculation of the growth of fishes from scale measurements. Publ. Ont. Fish. Res. Lab., 61: 5-18, 11 figs.

Hile, Ralph. 1941. Age and growth of the rock bass, Ambloplites rupestris (Rafinesque), in Nebish Lake, Wisconsin. Trans. Wis. Acad. Sci., Arts and Lett., 33: 189-337, 14 figs.

Järvi, T. H. 1920. Die kleine Maräne (Coregonus albula L.) im Keitelesee, eine ökologische und ökonomische Studie. Annales Academiae Scientarum Fennicae, Series A, 14(1): 1-302.

Lea, Einar. 1910. On the method used in the herring investigations. Cons. Permanent International pour l'Exploration de la Mer, Publications de Circonstance, 53: 7-174, 10 figs.

Lea, Einar. 1911. A study on the growth of herrings. Cons. Permanent International pour l'Exploration de la Mer, Publications de Circonstance, 61: 35-57, 7 figs.

Lea, Einar. 1933. Connected frequency-distributions a preliminary account. Rept. Norwegian Fish. and Marine Invest., 4 (2): 1-12, 2 figs.

Lee, Rosa M. [Mrs. T. L. Williams]. 1920. A review of the methods of age and growth determination in fishes by means of scales. Ministry of Agric. and Fish., Fish. Invest., Ser. II, 4(2): 1-32, 8 figs., 1 pl.

Monastyrsky, G. M. 1930. Über Methoden zur Bestimmung der linearen Wachstums der Fische nach der Schuppe. Rept. Sci. Inst. for Fish Cult., 5(4): 3-44. (Moscow)

Segerstråle, Curt. 1933. Uber scalimetrische Methoden zur Bestimmung der linearen Wachstums bei Fischen, insbesondere bei *Leuciscus idus* L., *Abramis brama* L., und *Perca fluviatilis* L. Acta Zoologica Fennica, 15: 1-168, 37 figs.

Sherriff, Catherine W. M. 1922. Herring investigations. Report on the mathematical analysis of random samples of herrings. With an introductory note by Prof. D'Arcy Thompson. Fish. Bd. of Scotland, Sci. Invest., 1922, No. 1, 25 p.

Van Oosten, John. 1929. Life history of the lake herring (*Leucichthys artedi* LeSueur) of Lake Huron as revealed by its scales, with a critique of the scale method. Bull. U. S. Bur. Fish., 44 (1928): 265-428, 43 figs.

Weese, A. O. 1950. Age and growth of Lepibema chrysops in Lake Texoma. Proc. Okla. Acad. Sci. 1949: 45-48.

Whitney, Richard R., and Kenneth D. Carlander. 1956. Interpretation of body-scale regression for computing body length of fish. Jour. Wildlife Mgt., 20 (1): 21-27.

Chapter XI

Length-Weight Relationship and Condition

The relationship between length and weight of fish has often been studied biologically. One principal approach has been to examine the **length-weight relationship** from the purely academic point of view of growth. The results of this method, if properly applied, do have practical value since they make it possible to convert length into weight and vice versa. Another approach has been to determine the **coefficient of condition** (also called condition factor, ponderal index, etc.), with the objective of expressing the condition of fish in numerical terms (degree of well-being, relative robustness, plumpness or fatness). The length-weight relationship of most fish can be expressed in the general equation

$$W = aL^n, \tag{1}$$

where W = weight, L = length, a is a constant, and n, an exponent Values for a and n are determined empirically. Calculations of the coefficient of condition (e.g., K) are based on the cube law, hence the equation

$$W = K \, L^3 \tag{2}$$

or

$$K = W/L^3 \tag{3}$$

Because the foregoing expression has failed always to function adequately independent of length and other variables in fish LeCren (1951) has proposed a *relative condition coefficient*, K_n, calculated from the formula

$$K_n = W/aL^n \tag{4}$$

In practice, LeCren indicates, the length-weight relationship would first be calculated as the logarithmic formula

$$\log W = \log a + n \log L \tag{5}$$

and the smoothed mean weights, W, for each length group would be computed from this log formula or read on an accurate graph. The relative condition factor would then be calculated from the formula for an individual from the average weight for length (i.e., deviation from the length-weight regression), whereas K is designed to reflect fluctuations of volume (weight) of three-dimensional objects in general in relation to length measurement. LeCren's proposal may have merit within a given population, provided the length-weight regression does not vary too erratically with year, season, etc. An obvious difficulty lies in the impossibility of comparing indices based on different regressions. Hence, in general practice, K is favored, in spite of its limitations.

159

Weight in fishes may be considered a function of their length (Hile, 1936.) If form and specific gravity were constant throughout life, the relationship could be expressed by the well-known cube law in equation (2). But actually, in nature, it has been found that the value of K is not constant for an individual, a species, or a population, but that it is subject to wide variation.

CONDITION

The values of the coefficient of condition have been used widely by fishery investigators to express the relative robustness of fishes. They have also been used as an adjunct to age and growth studies, to indicate the suitability of an environment for a species by a comparison of the value for a specific locality with that for a region (an average). They have even been employed to measure the effects of environmental improvement, including stocking (Cooper and Benson, 1951).

Obviously values for the coefficient of condition may be computed on the basis of measurements made by different systems. In the interest of uniformity the following designations are made:

K = coefficient of condition for Metric system;

C = coefficient of condition for English system; and

R = coefficient of condition for English-Metric system

where length, say, is in inches and weight in grams (e.g., Cooper and Benson, 1951). Furthermore, since there seems to be little hope for standardization in techniques of length measurement, the basis of length indication should be shown, with SL signifying standard length, FL, fork length, and TL, total length. Thus K might be labelled K_{SL} when standard length is employed, K_{FL} for fork, and K_{TL} for total. In addition it is desirable to state the variant of any of these length measurements used.

The worker may expect to find the following characteristics of K. C, or R values:

(1) Change with age.

(2) Sexual difference. One may not assume absence of such a difference, but must test to see if it is present. If it is present and is sufficiently great, the sexes should be kept separate when computing mean values.

(3) Change with season. Consider the condition of a fish just before spawning and right after spawning.

For best practice, values of the coefficient of condition which are to be compared should be for fish of the same length, age, and sex, and the fish should be collected from the same or different waters on one single date. Obviously, this ideal cannot be realized in practice. But most workers strive to base comparisons at least on same sex, length, and age for fish collected in the same season of the year. If comparison of values for K (C, or R) is to be made among individuals from a single body of water, not only should the collections be made as nearly on one date as possible, but they should be carried out with precaution against the selectivity of the collection method (gear plus mode of operating gear).

Unfortunately, coefficients of condition based on (3) have also been employed to describe the general length-weight relationship in populations of fishes, and thus to serve as the basis for calculating the unknown weight of fish of known length, or unknown length of fish of known weight. The use of equation (2) in this capacity has met with indifferent success, because, as Hile (1936) pointed out, the cube law on which it is based fails to describe accurately the relationship of length to weight in many forms of fishes (for example, some fishes increase somewhat more in other dimensions than in length since their weight at a given length is greater than the weight calculated from the law).

The instances where the cube law does appear to apply to the length-weight relationship are probably the exceptions, and are coincidences. The more general equation (1) is a much more satisfactory method of describing the length-weight relationship. In this equation the values of both a and n are determined empirically, that is they are derived from data taken directly from specimens in large series.

We may conclude, therefore, that the description of condition and the expression of the length-weight relationship are most often two entirely different, though related, things. Coefficients calculated from the cube relationship and those from empirically determined exponents are in no sense of parallel significance as measures of condition. One may test this statement by working through the following example from Hile, 1936:

A fish with a length of 1 foot and a weight of 1 pound will show on the basis of the cube relationship a coefficient of condition (C) of............. (calculate using $W = CL^3$).

If the fish doubles its length without change of form or of specific gravity, its weight at the length of 2 feet will be 8 pounds if the value of C continues to be 1.00 (as you calculated in the previous paragraph).

If, however, the weight at 2 feet is 10 pounds rather than 8 pounds, the value for C at this greater length will be...................(calculate). It will be thus known that a change in form has occurred along with growth in length. In other words, the fish has become relatively heavier than its increase in length would indicate. Use the new value of C calculated here (answer, 1.25) and compute the weight of a 1-foot fish on this basis to see that the formula cannot be used with confidence for this purpose (the answer obtained is 0.25 pounds out of line).

Thus it may be seen that values for coefficients of condition, by reason of their calculation from the cube relationship, are direct and quantitative measures of form or relative heaviness, and in this sense they are not directly comparable for fishes of various lengths and really are descriptive of condition only.

If a weight of 1 pound at the length of 1 foot, and of 10 pounds at 2 feet, were to represent actual average conditions within a population (that is, if these weights represent empirically determined values), what would be the corresponding empirical exponent calculated from the

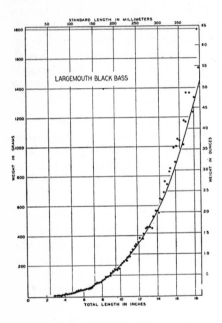

Fig. 47. LENGTH-WEIGHT RELA-TIONSHIP OF THE NORTHERN LARGEMOUTH BASS. In Figs. 47-48, the dots represent empirical averages and the curves are graphs of the length-weight equation. (Photocopied from Beckman, 1948).

length-weight equation $W = aL^n$ where these letters carry meanings as previously indicated, and with $a = 1.00$? (Ans: $n = 3.32193$)

The coefficients of condition calculated from this higher exponent would be 1.00 (calculate to verify), both for the fish at the length of 1 foot and weight of 1 pound and for the fish at the length of 2 feet and weight of 10 pounds; thus a fails to measure in any way the change of form that occurred with increase in length and so cannot be used when C (K or R) is meant. The value of a for a fish that weighs 8 pounds at the length of 2 feet is 0.80, which would make it appear that a fish which doubles its length without change of form actually suffers a loss of condition, which is hardly possible. It must be concluded that values of a calculated from empirically determined exponents do not serve as satisfactory measure of condition; these values for a do, however, express the relationship between length and weight (Hile, 1936).

LENGTH-WEIGHT RELATIONSHIP

In solving taxonomic problems (Speirs, 1952), and generally in fishery management it is often very useful to be able to determine the weight of a fish when length alone is known (or vice versa). To provide a basis for such estimates, an empirical curve may be fitted by inspection to points plotted from lengths and corresponding weights.

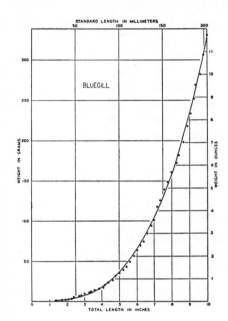

Fig. 48. LENGTH-WEIGHT RELATIONSHIP OF THE BLUEGILL. (Photocopied from Beckman, 1948).

The nature of such a curve may also be computed mathematically from length-weight data (Figs. 47-48). From graphs of such curves length may be estimated when the weight alone is known or vice versa, as indicated on previous pages. If the mathematical relationship between length and weight has been formulated, the formula giving the best fit may be used to calculate a corresponding length or weight where only one of the two is known (see following length-weight exercise).

An example of the utility of a knowledge of the length-weight relationship for a species would be the following. Let us suppose that you wish to compute the poundage of fish cropped from a lake by anglers. Your staff is able to get lengths and numbers of fish caught but does not have time to get weights. In the laboratory you can estimate weights from existing length-weight data with reasonable accuracy. You have thus been able to extend the value of your creel census data into a better measure of yield (pounds of fish) than number and sizes of fish. Similarly, you may be able to draw important comparisons from other studies in the literature where lengths alone are given.

Length-weight knowledge may also be useful in regulating fisheries. If, for example, there is no market value for a fish unless it weighs one-half pound or more, and if you can estimate the length for this weight from an existing curve, you may without additional, time-consuming field work set the mesh size of the gear to provide escapement of smaller individuals. They may then grow to the desired weight before being taken.

STUDY PROGRAM ON CONDITION

Complete the following exercise on condition, using available, paired data on lengths and weights for one species of fish. Follow the practice of designating the system of measurement used, and designate standard, fork, total, or other length as a subscript to the coefficient.

1. For each individual compute the value of the condition coefficient.

In your actual practice, and as customary, the calculated value for the coefficient should be multiplied by the necessary multiple of 10 to make it read with one digit to the left of the decimal (e.g., 2.9 rather than 0.00029).

2. Obtain average values for the coefficient sexes separately, in small (5 mm or so) size groups.

3. Look for differences in values between the sexes, and with increasing size. If differences exist, work out plausible explanations.

4. Observe fluctuations in the values; most likely these will be found in length intervals represented by small numbers of specimens. Beckman (1948) has given a formula for smoothing out such irregularities.

5. If desired, the metric coefficient of condition, K, may be converted into an English coefficient, C by the following equation:

$$C_{TL} = 36.1 \ r^3 \ K_{SL}$$

where $r =$ the ratio of standard length to total length and $K =$ coefficient of condition in metric system.

6. Alinement charts have been prepared for use in estimating both K and C. Compare your calculated values for these coefficients with those which you obtain from the nomographs in Carlander, 1953. Explain any differences in the comparable sets of values.

STUDY PROGRAM ON LENGTH-WEIGHT RELATIONSHIP

Complete the following exercise on length-weight relationship.

1. Determine the actual (empirical) value of the exponent (n) which will express the relationship of length to weight in the equation $W = aL^n$ by using the same paired length and weight values that you employed in the exercise on coefficient of condition in a tabulation with the following headings:

L	log L	W	log W	$\begin{array}{c}\log L \\ \times \\ \log W\end{array}$	$(\log L)^2$	Calc. log W	Calc. W

Find the logs of the individual lengths and weights and record.

Multiply these by one another and record.

Square the log of the length and record

Summarize the columns and substitute in the following equation (for fitting a parabola), where N = the number of individuals (or the number of groups in grouped data).

$$\log a = \frac{\Sigma \log W \cdot \Sigma (\log L)^2 - \Sigma \log L \cdot \Sigma (\log L \cdot \log W)}{N \cdot \Sigma (\log L)^2 - (\Sigma \log L)^2}$$

With the value for log a now in hand, find n in the equation

$$n = \frac{\Sigma \log W - (N \cdot \log a)}{\Sigma \log L}$$

2. Substitute values for log a and for n in the following equation to determine calculated weights by obtaining antilogs of calculated log W for each individual or group in the data from the equation

$$\text{Log } W = \log a + n \log L$$

3. Compare calculated weights and empirical weights by constructing a graph for both in relation to length (Figs. 47-48). Grouping and the use of mean values will facilitate this operation. Do the calculated data fit the actual weights well enough so that you could determine weight for a fish when its length alone is known? Explain deviations, if any.

4. Select a weight and calculate the corresponding length. Using the values of a and n obtained, verify result from your graph.

REFERENCES

Beckman, William C. 1948. The length-weight relationship, factors for conversions between standard and total lengths, and coefficients of condition for seven Michigan fishes. Trans. Amer. Fish. Soc., 75 (1945): 237-256, 7 figs.

Carlander, Kenneth D. 1953. Handbook of freshwater fishery biology with the first supplement. Dubuque, Wm. C. Brown Co., v, 429 p., 5 charts.

Cooper, Edwin L., and Norman G. Benson. 1951. The coefficients of condition of brook, brown, and rainbow trout in the Pigeon River, Otsego County, Michigan. Prog. Fish-Cult., 13 (4): 181-192, 4 figs.

Hile, Ralph. 1936. Age and growth of the cisco *Leucichthys artedi* (LeSueur) in the lakes of the northeastern highlands, Wisconsin. Bull. U. S. Bur. Fish., 48 (1935): 209-317, 11 figs. (Excellent on methodology; bibliography of 109 titles)

Le Cren, E. D. 1951. The length-weight relationship and seasonal cycle in gonad weight and condition in the perch (*Perca fluviatilis*). Jour. Animal Ecol., 20 (2): 201-219, 8 figs.

Speirs, J. Murray. 1952. Nomenclature of the channel catfish and the burbot in North America. Copeia, 1952 (2): 99-103, 1 fig.

Chapter XII

Fish Populations

In a special sense, it is an aim of work in fishery management to create and maintain the maximum possible standing crop of fish, and thereby to assure the greatest possible and continuing yield to sport and commercial fishermen. Thus it is often of extreme importance to know the magnitude of the fish population upon which a given measure of fishing success depends, or from which quality of fishing may be predicted. As is generally recognized for inland fresh waters, both the standing crops of fish and the fishing success differ greatly from one body of water to another and fluctuate in each from year to year. The population differences are exemplified in a partial compilation of existing data (Carlander, 1950), even though these estimates are not strictly comparable in themselves because of the various methods used in obtaining them: trout lakes and ponds, maximum between 40 and 50 pounds, but mostly less than 10 pounds per acre; trout streams, maximum between 300 and 400 pounds, but mostly less than 60 pounds per acre; ponds and lakes, maximum between 2700 and 2800 pounds, but mostly less than 300 pounds per acre; bays of rivers and of reservoirs, maximum between 800 and 900 pounds, but mostly less than 300 pounds per acre.

The composition of a fish population by numbers, sizes, and kinds at any instant is the result of the interaction of many factors. These factors are of two kinds: those stemming from the genetics and physiology of the fish species present, and those made up by the total environment of each species. The interplay of these forces results in the survival of only some individuals, and as time passes it may cause a progressively smaller egg production. The interaction of organism and environment also determines the population composition by species and numbers, and, within a species, the rate of growth and the condition of the individuals. A first step in population analysis thus is to learn makeup by species, and, within any chosen species, the constituency by numbers (relative or absolute) and age-groups. When these are known, mortality and turnover can be computed and the future composition of a species-stock predicted.

If one obtains a random sample of the total size range of a species-stock, assesses the age of each individual, and charts age-group composition of the stock from youngest to oldest, the rate of mortality will be shown. If, in addition, the relative abundance (or better, actual abundance) at any moment can be learned, rational management becomes possible.

METHODS OF POPULATION ENUMERATION

Recently, increased use has been made of fish population studies in several aspects of management. Some of the most valuable topics explored have been: (1) standing crop per unit of area—by numbers, by kinds, and by weight of fish; (2) role of various species combinations in obtaining maximum yield; (3) effects of fishing and fishery regulations on numbers of fish (and vice versa).

Methods employed in inland lakes and streams are much alike. Procedures for the enumeration of fish populations in inland waters are of two kinds—direct (actual counts) and indirect (estimations), as summarized by Cooper and Lagler, 1956.

Direct Methods

Methods employed in making actual counts of fish are several. One has been to drain bodies of water such as small ponds, and to recover all the individuals in them. In streams inhabited by migratory fishes, use has been made of counts (either by eye or with traps) of the individuals moving upstream or downstream. Enumerations have arisen from inadvertent, accidentally or naturally induced mass mortalities. Deaths of fishes from pollution, or from such events as the red tide in the Gulf of Mexico, have given some convenient measures of population. Some counts have also come about as a result of intentional poisoning of lakes and streams for management and/or population-study purposes. The use of toxicants in aquatic environments has further provided a means for verifying estimations based on mark-and-recapture methods, or such methods have been employed in conjunction with poisoning by previously releasing into the body of water a known number of tagged or marked fish which could be recognized on recovery. Application of the Petersen method to the percentage recovery of marked individuals has provided a means for estimating total population in these instances.

A few counts of fish populations have been made from airplanes or stream banks, sometimes using photography as an adjunct. Photoelectric eyes, underwater telescopes and television, and various kinds of diving apparatus have also provided means for counting fish. Recently, the swimming of transects by free divers, singly or in large teams, has offered promise of yielding an approximate population count in waters of sufficient clarity. Angling, trapping, or netting of fishes to the point of repeated "no return" have also been employed, but their completeness has not been tested adequately.

Indirect Methods

There are several methods of indirect numerical approximation, most of which involve mark-and-recapture means. These methods have been used rather extensively in inland waters (Carlander 1955), but only in a few marine populations. The techniques of indirect estimation of standing crops are of two kinds. One of them depends on the reduction in the catch per unit of effort (or in successive trials) as a result of diminution of the population by the fishing. The other is based upon the occurrence of previously marked fishes in the catch. The first of the two has been termed the DeLury regression method. The second is largely an outgrowth of the simple, direct proportion estimation device proposed by Petersen, 1896.

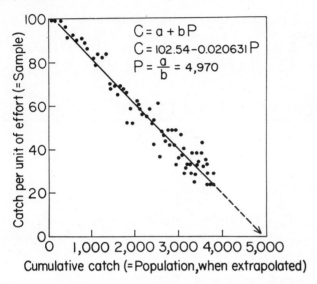

Fig. 49. Experimental model of the regression method (DeLury, 1947) for indirect estimation of fish population size from catch-effort data. (From Cooper and Lagler, 1956, courtesy Trans. North Amer. Wildlife Conf.)

The DeLury method employs data on catch per unit of effort to arrive at an estimate of population. Regrettably, the procedure cannot be applied unless the decrease in population due to fishing shows in a reduction of the subsequent take per unit of fishing effort. The reduction is proportional, ideally, to the extent of the depletion. The simplest means of estimating population numbers by this method is to graph the data, and by inspection to fit the expected straight regression line (Fig. 49). In such a graph, the catch per unit of effort becomes the ordinate, and the total catch to and including the latest sample becomes the abscissa. Extrapolation of the regression line fitted by eye or by formula to its intercept with the x axis yields a value at the intercept which is the approximation of the population number.

The assumptions upon which the DeLury method, according to the author, rests are: (1) the population is closed, that is, the effects of migration and natural mortality are negligible; (2) the units of effort employed do not compete with one another or else they are constant during the period involved; and (3) the response of the fish to the gear, i.e., their catchability, remains constant for the period under investigation.

The indirect estimation of fish populations by various mark-and-re-capture methods involves, first, the capture and release of a number of marked fish (m) into the population; second, the subsequent recapture of marked fish (r) along with the capture of unmarked fish (u) from the population; and third the computation of the population numerically from the equation $P = m\ (u + r)\ /\ r.$

The basic proposals carrying forward the idea of Petersen which have been advanced thus far for population estimation by the foregoing means are those of Schnabel, 1938, Schumacher and Eschmeyer, 1943, and Chapman, 1951. The formulas for their proposals follow:

Formulas for Population Estimates

Petersen.
$$P = m(u + r)\big/r$$

Schnabel:
$$P = \Sigma m(u + r)\big/\Sigma r$$

Schumacher-Eschmeyer:
$$P = \Sigma m^2 (u + r)\big/\Sigma mr$$

Chapman:
$$P = \Sigma \frac{[m(u+r)]^3}{(r)(u)(m-r)}\Big/\Sigma \frac{[m(u+r)]^2}{u(m-r)}$$

Mark-and-recapture methods such as the foregoing are also based on certain assumptions: (1) that marked fish do not lose their identifying marks throughout the period of study and that they are recognized by the operators on recapture; (2) either that the marked individuals are randomly redistributed throughout the population, or that the effort spent in netting is somehow proportional to the density of the population throughout the body of water; (3) that both the marked and the un-marked fish are susceptible in the same degree to capture; (4) that the numbers of fish entering the experiment are not increased as a result of recruitment from growth or immigration; and (5) that losses through death or emigration have the same proportion for both the marked and unmarked fish. If any of the foregoing do not apply in field trials, workers must gain the information needed to make required adjustments in the estimates of the population.

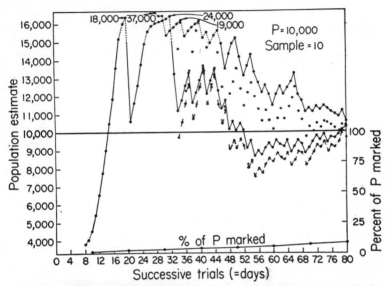

Fig. 50. POPULATION ESTIMATES by mark-and-recapture method based on two experiments using beans (as fish) in a pail (for a lake). Solid dots connected show two runs with estimates based on the Schnabel formula. Simple circles and tailed circles show corresponding estimations by the Schumacher-Eschmeyer formula. Known population size (P) was 10,000; each sample drawn was 10. Percentage of population marked at time of each trial is also shown.

In order actually to see how the various methods here described for the estimation of population work in practice one may use colored beads or other similar objects after the experiments of DeLury, 1951, and Cooper and Lagler, 1956. Such experiments would eliminate sources of bias which might be present in field work. Such tests furthermore give estimations of population which set the minimum limits of accuracy in field operations. Field estimates can be no more accurate than the experimental models; when one examines Figure 50, it is seen that a number of trials or days are required in order to attain a reasonably satisfactory estimate. For practical purposes it would seem that to achieve an approximation within 5 per cent of the known population is doing rather well. In Figure 50, comparison between the Schnabel and the Schumacher-Eschmeyer formulas, using same data, are shown.

The length of time required to achieve a good estimate depends on the number of marked individuals which are recaptured. This rate of recapture is in turn dependent upon the proficiency with which one can catch fish from the population, and upon the total number involved. Fredin, 1950, has made a proposal which would make it possible to identify the number of samples required to obtain a good estimate in field operations.

In estimating fish populations the operator must be sure that he has carefully set forth parameters of the entity which he seeks to measure. Almost certainly his estimates of the total population over any wide size-range of individuals will by the previous methods be too low if the data for the entire size-range are used en masse in making calculations. It would seem that in many investigations more accurate estimates would result from making detailed analyses of numbers of individuals in successive size groups, perhaps the smaller the better within the limits of practicality. Cooper and Lagler (1956), for example, have shown in one experiment that when size groups were not taken into consideration estimates were as much as 28 per cent too low, whereas the same data when broken into smaller units gave estimates less than 10 per cent off actual.

The foregoing indirect methods of population enumeration have been used in streams, with seining and with electrical shocking. They have also been employed for salmon populations where fish to be counted could be readily seen. In some instances, single large sections of streams have been used, in other sample sections only. The study portion has sometimes been blocked off at both ends, at other times left open. Both approaches have given satisfactory results. When a shocker is used,

Fig. 51. FIN CLIPPING. Fin-clip method of marking live fish for future recognition.

repeated passes are made through the area to be sampled, marking and returning fish and recording the numbers caught once only as well as those caught repeatedly. In standing waters, hoop, fyke, and trap nets have been most popular. In practice, the nets are run daily and the unmarked fish are marked and returned to the water, as are those which have been previously marked and recaptured. Days of such sampling are repeated, in practice, until estimates become relatively constant on the basis of the formula in use. There are variations in the procedures for selecting the location for nets, and the site for returning marked fish.

Because of the differences in response to netting among species and among different size-groups within species, any given method of netting or shocking or other means of collecting will be more efficient for some kinds and sizes of fish than for others. Care must be taken to recognize such sources of bias and to adjust them, as previously indicated.

METHODS OF MARKING LIVING FISH FOR FUTURE RECOGNITION

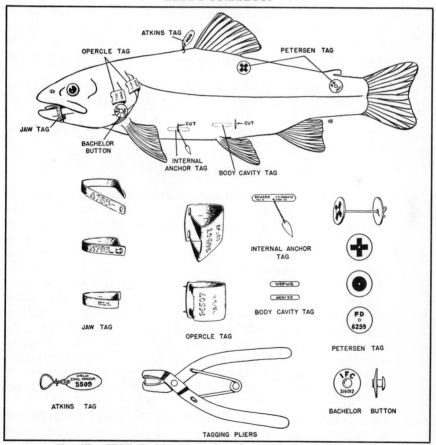

Fig. 52. FISH TAGS. Examples of tags used in marking fish.

Very many different methods have been employed to mark fish so that they may be recognized on recapture (Rounsefell and Kask, 1946). Basically the means are two, mutilation of the fish (Fig. 51) or attachment of some kind of a tag (Fig. 52). The former includes fin-clipping (most common), tattooing, and branding, and in general is less satisfactory for most purposes than tagging. The chief failing of fin-clipping, for example, is that fins regenerate unless deeply excised and that individual fish, identically marked, can hardly be told from one another. The method is fast, however, and requires no special equipment; for these reasons its greatest application is in short-term population studies.

A common but not universal deficiency in the marking of fish has been that investigators have failed to set up controlled experiments (Rounsefell and Kask, 1946) in order to determine: (1) comparative value of different types of tags; (2) rate of disappearance of marks, including rate of loss of tags; (3) mortality of fish due to handling and/or the marking means employed; and (4) effect of mutilation or tagging on the condition (as shown in changes of the coefficients K, C, or R) or on the habits of the subjects. A minimum safeguard would be to hold some marked and some unmarked (but similarly handled) fish together in an enclosure for observation in connection with each field use of any one technique.

There are many fishery topics related to populations which may be explored by the use of the proper tag in a well-designed experiment (Rounsefell and Kask, 1946). Among these are homing behavior, speed and rate of migration, territoriality, mortality, survival of stocked fish, and age and growth.

ANAESTHESIA

Fish can be marked more readily with less harm done to them in handling if they are anaesthetized. Also, the worker is less likely to be injured by sharp teeth or fin spines when the reactions of the fish have been slowed. Ether and urethane have been applied for this purpose (Gerking, 1949). For comfort of the operator, at least, the latter is to be preferred. These anaesthetics are added to water for use. The amount of ether required varies with the size of the fish and can easily be determined by trial and error. The solution strength of urethane needed to induce anaesthesia is about 0.5 per cent (about 19 grams or .66 oz. per gallon of water) (Gerking, 1949). Fish may be left in such a concentration of urethane for as long as 15 minutes; the chemical (ethyl carbamate) is held to be non-toxic in this amount for certain species and sizes. For early life history stages of some fishes, and for repeated or prolonged use, urethane is perhaps to be avoided (Battle and Hisaoka, 1952). The strength of the solution may be increased if more rapid action is desired; limits of toleration will then have to be learned by experiment. The possible carcinogenic action of urethane on human skin requires caution on the part of repeated users. This objection apparently does not apply to Tricaine Methanesulfonate (MS 222) (Sandoz Chem. Co., N. Y.). A 0.2% stock solution of the foregoing compound made up of 1.0 gm. in 500 cc. of water is diluted 1 to 6 for use. It seems most satisfactory and without deleterious physiological effects. Pickford (1953) has found it suitable for use with a topminnow, and Bjorklund, currently, with goldfish. Electronarcosis may also be used for the general purpose of quieting fish.

STUDY PROGRAM

If a suitable situation is available locally, conduct a population study in the field by the mark-and-recapture method; a small, easily seinable stream-side pool or hatchery pond with a few hundred fish in it will suffice. Or, as an alternative, an exercise may be done experimentally in the laboratory as follows:

1. Set up data paper with the following headings (letters and symbols are explained in preceding text material).

Trial Number (and Date)	$u+r$	Number Marked and Returned	m	$m(u+r)$	$\Sigma m(u+r)$	r	Σr	P

2. Place a few handfuls of dried corn or beans (the "fish") in a pan (the "lake").

3. With eyes closed to ensure a random sample remove a few fingers full.

4. Count the seeds, mark each with pencil or ink, record numbers in proper place on data paper, return to pan, and mix by stirring vigorously.

5. With eyes closed again, take another like sample, count, record marked and unmarked ones; mark the unmarked ones, and return all to pan; mix; calculate total number in pan.

6. Repeat (5) until estimates begin to approximate one another.

7. When estimates become more or less constant, verify estimate last obtained (presumably the best of the series) by actually counting all seeds in the pan. In counting, separate the marked and unmarked seeds in order to verify your previous counts of marked ones.

8. State error of estimate in per cent and explain deviations in the light of the requirements of fish population studies by the mark-and-recapture method previously given.

9. Propose means by which the mark-and-recapture method could be verified; there is need for further verification of this tool.

10. Summarize your information on the utility and limitations of the method as now known.

176   FRESHWATER FISHERY BIOLOGY

REFERENCES

Adams, L. 1951. Confidence limits for the Petersen or Lincoln index used in animal population studies. Jour. Wildlife Mgt., 15 (1): 13-19.

Battle, Helen I., and Kenichi K. Hisaoka. 1953. Effects of ethyl carbamate (urethan) on the early development of the teleost (Brachydanio rerio). Cancer Res., 12 (5): 334-340, 12 figs.

Carlander, Kenneth D. 1950. Handbook of freshwater fishery biology. Dubuque, Wm. C. Brown Co., v, 281 p., 5 charts.

Carlander, K. D. 1955. The standing crop of fish in lakes. Jour. Fish. Res. Bd. Canad., 12 (4): 543-570.

Chapman, D. G. 1951. Some properties of the hypergeometric distribution with applications to zoological sample censuses. Univ. Calif. Publ. Statistics, 1 (7): 131-160.

Cleary, Robert E., and John Greenbank. 1954. An analysis of techniques used in estimating fish populations in streams, with particular reference to large non-trout streams. Jour. Wildlife Mgt., 18 (4): 461-476.

Conseil Permanent International pour l'Exploration de la Mer. 1953. A guide to fish marks used by members of the International Council for non-participant countries. Jour. du Conseil, 19 (2): 241-289, illus.

Cooper, Gerald P., and Karl F. Lagler. 1956. The measurement of fish population size. In press, Trans. 21st North Amer. Wildlife Conf., in press, 10 figs.

Davis, Claude S. 1955. The injection of latex solution as a fish marking technique. Invest. Ind. Lakes and Streams, 4: 111-116.

DeLury, D. B. 1947. On the estimation of biological populations. Biometrics, 3(4): 145-167, 7 figs.

DeLury, D. B. 1951. On the planning of experiments for the estimation of fish populations. Jour. Fish. Res. Bd. Canad., 8 (4): 281-307.

Eschmeyer, R. W. 1938. The significance of fish population studies in lake management. Trans. 3rd North Amer. Wildlife Conf., pp. 458-468.

Fredin, R. A. 1950. Fish population estimates in small ponds using the marking and recovery technique. Iowa St. Coll. Jour. Sci., 24 (4): 363-384.

Gerking, Shelby D. 1949. Urethane (Ethyl carbamate) in some fishery procedures. Prog. Fish.-Cult., 11 (1): 73-74.

Haskell, David C. 1940. An electrical method of collecting fish. Trans. Amer. Fish. Soc., 69(1939): 210-215.

Kanaly, Jack J., Fred T. Williams, and Robert L. Millis. 1956. A study of the survival of hatchery reared trout in the Big Laramie River, Albany County, Wyoming. Wyo. Fish and Game Comm., Quart. Prog. Rept. Surv. and Invest., 4 (1): 1-31 (multilith.).

Krumholz, Louis A. 1944. A check on the fin-clipping method for estimating fish populations. Pap. Mich. Acad. Sci., Arts, and Lett., 29 (1943): 281-291, 2 figs.

Lagler, Karl F., and William E. Ricker. 1943. Biological fisheries investigations of Foots Pond, Gibson County, Indiana. Invest. Ind. Lakes and Streams, 2(1942): 47-72, 6 figs.

Leonard, Justin W. 1939. Notes on the use of Derris as a fish poison. Trans. Amer. Fish. Soc., 68(1938): 269-280.

Leslie, P. H. 1952. The estimation of population parameters from data obtained by means of the capture-recapture method. II. The estimation of total numbers. Biometrika, 39 (3-4): 363-388.

Parker, Richard A. 1955. A method for removing the effect of recruitment on Petersen-type population estimates. Jour. Fish. Res. Bd. Canada, 12 (3): 447-450.

Petersen, C. G. J. 1896. The yearly immigration of young plaice into the Limfjord from the German Sea, . . . Rept. Danish Biol. Sta., 6 (1895): 1-77. (Original not seen).

Pickford, Grace E., et al. 1953. Fish endocrinology. Bull. Bing. Ocean. Coll., 14 (2), 116 p.

Ricker, William E. 1943. Creel census, population estimates and rate of exploitation of game fish in Shoe Lake, Indiana. Invest. Ind. Lakes and Streams, 2(1942): 215-253.

Ricker, W. E. 1948. Methods of estimating vital statistics of fish populations. Indiana Univ. Publ. Sci. Ser., 15, 101 p.

Rounsefell, George A., and John Lawrence Kask. 1946. How to mark fish. Trans. Amer. Fish. Soc., 73 (1943): 320-363, 4 figs.

Scattergood, Leslie W. 1954. Estimating fish and wildlife populations: a survey of methods. [In] Statistics and mathematics in biology. Ames, Iowa, The Iowa St. Coll. Press, pp. 273-285.

Schnabel, Zoe E. 1938. The estimation of the total fish population of a lake. Amer. Math. Monthly, 45(6): 348-352.

Schumacher, F. X., and R. W. Eschmeyer. 1943. The estimate of fish population in lakes or ponds. Jour. Tenn. Acad. Sci., 18 (3): 228-249.

Shetter, David S., and Albert S. Hazzard. 1939. Species composition by age groups and stability of fish populations in sections of three Michigan trout streams during the summer of 1937. Trans. Amer. Fish. Soc., 68(1938): 281-302.

Shetter, David S., and Justin W. Leonard. 1943. A population study of a limited area in a Michigan trout stream, September, 1940. Trans. Amer. Fish. Soc., 72(1942): 35-51, 4 figs.

Smith, M. W. 1940. Copper sulphate and rotenone as fish poisons. Trans. Amer. Fish. Soc., 69(1939): 141-157.

Chapter XIII

Yield

Fishery management obviously entails consideration of yield, since one of its fundamental aims is to predict the quality and the quantity of the fishery product, and to maintain both at the highest level. Failing catches are often the first indication of the need for management that come to the attention of the fishery worker. The prediction of future production, as well as an appraisal of man's efforts to improve and maintain it, depend on a knowledge of previous and current harvests. Records of fishing effort and degree of success are required for this. In commercial fisheries, statistics on landings at fishing ports are kept by governmental agencies. As a result, much has become known of the order of magnitude of organized harvest of aquatic crops, along with its fluctuations, trends, and responses to regulation. For sport fisheries, which are found wherever there are men, such convenient and broadly inclusive records do not exist. However, considerable information has been gained by innumerable localized studies on angling effort and returns to fishermen.

Analyses of yield based on catch statistics thus can give information of very great value in the management of sport (Eschmeyer, 1937) or commercial fisheries (Clark and Marr, 1955). Such analyses are often called creel census studies in recreational fisheries, and production studies in commercial fisheries. They may show or lead directly to a knowledge of: (1) catch (annual or otherwise) in kinds, numbers, sizes and weight; (2) amount of fishing effort (fishing intensity, fishing pressure); (3) catch per unit of effort (per unit of time such as hour, day, trip, or year, and/or per unit of gear—line, boat, net, etc.); (4) rate of exploitation.

Catch statistics also afford information on the effectiveness of managerial efforts such as: (1) changes in fishing regulations (removal, intensification, and the like); (2) stocking or transplanting; (3) environmental improvement other than (2) above, such as pollution control, water level regulation, fertilization, etc.; (4) alterations in methods of fishing (methods of use, gear, lures, etc.).

In addition, data taken in catch studies have been used to show: (1) interrelations between species; (2) ecological and geographical distribution of fish; (3) relation of meteorological conditions to fishing; (4) characteristics of fishermen (sex; residence; skill; species and gear preferences); (5) costs and returns of fishing; (6) effects of fishing in one season upon that in another (e.g., does winter fishing through the ice affect summer angling quality for bluegills?).

In yield studies based on creel census, three techniques are of most common use: **general census, complete census,** and **stratified-sample census.** The objectives of these differ somewhat, as do the kind, and the reliability, of information obtained. Techniques involving voluntary reporting by anglers have been used; attempts to verify these techniques have shown that sometimes few, at other times most of the fishermen do not report voluntarily.

General creel censuses aim at attaining broad information on trends in kinds of fishing, time of fishing, time spent, species and sizes of individuals caught, and catch per unit of fishing effort (usually in terms of numbers of legal fish per fisherman-hour). Frequently the data are haphazard in point of the time and the place where they are collected. This is particularly true when they are gathered by wardens or conservation officers as an irregular assignment competing with many other duties.

Complete censuses, in addition to the foregoing, aim at highly individualized information on fishing type, time, effort, success, and other variables. They further seek complete information on the fishing pressure and yield for individual bodies of water or parts thereof. Obviously, the operation of such a census by competent persons is costly and time consuming even for small water areas. The resultant data, however, may be of high quality and value. Where checking stations are maintained and manned by trained personnel, excellent results have been obtained. As indicated, complete censuses are probably unattainable on a voluntary basis.

The great cost and effort involved in complete censuses have led to the use of partial censuses. From early crude procedures, based on a rough guess of the number of men or boats not encountered, partial procedures have now advanced to a sound basis of stratified random sampling (Moore et al., 1952). When such sampling is distributed among days according to the amount of fishing and the degree of variability of catch-effort data for each type of day, greater efficiency may be achieved than if an equal census effort is given to each day (Tait, 1953). The gain in efficiency over a complete census, with results nearly as reliable, is seen in Tait's conclusion for his data that the number of angler contacts made in a schedule including three half-days each week is usually adequate for estimating the mean catch per hour in a season with considerable fishing effort. Future improvements in technique may be anticipated, to judge by the 1956 spring seminar on the subject held under the leadership of Kenneth Carlander at Iowa State College.

One of the most promising utilitarian and theoretical aspects of yield studies lies in their relation to simultaneous studies of population. Since it has been shown repeatedly that there is a direct relation between the size of a fish population and fishing success, one wonders why there have not been more investigations of the population-yield type as exemplified in the sport fisheries by Cooper, E. (1952), Cooper, G. (1953),

Cooper, G. and Latta (1954), Lagler and deRoth (1953), and Ricker (1943 and 1945) and others. Such analyses go a long way toward defining the magnitude of fish stocks required to provide predictable levels of fishing success. In this sense they may afford real objectives for management, or become the basis for management procedures such as use-regulation.

CREEL CENSUS—Michigan Department of Conservation

Check, If Stream.................... If Lake.................... County....................

Name of Lake or Stream.................... Township....................

SPECIES CAUGHT	LEGAL SIZE		UNDERSIZE	
	Number	Av. Lgth.	Number	Av. Lgth.
Brook Trout				
Rainbow Trout				
Brown Trout				
Large Mouth Bass				
Small Mouth Bass				
Bluegills				
Sunfish				
Yellow Perch				
Pike Perch (Walleyes)				
Northern (Grass) Pike				
Rock Bass				
Crappies (Speckled Bass)				

(Enter other kinds taken on blank spaces above)

Date.................... 19......

Number of fishermen in party: Male.......... Female..........

Residence: City.................... State....................

One card to be used for each fishing party contacted, whether or not any fish are caught.

Number of fishermen in party who did not catch fish?....................

Kind of Fishing:

Ice?.......... Still Fishing?..........

Boat?.......... Trolling?..........

Shore?.......... Casting?..........

Bait used: Natural.......... Artificial..........

If taken by spear, dipnet or other means, state how....................

(Use other side of Cards for Remarks)

TIME FISHED ....HRS. A.M. / P.M. 12 1 2 3 4 5 6 7 8 9 10 11 12

Draw line through hours and quarter hours fished. 50M—8-11-39

Fig. 53. GENERAL CREEL CENSUS BLANK. An example of the blanks used in regional censusing of returns to anglers.

SPORT FISHING INSTITUTE
CREEL CENSUS CARD

Name of Lake____________ Date____________

Name of Fisherman____________ Address____________

Kind of Fishing: Fly fishing, casting, trolling, other____________ Boat Yes No

Species of Fish	Total Number of Fish: Legal Size	Sub Legal
Largemouth Bass		
Bluegill		
Pumpkinseed		
Yellow Perch		
Northern Pike		
Rock Bass		
Crappies		
Other		

Time fished (to nearest 1/4 hr.).
________hrs.________min.

From ______ a.m./p.m. to ______ a.m./p.m.

Number of bass which struck and were not landed________.

Directions

1. Use one card per fisherman
2. Fill in blanks, including numbers of fish caught and time fished.
3. For each keeper bass, cut off dorsal fin and left pelvic fin close to body and place in envelope with scale sample.
4. For scale sample, take a dozen scales from designated area and place in scale envelope.
5. Record for T L the greatest over all total length with mouth closed

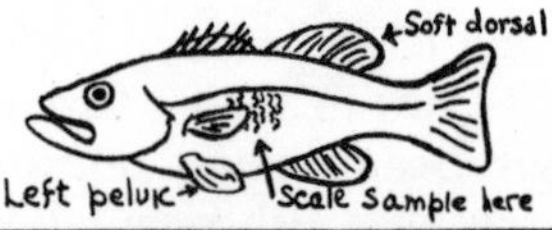

Fig. 54. SPECIAL CREEL CENSUS BLANK. An example of the blanks used in special project waters; in this instance note request for scale samples and for remains of fins previously clipped.

When isolated yield studies are combined they may serve to disclose both economic and recreational values of fishes. They may also indicate behavioristic features of various kinds of fishes, such as responsiveness to various kinds of fishing gear or methods of fishing. The table below, compiled from several creel censuses, illustrates the range in the rate at which common sport fishes are taken.

RANGE AND MAXIMUM AVERAGE CATCH PER HOUR
REPORTED FOR CERTAIN SPORT FISHERIES
IN AMERICAN FRESH WATERS

Summarized from Carlander, 1953

Kind of Fish	Number of Bodies of Water Included	Average Catch (Number of Fish) per Fisherman Hour*	Maximum Average Catch per Hour
Pike—Pickerel	6	1.44	5.25
Bullheads	3	1.90	3.75
Perch	4	.25	.55
Yellow Walleye	5	.21	.45
Largemouth Bass	20	.28	1.45
Smallmouth Bass	24	.36	1.35
Sunfishes	16	1.83	12.85
Trout (in lakes)	405	1.13	16.00
Trout (in streams)	608	1.36	14.00

*The average catch for all bodies of water was determined by weighting each unit of catch per hour by the number of water bodies from which each unit was reported.

STUDY PROGRAM

Obtain some raw creel census data and summarize them under appropriate headings to obtain all pertinent averages including catch per fisherman hour both in pounds of fish and in number of legal fish.

What are the management implications of your data? Read references, and tie creel census possibilities (and facts if available) in with work in biological fishery surveys (see later chapter in this book).

What are some of the evident limitations and possibilities for improvement of censuses with which you become familiar?

How might "experimental design" of mathematicians be employed to increase the efficiency of sampling in creel censuses?

182 FRESHWATER FISHERY BIOLOGY

REFERENCES

Carlander, Kenneth D. 1953. Handbook of freshwater fishery biology with the first supplement. Dubuque, Wm. C. Brown Co., v, 429 p., 5 charts.

Christensen, Kenneth E. 1953. Fishing in twelve Michigan lakes under experimental regulations. Mich. Inst. Fish. Res. Misc. Publ., 7, 46 p., 17 figs.

Cooper, Edwin L. 1952. Rate of exploitation of wild eastern brook trout and brown trout populations in the Pigeon River, Otsego County, Michigan. Trans. Amer. Fish. Soc., 81 (1951): 224-234, 1 fig.

Cooper, Gerald P. 1953. Population estimates of fish in Sugarloaf Lake, Washtenaw County, Michigan, and their exploitation by anglers. Pap. Mich. Acad. Sci., Arts, and Lett., 38 (1952): 163-186.

Cooper, Gerald P., and William C. Latta. 1954. Further studies on the fish population and exploitation by angling in Sugarloaf Lake, Washtenaw County, Michigan. Pap. Mich. Acad. Sci., Arts, and Lett., 39 (1953): 209-223, 1 fig.

Eschmeyer, R. W. 1937. The Michigan creel census. Trans. 2nd North Amer. Wildlife Conf., pp. 625-634.

Eschmeyer, R. W. 1939. Summary of a four-year creel census of Fife Lake, Michigan. Trans. Amer. Fish. Soc., 68(1938): 354-358.

Hazzard, A. S., and R. W. Eschmeyer. 1938. Analysis of the fish catch for one year in the Waterloo Project area. Pap. Mich. Acad. Sci., Arts, and Lett., 23(1937): 633-643.

Lagler, Karl F., and Mary Jane Lagler. 1943. A summer creel census for Foots Pond, Indiana. Invest. Ind. Lakes and Streams, 2(1942): 111-115.

Lagler, Karl F., and Gerardus C. deRoth. 1953. Populations and yield to anglers in a fishery for largemouth bass, *Micropterus salmoides* (Lacépède). Pap. Mich. Acad. Sci., Arts, and Lett., 38 (1952): 235-253, 5 figs.

Moore, Harvey L., Oliver B. Cope, and Richard E. Beckwith. 1952. Yellowstone Lake trout creel censuses, 1950-51. U. S. Fish and Wildlife Service, Spec. Sci. Rept.: Fish., 81, 41 p., 19 figs.

Ricker, William E. 1943. Creel census, population estimates and rate of exploitation of game fish in Shoe Lake, Indiana. Invest. Ind. Lakes and Streams, 2 (12) (1942): 215-253, 7 figs.

Ricker, William E. 1945. Abundance, exploitation and mortality of the fishes in two lakes. Invest. Ind. Lakes and Streams, 2 (17): 345-448, 7 figs.

Tait, Howard D. 1953. Sampling problems in the Michigan creel census. Univ. Mich. Ph. D. thesis, 131 p., 14 figs. (Microfilm copy in U. S. Library of Cong.).

Chapter XIV

Fish Pathology

Like all animals, fish have their full complement of diseases and parasites and of abnormalities both malignant and benign. There is no question that most fish die from such disorders, natural enemies other than man, or old age — certainly not from being caught by fishermen. Usually the ailments of fish may be placed in one of the following four categories: (1) disorders resulting from external physical and chemical agencies such as temperature, pH, dissolved gases, mechanical injuries, or pollution; (2) dietary or developmental deficiencies such as stunting, anemia, fatty degeneration, nutritional gill disease, cataract, and certain other types of misfunctions and malformations; (3) tumors and atypical cell growths; (4) diseases including those caused by infectious agents and parasites. Studies of these disorders constitute the field of fish pathology (and teratology), with etiological, morphological, physiological, prophylactic and therapeutic aspects.

Few workers have entered fish pathology, in spite of the fact that work in this field is of great significance in certain management activities such as fish culture, diagnoses of catastrophic epidemics in nature, and detection and control of pollution. Consequently, only little information exists on most aspects of the subject, and the actual effect of most disease organisms on their host fish is poorly known, particularly in nature. Furthermore, there are programs in fish pathology in only a few American universities (Cornell, Michigan, N. Y. U., and Washington), and there is no full-time professor of the subject in any of these. The outstanding fish disease laboratories on this continent are those of the U. S. Fish and Wildlife Service at Leetown, W. Va., and at Seattle and Cook, Wash. Only a few states, and the New York City Aquarium, have a fish pathologist (Snieszko, MS). A prospective worker must enter the field through general training in parsitology, protozoology, bacteriology, physiology, fish anatomy (both gross and microscopic), chemistry, pharmacology, epidemiology, biochemistry, nutrition, and genetics (e.g., see Appendix D).

SOME COMMON PATHOLOGICAL CONDITIONS

We can do little more here than briefly to survey major aspects of fish pathology. The following pages serve merely as a summary of common pathological conditions. Emphasis is on the diseases or disorders of biological origin (but those due to senility are omitted). Upsets due to physical and chemical factors of the environment are treated in the chapter on pollution. Although heredity is important in disease (Gordon, 1954; Wolf, 1954) no special treatment is given to it.

Developmental and/or Hereditary and Other Anomalies
A. Albinism (in hatchery reared trout).
B. Monstrosities and other terata.
  1. Siamese twinning (often found in hatchery trout—developmental anomaly).
  2. Two-headedness (often found in hatchery trout).
  3. Permanent flexure of vertebral column, not uncommon either in wild or in artificially reared fishes.
  4. Shortening of operculum, not uncommon in hatchery trout or aquarium fish; an indication of dietary deficiency, most likely of rachitic nature; may be hereditary.

Terata Resulting from Injuries
A. Broken gill arches, torn jaws, etc. (resulting from angling).
B. Disfigurements resulting from attacks by predators or collisions (heron spear marks, lamprey scars, otter tooth lesions, kingfisher pincer injuries, boat propellor scars, turbine damages).

Atypical Cell Growths
A. Ovarian tumors.
B. Visceral tumors.
C. Carcinoma of epithelium (epithelioma) or of lateral body musculature (myoma).
D. Cranial carcinomas.
E. Carcinoma of the thyroid.
F. Melanomas.

Parasites
A. Bacteria
  1. Furunculosis, an infectious systemic disease, frequently characterized by boils or furuncles caused by *Aeromonas* (*Bacterium*) *salmonicida*.
  2. Ulcer disease. Superficial ulcers and systemic infections caused by several types of bacteria. The typical ulcer disease is caused by *Hemophilus piscium* (Snieszko, 1952). Another kind caused by *Aeromonas liquefaciens* (*Pseudomonas hydrophila*) has been described by Reed and Toner (1941).
  3. Pseudomonad infections. Numerous pseudomands such as *A. liquefaciens* cause many systemic and localized infections in

cold- and warmwater fishes (Snieszko, et al., 1954; Schäperclaus, 1954).

4. Kidney disease. Bacterial infection of trout and salmon causing heavy losses (Earp, Ellis and Ordal, 1953; Snieszko and Griffin, 1955).

B. Viruses

There are several virus diseases of fishes. The best known are lymphocystis, European kidney disease of rainbow trout, and a disease of sockeye salmon, sockeye virus. The latter was most likely transmitted from adult salmon by salmon viscera used as food for young fish (Watson, 1954; Watson, Guenther, and Rucker, 1954).

C. Fungi

1. *Saprolegnia* or water mold is the most frequently encountered fungus infection in fish (Davis, 1953). Individuals from egg to adult are attacked; often the infection is secondary upon a lesion of non-fungus origin.

2. *Ichthyosporidium (Ichthyophonus) hoferi* is a fungus which causes systematic infections in marine fishes. Recently it has been recognized as a pathogen of warmwater fishes in ponds (Schäperclaus, 1954).

3. Mycosis-like granuloma is a recently recognized disease of salmonoid fishes, brook trout in particular. To May, 1956, the identity of the fungus seen in the tissues had not been completed (Snieszko).

D. Protozoa (Fish, 1935b; Davis, 1947).

1. "Ichthy" (*Ichthyophthirius* sp.), "the itch," sometimes found on rearing-pond fish. Often causes heavy losses of fish in raceways or rearing ponds.

2. *Costia necatrix* (Fig. 55). External protozoan parasite often found on trout in hatcheries. May cause substantial mortalities in crowded hatchery waters.

3. *Trichodina spp.* (Fig. 56). Protozoan ectoparasites of trout, bass, and other fishes. May cause serious mortalities in hatcheries.

4. *Octomitus salmonis* (Fig. 57). Internally parasitic, flagellate protozoan, occurs in hatchery trout. May cause serious mortalities.

E. Worms (see also the table on page 195).

1. *Gyrodactylus spp.*, (Fig. 58). Monogenetic trematode. 2 large anterior hooks and 16 small hooks on posterior disk. No eye spots. Viviparous. Parasitic on skin and gills of freshwater

fishes. May cause serious damage and even death of host, especially in rearing ponds or hatcheries.

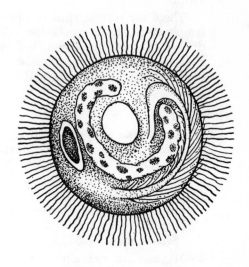

Fig. 55. PROTOZOAN ECTOPARA-
SITE OF TROUT. Ventral view of
Costia necatrix. Greatly enlarged.
(After Davis, 1946).

Fig. 56. ECTOPARASITIC PROTO-
ZOAN OF TROUT AND BASS. *Tri-
chodina myakkae*. Greatly enlarged.
(After Davis, 1946).

Gyrodactylus and its relatives pass their entire life cycle on the outside of the host, which may be almost any species of fish (freshwater or marine). They are about 1 mm. in length, and possess an elaborate posterior sucking disc equipped with hooks, by which they attach themselves to the skin and gills of the fish. If present in sufficient numbers, these parasites may cause fatality.

Characteristic of the genus *Gyrodactylus* is a type of paedogenesis in which a young individual may be sexually mature before it is born, indeed while it is still in the uterus of the parent. Not only that, but it may even have young in its own uterus—so that there may be three generations occurring, one inside of another.

In some species, the entire life of the parasite is passed attached to a host. The method of development provides for the attachment of successive generations in their turn, upon the parent's host.

2. *Dactylogyrus* spp. Monogenetic trematode. 2 large hooks and 14 marginal hooks on posterior disk. 4 eye spots. Oviparous. A parasite on gills of freshwater fishes. May be very harmful if occurring in large numbers.

3. *Ancyrocephalus* spp. Monogenetic trematode. 4 large hooks and 14 to 16 small hooks on posterior disk. 4 eye spots. Oviparous. Parasitic on skin and gills of freshwater fishes. May harm fish when it occurs in large numbers.

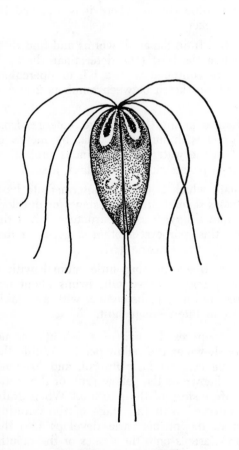

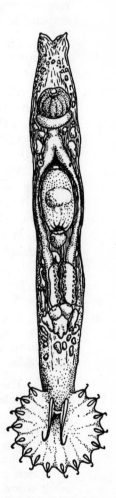

Fig. 57. INTERNALLY PARASITIC PROTOZOAN OF TROUT. *Octomitus salmonis*, flagellate form. Greatly enlarged. (After Davis, 1946).

Fig. 58. ECTOPARASITIC FLATWORM. *Gyrodactylus cylindriformis*, a trematode. Representative of several similar ectoparasitic flatworms of fish. Greatly enlarged. (After Mueller and Van Cleave, 1932).

4. *Clinostomum* spp., yellow grub (Fig. 59). Digenetic trematode. Clinostomidae. Metacercariae in flesh of freshwater fishes (Fig. 59, 5). Adult in pharynx and esophagus of fish-eating birds (Fig. 59, 1). Middle-sized distomes with flattened body. No pharynx, short esophagus, and long crura provided with lateral pockets. Apparently cause little damage to fish other than occasional emaciation.

The life cycle of the yellow grub, *Clinostomum marginatum* is complicated. The following numbered paragraphs correspond to the numbered items in Fig. 59.

(1) The adult stage of this parasite may be found in the oral cavity of the Great Blue Heron, where it is attached by means of its muscular suckers.

(2) The eggs are shed from the adult worms and find their way into the water when the bird (the determinate host) is feeding. These eggs are equipped with a lid, or operculum (shown open in the outline sketch between numbers 2 and 3, **Fig. 59**).

(3) The miracidium, a minute larval stage, emerges from the egg and is equipped with numerous cilia, by means of which it swims about in the water, and a spinous projection, or stylet, which aids it in penetrating its next host, a snail.

(4) Within the snail, which is the first intermediate host, the miracidium undergoes several successive stages of development. It grows first into a large sac-like structure called the mother sporocyst; from this sporocyst another stage, the redia, is developed, and finally the cercaria (5).

(5) The cercaria, a free-swimming little animal with a bluntly shaped forebody and a forked tail, swims about upside down in the water, and may make contact with a suitable kind of fish for its second intermediate host.

(6) The cercaria penetrates the skin of a fish, its second intermediate host, here shown as the yellow perch. Within the muscles of this host, the cercaria loses its tail, and becomes encysted, and now it is known as the yellow grub or the meta-cercarial stage in the life history of the parasite. When grubby fish, that is, fish infected with this stage of the parasite, are eaten by the heron, the metacercaria develops into the adult worm. The worm fastens onto the tissues of the mouth, throat, or esophagus of the bird (the final or determinate host). Now the cycle may begin over again.

(7) Final host, Great Blue Heron.

5. *Crepidostomum* spp. Digenetic trematode. Allocreadiidae. 6 oral papillae surround anterior end. Genital pore anterior to fork of intestine. Uterus short, with few eggs, between acetabulum, ovary and anterior testis. In intestines of freshwater fishes. Probably not harmful in ordinary numbers.

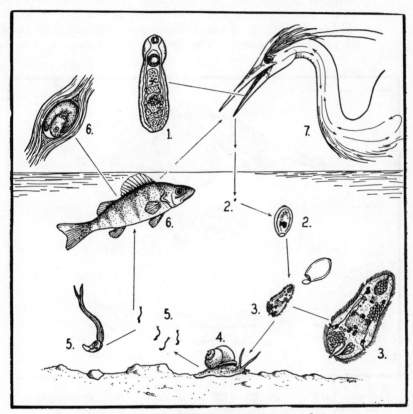

Fig. 59. LIFE CYCLE OF THE YELLOW GRUB, *Clinostomum marginatum*. (Adapted from Hunter, 1935).

6. *Neascus* spp., black-spot. Trematoda. Strigeid metacercariae with both fore and hind bodies well developed and distinctly set apart by a constriction; no lateral sucking cups; fore body leaf-like. Holdfast organ well developed. Reserve bladder well developed, the smaller branches are usually anastomosed. Calcareous granules mostly free in the circumambient fluid. Encysted.

   a. Black-spot. Pigmented cysts in the integument. Might be confused with glochidia of clams in the fall of the year.

b. Liver, kidney, and pericardium cysts. Non-pigmented cysts.
Neither a nor b above have been shown to be lethal to fishes.

7. *Proteocephalus ambloplitis,* bass tapeworm (Fig. 60). Cestode
of rock bass and many other game fishes, especially basses and
sunfishes. 280-410 mm. long by 2-2.5 mm. wide. Fifth sucker
vestigial. Mature and ripe proglottid broader than it is long.
Cirrus pouch pyriform, muscular, and 2/7 to 2/5 of proglottid breadth. Coils of vas deferens many, extending to middle
of proglottid. Larvae (Fig. 60, 4) may damage ovaries be-

Fig. 60. LIFE CYCLE OF THE BASS TAPEWORM, *Proteocephalus
ambloplitis.* (Adapted from Hunter, 1930).

yond repair; in hatcheries may inflict serious damage on brood
stock by causing sterility.

The life cycle of the bass tapeworm, *Proteocephalus ambloplitis,* may be summarized as follows (numbers correspond
to those in Fig. 60):

(1) The adult tapeworm commonly infests the intestine of
bass. Here it maintains its position by means of the muscular suckers on its head which attach to the intestinal wall of
the host. The body of the worm is comprised of a number

of segments, proglottids, the largest of which are at the caudal end of the worm, and the smallest near the head, where growth takes place. Each of these segments is an independent unit containing its own reproductive system. These worms maintain no digestive system; they absorb food from the host through the walls of each segment. As the segments mature and become filled with eggs, they break off from the rest of the adult worm and are shed through the anus of the fish into the water.

(2) In the water, the wall of the proglottid disintegrates and the eggs are released. For the life cycle of this parasite to continue, the eggs must be eaten by certain copepod crustaceans.

(3) Within the body of the crustacean (the first intermediate host), the egg hatches and develops into a bluntly shaped larva called the procercoid. The crustacean containing larvae in this stage may be eaten by the second intermediate host of the parasite.

(4) The second intermediate host may be almost any fish in which the parasite, as a procercoid larva, bores through the wall of the digestive tract and invades the tissues of the viscera (liver, spleen, or reproductive organs). Development of the parasite continues in these organs until the larva has grown from its procercoid to the plerocercoid stage.

(5) The final host, usually a piscivorous centrarchid (although perch, walleyes, and others will also serve) eats the infected, secondary fish host. As the secondary host is digested, the larvae are released into the intestine of the final host where they grow into adult tapeworms anchoring themselves in the intestine of the fish by means of an apical sucker. From this point on, the cycle may be repeated.

8. *Ligula intestinalis,* body-cavity tapeworm of fish. Cestoda. Diphyllobothriidae. Scolex triangular, very short, and lacking hooks. Larva a plerocercoid found free in body cavity of many fishes (including minnows, suckers, pike, and perch). External segmentation not evident in larva. Adults in gulls and other water birds which eat infected fish. Larvae may be numerous in host, and of larger sizes in larger fish (to about 1/2-inch broad and to 10 or more inches long) and smaller in smaller fish. May equal as much as 1/3 of the body weight of the host. Effects not known.

9. *Dibothriocephalus latus,* broad tapeworm of man (Fig. 61). Cestoda. Diphyllobothriidae. Scolex laterally flattened and

with 2 slit-like suckers; larva a plerocercoid up to 3 cm. long and found in perch and many other fishes. Adult in man, cats, and dogs which eat raw or inadequately cooked fish. The life cycle may be summarized as follows, with numbers corresponding to those in Fig. 61.

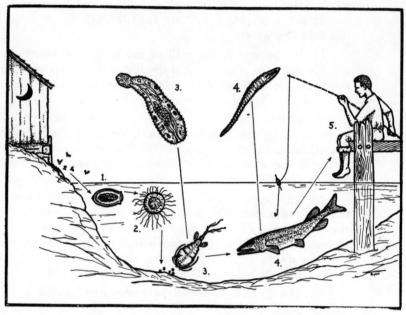

Fig. 61. LIFE CYCLE OF THE FISH TAPEWORM OF MAN, *Dibothriocephalus latus*. (Adapted from Belding, 1942, Textbook of Clinical Parasitology).

(1) Although we live in a comparatively enlightened age, and the life cycle of this parasite is well known, it is still not extremely unusual to find infections of *D. latus* where unsanitary conditions prevail. From man, who harbors the adult tapeworm in his intestine, segments of the worm (called proglottids) are shed with feces. If they find their way into a stream or other water area, the eggs, fully embryonated, will be released from the proglottid. These eggs, in turn, give rise to coracidia.

(2) A coracidium is a spherical larva with long cilia which escapes from the egg through a lid-like opening, the operculum. Swimming for several days with a characteristic alternating right and left movement, this ciliated larva may at length be devoured by a suitable copepod crustacean (3).

(3) In the intestine of the suitable copepod, the cora-cidium loses its cilia, penetrates the gut wall of this its first intermediate host, and develops into the next larval stage, the procercoid larva within the body cavity. The copepod con-taining this larval stage of the parasite must in turn be con-sumed by the second intermediate host (4).

(4) The second intermediate host is commonly the northern pike (*Esox lucius*) or the yellow walleye (*Stizostedion v. vitreum*). The larval parasite is liberated into the lumen of the gut by digestion of its first intermediate host. The pro-cercoid larva of the parasite works its way through the gut wall into the body cavity and hence to the muscles, viscera and connective tissues of the host. Here it is transformed into an encysted plerocercoid larva, which is known as a sparganum.

(5) The plerocercoid larva may find its way into the final host when man eats fish in which the parasite has not been killed by cooking or other treatment. The life cycle may thus continue, the plerocercoid (or sparganum) developing into an adult tapeworm in the intestine of man.

10. *Octospinifer* spp. Acanthocephala. A few ovoidal giant nu-clei in subcuticula. A large cement gland in the male. 8

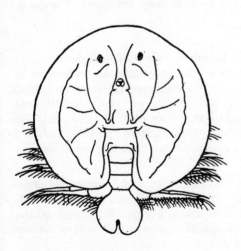

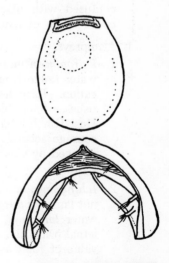

Fig. 62. ECTOPARASITIC COPEPOD. *Argulus catostomi,* a copepod parasitic on fish. Greatly enlarged. (After Wil-son, 1902).

Fig. 63. ECTOPARASI-TIC MUSSEL LARVA. Side view (upper figure) and open end view of a larval mussel or glochi-dium. Greatly enlarged.

hooks in 3 circles around globular proboscis. In intestines of freshwater fishes. May injure intestinal wall but is seldom lethal.

11. *Cystidicola* spp. Bladderworm. Nematoda. Occurs in swim bladder of *Coregonus artedii*. Apparently causes little damage.

F. Hirudinea. Annelida. Leeches occasionally parasitize fishes in small numbers. General effects probably harmful but details not known.

G. Copepoda. Crustacea; Arthropoda. Those which parasitize fishes are called fish-lice.

1. *Argulus* spp. (Fig. 62) Flat, horseshoe-crab shaped, having two ventral sucking disks. Parasitic on skin of many species of fishes. May change from one host to another. Injurious in hatcheries when present in large numbers. Small fishes eat the larvae and sometimes the adults for food.

2. *Salmincola* spp. Measures several millimeters in length; color yellowish white. A pair of long egg sacs at the posterior end. Easily seen on the gills of fishes. Head penetrates flesh of fish and the copepod remains attached until it dies. *S. edwardsii* is specific for brook trout. Other species infect other fishes.

H. Mollusca. Glochidia (Fig. 63), larval forms of clams, might be confused with black spot. Infection may be heavy enough to cause death of fish.

I. Lampreys.

1. *Petromyzon marinus*, sea lamprey. Adults landlocked in fresh water range from 15 to 24 inches in length, depending on location. Rasp hole and cling to commercial, sport, and other fishes. Suck blood and body fluids for their nourishment. Host fish become weakened and may die. Wounds may encourage secondary infection. The value of marketable fish is reduced by wound scars, and unknown numbers are killed outright.

2. *Ichthyomyzon unicuspis*, silver lamprey, and *I. castaneus*, chestnut lamprey are generally smaller than the sea lamprey. Freshwater lampreys feeding like sea lamprey. Presumed seldom lethal primarily. Wounds appear as ulcers and destroy esthetic value of food and sport fishes.

3. *Lampetra tridentata*, Pacific lamprey. Adults range from approximately 7 inches to more than 24 inches in length, depending on locality. Feed in sea (not in fresh water) on fishes and whales. Feeding habits and life history similar to those of sea lamprey. Commercially utilized for oil.

DESCRIPTIVE SUMMARY OF SOME IMPORTANT PARASITES
OF FRESHWATER FISH*

Common Name of Parasite	Scientific Name	Description and Location	Species of Fish Infected	Importance
1. Black grub of bass	*Uvulifer ambloplitis*	Small cysts about the size of a pin head. Occur on fins and in flesh.	Most species of sunfish, rock bass, basses (smallmouth and largemouth)	Severe infections may kill young fish or cause a significant loss of weight.
2. Black grub of perch	*Crassiphiala bulboglossa; Neascus* spp.	Small cysts about the size of a pin head occurring on or just under the scales. Sufficient numbers may be present in severe infections to give the impression of roughness when fish is touched.	Yellow perch, chain pickerel, banded killifish, and probably others.	No experimental evidence. Probably same as 1.
3. Black grubs	*Neascus* spp.	Same as in 2.	Other species of fish.	Unknown.
4. Sand grain grubs	*Tetracotyle* spp.	In flesh as minute but hard white or yellow cysts.	Yellow perch.	Unknown.
5. White grub of liver	*Posthodiplostomum minimum*	These white cysts occur in the liver and sometimes in kidney, spleen, or gonads. They are about the size of a pin head.	Nearly all species of fish.	Destroys liver and other tissue. May kill the fish in cases of severe infections.
6. Eye grub	*Diplostomulum scheuringi; Diplotomulum* spp.	In lens, or aqueous or vitreous humor of eye.	Nearly all species of fish.	Unknown. Parasites in lens may produce blindness. Heavy infections may kill fish.
7. Yellow grub	*Clinostomum marginatum*	In flesh, on gills or gill cover.	Nearly all species of fish.	Apparently may cause emaciation.
8. Red roundworm	*Eustrongylides* spp.	In flesh may cause sores. Dead parasites occur in hard nodules.	Eels, bass, sunfish, yellow perch.	Unknown. Heavy infections make fish unfit for food.
9. Bass tapeworm	*Proteocephalus ambloplitis*	In mesenteries, liver, spleen, or reproductive system. Sometimes makes fish soft and flabby.	Nearly all species of fish.	May cause sterility in bass.

*Adapted from Hunter, George W. 1942. Studies on the parasites of fresh-water fishes of Connecticut. Bull. Conn. St. Geol. and Nat. Hist. Surv., 63, pp. 228-288. (Also see Appendix D)

AUTOPSY

In conducting the autopsy of a fish, a procedure somewhat as follows may be carried out. Fresh material is better to work with than that which has been preserved. The routine described follows that outlined on the record card shown in Figure 64.

Make a systematic search for gross pathological conditions (enlargements, inflammations, etc.) and parasites on a fresh specimen. Follow the sequence of organs given on the blank form and fill in the record according to the directions below.

Where parasites are concerned, the data both qualitative and quantitative should be as nearly complete as possible. Use adequate optical equipment, the table on p. 195, and literature, and make accurate identifications and counts. Write careful notes on apparent effects of parasites or other pathological conditions with special reference to their management implications. Where there are no apparent effects, say so in your notes to indicate that you considered the point.

For additional points of autopsy technique, including methods for preserving materials, see Belding (1952).

Record information as follows on the autopsy record card.

HOST DATA

Species: Give either scientific name, or common name if there is no chance of confusion with some other species.

Date: Give date of collection.

Number: This is the serial number of the card and may be preceded by the initials of the pathologist.

Reference number: Fill in here the number of the scale envelope of this fish and the reference number to data taken when the specimen was collected.

Body length, weight, sex, maturity of gonads: Fill in from scale envelope or, if not yet obtained, do so and record. Follow directions given earlier under scale sampling procedure.

Annuli, Coefficient of Condition: Leave blank unless you determine it on the spot.

Fresh, preserved: Indicate by underlining, or crossing out, the condition at time of examination.

How taken: Indicate whether taken by gill net, seine, hook and line, or picked up dead, or other method of capture.

PARASITE DATA

In this section, including all remaining lines on the front of the record card except the last, fill in every blank with: (1) the pathological condition and/or the kind of parasites; (2) negative (neg.) if nothing was found; or (3) draw a line through the blank if organ was not examined.

INSTITUTE FOR FISHERIES RESEARCH
DIVISION OF FISHERIES
MICHIGAN DEPARTMENT OF CONSERVATION
COOPERATING WITH THE
UNIVERSITY OF MICHIGAN

PARASITE RECORD

County:

Lake or Stream   T.......... R.......... Sec..........

Host Data: Species.......... Date.......... No.......... Ref. No..........

Body Lengths.......... Weight.......... Sex.......... Maturity of Gonads..........

Annuli.......... Coeff. of Cond.......... Fresh, Preserved. How taken..........

Parasite Data: Skin.......... Fins: Pectoral..........

Pelvic.......... Dorsal.......... Anal.......... Caudal..........

Gills.......... Mouth Cavity..........

Orbit.......... Eyeball..........

General Musculature..........

Stomach.......... Pyloric caeca..........

Intestine.......... Rectum..........

Peritoneal cavity..........

Liver.......... Gall Bladder..........

Kidney.......... Air Bladder.......... Testes, Ovaries..........

Pericardial region.......... Stomach Surface.......... Intestine Surface..........

Are there any parasite/problems or disease in this body of water which would warrant detailed investigation? If so describe.

Parasite Identification: Investigator..........

Fig. 64. AUTOPSY RECORD CARD.

Parasitic Identification

Make a record here of the various parasites taken from the fish and what was done with them. Fill out as completely as possible.

GENERAL REMARKS

On the back of the Autopsy Record Card, record any general observations including statement as to probable cause of death if the specimen was originally collected when dead. It is also very important to indicate whether the specimen was alive and apparently normal in its behavior, or whether it was in distress, floating upside-down, or dead at the time it was taken for examination.

STUDY PROGRAM

Examine as many pathological conditions of fish as you can and learn the characteristics of the organisms involved. As a minimum achievement you should be able to recognize all conditions by their common names and be able to state general significance, symptoms, prophylaxis and/or therapy if known (for which see Appendix D). For parasitic worms, know life histories of representative types.

At least one autopsy should be conducted in the presence of an experienced worker.

Acquaintance should be gained with available general treatises, including Schäperclaus (1954), Davis (1953), and Amer. Fish. Soc. Symposium, 1954, "Research on fish diseases: a review of progress during the past 10 years" in volume 83 of the Transactions.

REFERENCES

Bangham, R. V. 1925. A study of the cestode parasites of the black bass in Ohio, with special reference to their life history and distribution. Ohio Jour. Sci., 25 (6): 255-270, 23 figs.

Bangham, R. V. 1928. Life history of bass cestode, *Proteocephalus ambloplitis*. Trans. Amer. Fish. Soc., 1927: 206-208.

Bangham, R. V., and G. W. Hunter, III. 1939. Studies on fish parasites of Lake Erie. Distribution studies. Zoologica, 24 (4): 385-448.

Belding, David L. 1952. Textbook of clinical parasitology. New York, Appleton-Century-Crofts, Inc., viii, 1139 p., illus.

Davis, H. S. 1946. Care and diseases of trout. U. S. Fish and Wildlife Service, Invest. Rept. 12, 98 p., 20 figs. (Bibliography of 144 titles)

Davis, H. S. 1947. Studies of the protozoan parasites of fresh-water fishes. U. S. Fish and Wildlife Service, Fish. Bull., 51, 29 p., 14 pl.

Davis, H. S. 1953. Culture and diseases of game fishes. Berkeley, Univ. Calif. Press, x, 332 p.

Elliott, A. M., and L. R. Russert. 1949. Some condition characteristics of a yellow perch population heavily parasitized by *Clinostomum marginatum*. Jour. Parasit., 35 (2): 183-190.

Essex, H. E., and G. W. Hunter, III. 1926. A biological study of fish parasites from the central states. Ill. St. Acad. Sci., 19: 151-181.

Ferguson, M. S., and R. A. Hayford. 1941. The life history and control of an eye fluke. Prog. Fish-Cult., 54: 1-13, 4 figs.

Fish, F. F. 1935a. The bacterial diseases of fish. Prog. Fish-Cult., 5: 1-9.

Fish, F. F. 1935b. The protozoan diseases of hatchery fish. Prog. Fish-Cult., 6: 1-4.

Fish, F. F. 1940. Formalin for external protozoan parasites. A report on the prevention and control of *Costia necatrix*. Prog. Fish-Cult., 48: 1-10, 3 figs.

Freund, L. 1923. Bibliographia pathologiae piscium. Collegit atque edidit auxilio ministerii pro agricultura czechoslovakiae. Prague, Hopfer, pp. 187-263.

Hindle, Edward. 1949. Notes on the treatment of fish infected with *Argulus*. Proc. Zool. Soc. London, 119: 79-81.

Hofer, Bruno. 1904. Handbuch der Fischkrankheiten. Munich. 369 p.

Hubbs, C. L. 1927. The related effects of a parasite on a fish. Jour. Parasit., 14: 75-84.

Hunninen, A. V. 1936. Studies of fish parasites in the Delaware and Susquehanna watersheds. Suppl. 25th Ann. Rept. N. Y. St. Cons. Dept., Biol. surv. Delaware and Susquehanna watersheds, 1935: 237-245.

Hunter, G. W., III. 1928. Contributions to the life history of *Proteocephalus ambloplitis* (Leidy). Jour. Parasit., 14: 229-243, 8 figs.

Hunter, G. W., III. 1937. Parasitism of fishes in the Lower Hudson area. Suppl. 26th Ann. Rept. N. Y. St. Cons. Dept., Biol. surv. Lower Hudson watershed, 1936: 264-273, 2 figs.

Hunter, G. W. III. 1942. Studies on the parasites of fresh-water fishes of Connecticut. Bull. Conn. St. Geol. and Nat. Hist. Surv., 63: 228-288.

Hunter, G. W., III, and Wanda S. Hunter. 1929. Further experimental studies on the bass tapeworm, *Proteocephalus ambloplitis* (Leidy). Suppl. 18th Ann. Rept. N. Y. St. Cons. Dept., Biol. surv. Erie-Niagara system, 1928: 198-207, 13 figs.

Hunter, G. W., III, and Wanda S. Hunter. 1930. Studies on the parasites of fishes of the Lake Champlain watershed. Suppl. 19th Ann. Rept. N. Y. St. Cons. Dept., Biol. surv. Champlain watershed, 1929: 241-260, 7 figs.

Hunter, G. W., III, and Wanda S. Hunter. 1931. Studies on fish parasites in the St. Lawrence watershed. Suppl. 20th Ann. Rept. N. Y. St. Cons. Dept., Biol. surv. St. Lawrence watershed, 1930: 197-216, 5 figs.

Hunter, G. W., III, and Wanda S. Hunter. 1932. Studies on parasites of fish and of fish-eating birds. Suppl. 21st Ann. Rept. N. Y. St. Cons. Dept., Biol. surv. Oswegatchie and Black river systems, 1931: 252-271, 3 figs.

Hunter, G. W., III, and Wanda S. Hunter. 1934. Studies on fish and bird parasites. Suppl. 23rd Ann. Rept. N. Y. St. Cons. Dept., Biol. surv. Raquette watershed, 1933: 245-254, 4 figs.

Hunter, G. W., III, and Wanda S. Hunter. 1935. Further studies on fish and bird parasites. Suppl. 24th Ann. Rept. N. Y. St. Cons. Dept., Biol. surv. Mohawk-Hudson watershed, 1934: 267-283, 3 pl.

Hunter, G. W., III, and Wanda S. Hunter. 1938. Studies on host reactions to larval parasites. I. The effect on weight. Jour Parasit., 24: 477-481.

Marshall, W. S., and N. C. Gilbert. 1905. Notes on the food and parasites of some fresh-water fishes from the lakes at Madison, Wisconsin. Rept. U. S. Fish Comm., 1904: 513-522.

Mueller, J. F. 1934. Parasites of Oneida Lake fishes. Pt. IV. Additional notes on parasites of Oneida Lake fishes, including descriptions of new species. Roosevelt Wild Life Annals, 3 (4): 335-373, 7 pl.

Mueller, J. F. 1938. Parasitism of fishes in the Allegheny and Chemung areas. Suppl. 27th Ann. Rept. N. Y. St. Cons. Dept., Biol. surv. Allegheny and Chemung watersheds, 1937: 214-225, 3 figs.

Phillips, Arthur M. Jr., Donald R. Brockway, Floyd E. Lovelace, Henry Podoliak and John M. Maxwell. 1952. The nutrition of trout. Cortland Hatchery Report No. 20 for the year 1951. N. Y. St. Cons. Dept., Fish. Res. Bull., 15, 25 p.

Plehn, M. 1924. Praktikum der Fischkrankheiten. [In] Handbuch der Binnenfischerei Mitteleuropas, Bd. I. Stuttgart. 479 p., 173 figs., pls. xi-xxxi.

Pratt, H. S. 1929. Parasites of fresh-water fishes. U. S. Bur. Fish. Econ. Circ. 42, 10 p., 11 figs.

Reed, G. B., and G. C. Toner. 1942. *Proteus hydrophilus* infections in pike, trout and frogs. Canad. Jour. Res., 20, Sect. D: 161-166.

Schäperclaus, Wilhelm. 1954. Fischkrankheiten. Berlin, Akademie Verlag, xii, 708 p., 389 figs.

Schlumberger, H. G. 1948. Tumors of fishes, amphibiams, and reptiles. Cancer Res., 8: 657-754.

Snieszko, S. F. 1952. Ulcer disease in brook trout (*Salvelinus fontinalis*). Prog. Fish-Cult., 14: 43-49.

Snieszko, S. F., in collaboration with Leonard Allison, Myron Gordon, Philip J. Griffin, John E. Halver, Ross F. Nigrelli, Robert R. Rucker, Brian J. Earp, Erling J. Ordal, Stanley W. Watson and Louis E. Wolf. 1954. Symposium, research on fish diseases: A review of progress during the past 10 years. Trans. Amer. Fish. Soc., 83 (1953): 217-349.

Snieszko, S. F., and Philip J. Griffin. 1955. Kidney disease in brook trout and its treatment. Prog. Fish-Cult., 17: 3-13.

Thompson, D. H.   1927.   An epidemic of leeches on fishes in Rock River. Bull. Ill. St. Nat. Hist. Surv., 17: 193-201.

Van Cleave, H. J., and J. F. Mueller.   1934.   Parasites of Oneida Lake fishes.   Pt. III.   A biological and ecological survey of the worm parasites.   Roosevelt Wild Life Annals, 3 (3): 159-334, 13 pl., 9 text-figs.

Ward, H. B.   1894.   Some notes on the biological relations of the fish parasites of the Great Lakes.   Proc. Nebr. Acad. Sci., 4: 8-11.

Ward, H. B.   1894.   On the parasites of lake fish.   Proc. Amer. Microscop. Soc., 15: 173-182, 6 figs.

Ward, H. B.   1912.   The distribution and frequence of animal parasites and parasitic diseases in North American fresh-water fish.   Trans. Amer. Fish. Soc., 41(1911): 207-241.

Wilson, Charles Branch.   1902.   North American parasitic copepods of the family Argulidae, with a bibliography of the group and a systematic review of all known species.   Proc. U. S. Nat. Mus., 25(1903): 635-742, 23 figs., 20 pl.

Wardle, Robert A., and James A. McLeod.   1952.   The zoology of tapeworms.   Minneapolis, Univ. Minnesota Press, xxiv, 780 p., 418 figs. (Extensive bibliography)

Watson, Stanley W., R. W. Guenther and R. R. Rucker.   1954.   A virus disease of sockeye salmon: interim report.   U. S. Fish and Wildlife Service, Spec. Sci. Rept.: Fish., 138, 36 p.

Wolf, Louis E.   1938.   Ichthyopthiriasis in a trout hatchery.   Prog. Fish-Cult., 42: 1-16.

Chapter XV

Pollution

Pollution and its effects constitute one of man's greatest crimes against himself. The extent of despoilment in rendering waters unfit for human consumption, and unsuitable for aquatic life and other important uses, is particularly alarming near large centers of population. The damaging effects of this scourge also appear in remote places, in the vicinity of coal mines, canneries, paper mills, and atomic piles. Streams are more frequently violated than lakes.

The uses generally recognized for inland waters are human consumption and other domestic uses, industrial and agricultural supply, waste disposal, recreation including fishing, and navigation. Although specialists in different fields vary the order of importance of the foregoing, there can be no question that each is essential. The problem is to reconcile them and to strive for a reduction of obvious conflicts. It is the duty of a fish manager to be able to recognize pollution from any source, and to recommend practicable ways to avoid it. He must have full understanding of the multiple interests and rights involved in water use in order to share wisely in the management of water as a natural resource.

The types of pollution that may affect the aquatic environment and its users have been classified by Tarzwell as follows:
1. Inert inorganic materials—erosion silt, etc.
2. Putrescible wastes—all organic wastes.
3. Toxic wastes—metals, insecticides, etc.
4. Radioactive wastes.
5. Wastes of significant heat content—hot water or other heated effluents.

DETECTION AND MEASUREMENT OF POLLUTION

Pollution may be detected and measured by various combinations of chemical, physical, and biological means. Chemical tests are used for such things as dissolved oxygen, hydrogen ion concentration, and the presence of particular chemical compounds or elements. Physical assays measure color, turbidity, specific conductance, and odor, among other things. The biological identification and mensuration of pollution involves test and index organisms; the occurrence of sudden large mortalities is often a tardy clue. Test organisms are those which are exposed to various dilutions of presumed pollutants in order to determine limits of tolerance and lethality. This is the method of bio-assay and it is best done under standardized conditions in order that the results obtained by workers in widely separated laboratories may be comparable (Doudoroff, et al., 1951). Several kinds of fishes and other organisms have been used for this purpose; Ellis (1937) employed the goldfish extensively but it is so hardy and tolerant that it is not now to be recommended.

As pollution progresses, the bottom life changes and permits the experienced worker to use certain plants and animals as indices to the situation. Living things that are sensitive to a particular pollutant cease to exist and are succeeded by more tolerant ones. In situations of organic pollution, as in that from domestic sewage, the following organisms tend to become dominant and may serve as indices when they are particularly abundant: tubificid worms; leeches; mosquito larvae; rat-tail maggots (larvae of *Syrphus* flies); filterfly larvae (Psychodidae); and "pollution fungus" *(Sphaerotilus natans)*. Such biological indices are only of moderate accuracy, however, because they inhabit such a wide range of natural situations (Huet, 1949; Gaufin and Tarzwell, 1952). The coliform group of bacteria serve as an index to the presence of human fecal material in waters.

Sudden large mortalities involving several fish species are sometimes an evidence of man made pollution. At other times, they may arise from natural causes such as seasonal anaerobiosis (Moore, 1942), lightning striking the water (Raney, 1941), or water toxification by another organism (Mackenthun, et al., 1948). Mortalities of a single species are more apt to be due to a life history event such as death after spawning (as in Pacific salmons or in lampreys) or to an epizooty.

WATER QUALITY AND AQUATIC LIFE

A natural property of lakes and streams is to overcome the effects of pollution by self-purification. This is accomplished through dilution, precipitation, and oxidation. However, the extent to which the purifying process can be carried by these means is limited.

Fundamentally, there are three zones downstream from any source of harmful pollution: (1) zone of immediate pollution; (2) septic zone; and (3) zone of recovery. In many situations the first zone is characterized by an accumulation of the pollutant, and by the color or odor of the polluting substance or its vehicle. The septic zone, in instances of organic pollution, may be without dissolved oxygen all or part of the time, is marked by the height of the effect of the pollutant, and is often accompanied by odors of decomposition and an increase in populations of index organisms. The immediate-pollution and the septic zones may be combined as one at toxic waste sites where organisms are destroyed at once by the outfall. The zone of recovery is characterized by progressive return to normalcy, reappearance of less tolerant organisms, and absence of odors. Not uncommonly the zones of immediate pollution and the zone of sepsis are devoid of fish. Not all pollution, however, is harmful. Certain substances, in proper proportion to the recipient water volume, may act as fertilizers (Hasler and Einsele, 1948).

Quality of water favorable to good populations of American stream fishes of the "warmwater" type is a complex partly defined as follows (Ellis, 1944: 12):

(a) Dissolved oxygen not less than 5 ppm.

(b) pH range between 7.0 and 8.5.

(c) Ionizable salts as indicated by a conductivity between 150 and 500 mho $\times$ 10^{-6} at 25° C. and in general not exceeding 1,000 mho $\times$ 10^{-6} at 25° C.

(d) Ammonia not exceeding 1.5 ppm.

(e) Suspensoids of a hardness of one or greater, so finely divided that they will pass through a 1,000-mesh (to the inch) screen, and so diluted that the resultant turbidity would not reduce the millionth intensity depth for light penetration to less than 5 meters.

The Aquatic Life Advisory Committee (1955) has redefined the dissolved oxygen criterion as follows:

"The dissolved oxygen content of warm-water fish habitats shall be not less than 5 ppm. during at least 16 hr. of any 24-hr. period. It may be less than 5 ppm. for a period not to exceed 8 hr. within any 24-hr period, but at no time shall the oxygen content be less than 3 ppm. To sustain a coarse fish population the dissolved oxygen concentration may be less than 5 ppm. for a period of not more than 8 hr. out of any 24-hr. period, but at no time shall the concentration be below 2 ppm."

"If such favorable conditions for fishes are to be maintained and fishes and other aquatic organisms are to be protected against the toxic actions of many stream pollutants, all pollutants not readily oxidizable or removable by the stream should be excluded, including particularly all cellulose pulps, wastes carrying heavy metallic ions and gas factory effluents. Other types of wastes should be diluted to concentrations nontoxic to the aquatic life of the particular stream. No substance should be added to stream waters which would cause a deviation in general conditions beyond the limits outlined above." (Ellis, 1944:12)

The Aquatic Life Advisory Committee (1955) further suggests:

"That pH be recognized as a poor criterion for the expression of toxicity of acids and alkalies in general, and that its use be restricted to the control of the addition of highly dissociated inorganic acids and alkalies known to be non-toxic within the pH range of 5 to 9.

"That at no time shall acid be added in quantities to lower the pH below 5, nor alkalies sufficient to raise the pH above 9; and that, insofar as possible, pH values be maintained between 6.5 and 8.5 to maintain the productivity of the water for aquatic life.

"That the addition of ammonia (as NH_3 or NH_4OH), poorly dissociated inorganic acids, and organic bases and acids shall be regulated not in terms of pH, but in terms of their own toxicities as established by bioassay."

EFFECTS OF POLLUTANTS

An ordinary pollutant harms a fish either indirectly or directly (Ellis, 1936). Indirect damage occurs largely through destruction of the habitat. Starvation may result from the elimination of plankton and bottom organisms by chemical or physical agencies. Defiling materials which settle out may cover spawning grounds, besides laking down the bot-

USUAL FISHERIES HAZARDS OF 30 COMMON TYPES OF MUNICIPAL AND INDUSTRIAL EFFLUENTS (Ellis, 1937)[1]

Types of wastes	Changes in water affecting fishes						Bottom pollution blanket	Specific toxic action on fishes
	Decrease in dissolved oxygen	Hydrogen-ion concentration		Increase in specific conductance	Increase in turbidity	Increase in ammonia		
		Increase in acidity	Increase in alkalinity					
MINERAL WASTES, LITTLE BACTERIAL ACTION								
1. Erosion silt	None	None	None	None	Critical	None	Critical	None.
2. Limestone sawmills	do.	do.	Possible	Moderate	do.	do.	do.	Do.
3. Asbestos works	do.	do.	do.	do.	do.	do.	do.	Possible.
4. Mine flotation	Possible	Possible	do.	do.	None	do.	Possible to critical	Possible.
5. Coal- and iron-mine drains	do.	Critical	do.	do.	do.	do.	Possible to critical	Possible to critical.
6. Crude oil	do.	None	do.	None	do.	do.	do.	Possible to critical.
7. Salt water from oil wells	None	do.	Possible	Critical	do.	do.	None	Do.
ORGANIC, BACTERIAL ACTION								
8. Municipal sewage	Critical	Possible	do.	Possible	Possible	Critical	Possible to critical	Do.
9. Dairy industries	do.	Critical	None	Moderate	Moderate	Moderate	do.	Possible.
10. Packing plants	do.	Moderate	do.	do.	do.	Critical	Critical	Do.
11. Canning factories	do.	None to moderate	Possible	do.	Possible	do.	Possible to critical	Do.
12. Breweries and distilleries	do.	do.	None to moderate	do.	do.	Possible	do.	Do.
13. Beet sugar, pulp wastes	Possible to critical	Critical	None	do.	do.	do.	do.	Possible to critical.
14. Paper pulp		Possible	Possible	Possible	do.	do.	Critical	Possible.
15. Sawdust	do.			do.	do.	do.	Critical	Do.
CHEMICAL PROCESSES								
16. Coal-gas wastes	Possible	None	do.	Moderate	None	Critical	do.	Critical.
17. Spent lubricants	do.	do.	None	Possible	do.	None	Possible to critical	Possible to critical.
18. Metal refineries	None	do.	Possible	do.	Possible	Possible to critical	Possible	Critical.
19. Laundries and wool washings	Moderate	None	Moderate to critical	Moderate	Moderate	Moderate to critical	Possible	Possible.
20. Steffens house waste	Moderate to critical	do.	Critical	Critical	None	None	do.	Critical.
21. Sulphite pulp	do.	Possible	Moderate to critical	Moderate	do.	Possible	Possible to critical	Do.
22. Strawboard waste	None	None	Critical	do.	Possible	None	do.	Do.
23. Chemical works (a)	Possible	do.	do.	do.	None	do.	None	Do.
24. Chemical works (b)	Moderate	Critical	None	do.	Possible	Possible to critical	do.	Do.
25. Tanneries	Possible	Possible to critical	Possible to critical	do.	None	None	Critical	Do.
26. Dye works	Possible	None to moderate	None to moderate	None	None	None	Possible	Do.
27. Bittern liquors	None	Critical	None	Critical	None to possible	do.	None	Possible to critical.
28. Tin-plate and wire mills	None to possible	do.	do.	Moderate	do.	do.	Possible to critical	Do.
29. Starch factories	Possible to critical	Possible to critical	do.	Possible	Possible	Possible	do.	Do.
30. Cloth sizing	do.	Possible to critical	do.	Moderate	Moderate	do.	do.	Possible.

[1] In this table increases in both acidity and alkalinity are noted in some cases, due to the facts that two or more kinds of effluents are mixed, with one predominating at times and to changes which take place in the stream after the effluent is added.

tom foods. In addition, indirect influences may be exerted through changes in the gaseous and salt contents of the water.

Direct effects of pollution on fish life are either catastrophic or gradual, depending on the amount and kind of the undesirable affluent in relation to the quantity of the recipient water mass (Ellis, 1936). Sudden discharge of a large volume of boiling water or heavy salts or other chemicals may kill instantly. Some substances when absorbed are directly toxic to fishes, even in small quantities. Certain derivatives of crude oil and ammonium compounds are of this nature. Many commercial pollutants, however, need not be absorbed but act primarily by damaging the gill filaments. The filaments may actually be eroded (some strong acids do this) or they may become clogged by having the desecrating substance cause oversecretion of mucus (e.g., heavy metal salts). Certain other poisons need to be swallowed to damage the internal organs. Some such agents will do this at once when absorbed; whereas others, such as arsenic and selenium, are stored up by the fish until the accumulation becomes injurious. Still other things irritate the surface of the fish and bring on secondary infections of bacteria or mold.

POLLUTION ABATEMENT

The fishery biologist encounters several weighty impediments in his efforts to regulate pollution (Beatty, 1948). For one thing, the effects of many polluting substances are not known. For another, it is very difficult to appraise in dollars the damages wrought by a violating agency. Yet, many instances of offence will not be brought under control until an economic scale is established against which the cost of abatement may be justified or on the basis of which damages may be assessed. The aquatic resource is generally endangered by the lack of adequate or commensurate penalties for destruction by pollution, and by the lack of sufficient authority in fish and game departments for the administration of pollution laws as they apply to the fish crop; the ultimate jurisdiction is often left to state health departments. Federal control of pollution is virtually non-existent (although this situation is improving), in spite of the fact that pollution problems are often interstate in nature.

Needed for the furtherance of pollution abatement are public education, direct aid to communities and industries, and research on the effects of pollutants, singly and in likely combinations, on aquatic organisms. Reasonably precise standards are required for both qualitative and quantitative aspects of toxicants, such as were given above for dissolved oxygen and pH. However, for many substances the concentrations which are tolerable to aquatic life are not accurately known. The problems of establishing criteria are amplified by differences in quality of receiving waters, in species responses to the same pollutant, in synergesis of polluting substances, and in variations in the volume of flow and natural chemical content of recipient streams. Permissible concentrations of toxicants in waste-receiving waters are those which can be tolerated indefinitely by all or a selected group of the kinds of aquatic organisms present. It has been recommended (Aquatic Life Advisory Committee, 1955) that rigidly controlled bio-assay toxicity tests form the basis for determining permissible concentrations of pollutants. Programming and conduct of such tests calls for careful selection (as well as handling, and conditioning and control, where applicable) of test animals, experimental water, temperatures, test containers, procedure, and method of interpretation and reporting. The results of toxicity tests are best expressed as the median tolerance limit (TL$_m$) which is the concentration of the substance or waste that kills one-half the aquatic test animals in a specified period of exposure (e.g., 48-hr. TL$_m$). Application of median tolerance limits to the establishment of permissible levels of concentration of a pollutant in natural waters is based on the general experience that 0.1 of the concentrate of the 48-hr. TL$_m$ usually has no adverse effect on animals represented in the tests. The application factor 0.1 requires further testing but is thought to approach a safe average. Recommendations of the Aquatic Life Advisory Committee (1955) in this regard are:

"1. The toxicity of wastes to aquatic life in the receiving water can most effectively and reliably be determined by means of bioassays.

"2. The bioassay methods for the evaluation of acute toxicity of industrial wastes to fish described and recommended by the Committee on Research, Sub-committee on Toxicity, Section III, Federation of Sewage and Industrial Wastes Associations [Doudoroff et al., 1951] are endorsed.

"3. The final concentration of any waste in the receiving water should be no greater than the 48-hr. TL$_m$ $\times$ 0.1 (that is, the 48-hr. TL$_m$ as determined by the bioassay methods recommended multiplied by 0.1, the tentative application factor). Other application factors may be used in specific cases, but only after thorough investigations justifying their use have been made."

STUDY PROGRAM

Bio-Assay of a Pollutant

The exercise outlined here is simplified for classroom use, from the detailed procedures given by Doudoroff et al., 1951—which should be studied before proceeding, if possible. The object is to introduce a worker to the methodology of determining the effects on fish of a chemical or a pollutant from an industrial source. For convenience, concentrated commercial Formalin may be used as the test substance, because of its universal presence in fishery laboratories and because of its fishery uses in the preservation of specimens and in disease control.

1. Secure a series of warmwater fish of one species and of nearly uniform size from an unpolluted source. Sunfish or minnows about two inches in total length should be satisfactory and easily obtained.

2. Acclimatize the fish for at least one week by holding and feeding them in the laboratory at conditions as nearly as possible like those under which the experiments will be run, with special regard to temperature

and chemical quality of water. Recommended test temperature, hence acclimatizing temperature, should be held constant ± 2° F., within the range of 68° to 77° F. for warmwater fishes.

3. Place an equal volume of water in each of five clean aquaria with a minimum individual capacity of five gallons. Use water from acclimatizing tank, or unpolluted water from the same source. One container is for control, the other four are for various concentrations of test solution. Measure volumes of commercial formalin (or pollutant) to obtain the following percentages of test solutions: 0.1%; 0.18%; 0.32%; and 1.0%. A 1.0% solution of Formalin by volume contains 99 cc. of the water to each 1.0 cc. of the concentrated commercial solution.

4. Aerate the tanks with dispersed, compressed air or with oxygen to keep the concentration of dissolved oxygen above 4 ppm. for warmwater fishes. Determine amount of dissolved oxygen, free carbon dioxide, pH, and as many of the other items as possible which are called for on the sample record blank shown on page 210. Use methods given in the chapter on Lake, Pond, and Impoundment Surveys, or in Standard Methods for the Examination of Water, Sewage, and Industrial Wastes, 10th Ed., 1955.

5. Add four fish to each tank, taking care not to exceed the ratio of about one fish to every two quarts of test solution.

6. Record observations on a form like the following sample and convert numbers of fish surviving in each tank at the end of 48 hours into percentages for that concentration of test solution. If none die in this time interval, see item 9 below.

7 Estimate the 48-hr. TL_m by straight-line graphic interpolation using semi-logarithmic paper. The 48 hr. TL_m is the concentration of a pollutant at which just 50 per cent of the test animals used can survive for 48 hours. In order to do this, graph the percentages of survival on the arithmetic scale and the units of concentration on the log scale (see sample graph) of semi-log paper. Connect the point representing the concentration and percentage at which more than 50 per cent of the fish died in 48 hours with the nearest point representing concentration at which less than 50 per cent of the fish died in that interval. Then estimate the 48-hr. TL_m for a theoretical survival of 50 per cent. Under ideal conditions, the concentrations which are survived by none of the test fish or by all of the test fish are only slightly higher or lower respectively than the 48-hr. TL_m. Thus, this index, if carefully achieved, is of great use to the fishery worker in appraising the effects of pollutants and the dilutions required if a pollutant of the non-accumulative kind is to be rendered innocuous.

8. If none of the fishes should die in 48 hours, allow the experiment to run up to 96 hours or longer as needed to get results. Increase the concentration of each test solution tenfold and repeat, if needed.

9. Test 0.1 concentration for 48-hr. TL_m to see if this would be a permissible concentration of the toxicant in your test water.

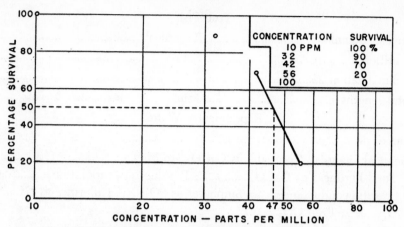

Fig. 65. TOLERATION OF POLLUTANTS BY FISH. Estimation of the mean tolerance limit (TLm) by straight-line interpolation. The TLm in this example is a concentration of 47 ppm. (Redrawn from Hart, et al., 1945).

10. Prepare a brief statement on the toxicity of the substance tested and state conditions of the test which may have influenced the results. Consider here the nature of the pollutant, the techniques of the test, and the condition and size of the fish. Also state a probable permissible, "harmless" concentration in natural water of similar quality to that used in the experiments.

REPORT OF TOXICITY ANALYSIS

Substance investigated... Date.........................
Properties of substance...
Source of sample...
Purpose of investigation...

Test Results

TLm	Temperature	Concentration of Test Solution	Number Surviving	Percentage Survival
24-hr. TLm				
48-hr. TLm				
96-hr. TLm				

Test Fish

Names: Common ....Technical ....

Identifier ....Source ....

Acclimatization ....

Total lengths ....Min. .... Max. .... Mean............

Experimental Water

Source ....

Chemical analysis: Total alk. as $CaCO_3$ (to M.O.)..............; pH................;

Total hardness as $CaCO_3$..............; Residue on evaporation..............or

Specific conductance........; Sulphates as SO_4........; Chlorides as Cl.......;

O_2..........; Free CO_2............

Manner of aeration of test solution...

Remarks ....

Investigator...

Field Study of Industrial Pollution

Visit a local site of industrial pollution, list evidences, and determine nature and evident effects of the pollutants. Keep record of observations on a blank form such as the one which follows. Design and, if possible, conduct experiments on the polluting material along the lines of the previous exercise. Ascertain probable effects of the pollutant from Ellis (1944) or from references in Doudoroff and Katz (1950 and 1953). Try to affix dollar value to the damage done and include the figure in a statement of the esthetic, recreational, and other benefits which might accrue were the situation alleviated. Work out a control plan and estimate its cost and feasibility. If possible, get reaction of polluting agency to your proposal.

Field Study of Pollution Control

Visit a sewage disposal plant (or see the movie CLEAN WATERS, cited in References). If descriptive literature and a flow diagram are available, obtain them and become acquainted with the steps in the treatment process. If no diagram is to be had, prepare one. Systematize your observations and keep a record of your findings by using a blank form such as that which follows.

Since most sewage plants do not continually achieve the desired ends, evaluate the one visited as to its objectives, general efficacy, and shortcomings, and make recommendations for its improvement. Remember that recommendations, in order to have a chance of being adopted, must show the need, the probable desirability of the results to be obtained, and the feasibility of the operation in relation to present facilities, available capital, and location. Discuss your proposals with the person in charge of the treatment establishment, if possible.

Legal Aspects of Pollution

Study a copy of the laws of your state or province regarding pollution and riparian rights. How might they be strengthened? Compare with situation in other areas using Beatty, 1948, as a basis.

INDUSTRIAL POLLUTION ANALYSIS FORM

Location ....

Polluting agency (and responsible person)...

Nature of pollution and how detected

Continual................................ Intermittent...

Physical evidence ....

....

Chemical evidence ....

....

Biological evidence ....

....

Specific pollutant(s) ....

Ellis' (1937) or other reliable limits of toleration for fish.....................

....

Toxicity to aquatic life

At point of effluence (include measurement of amount and concentration of effluent and volume of stream flow).....................................

....

Extent of toxic zone (compute from dilution)...

....

Zone of recovery (compute from dilution)..

....

Damage of pollutant (give dollar value where possible)............................

Esthetic ....

....

Recreational ....

....

On fish, etc. ....

....

Abatement of pollution

What is being done, if anything?..

....

....

Recommendation for, and description of control..

....

....

....

Date.. Analyst..

DOMESTIC SEWAGE TREATMENT ANALYSIS FORM

Location of plant...

Community served.. Population.....................

Plant superintendent ....

Date of construction........Rated capacity......gallons. Expected life......years

Flow in gallons: Peak............and time of day...
Minimum............and time of day.................................
Average............and time of day.................................
Excess of peak over rated capacity.....................

Location and number of lift or pumping stations.............................

Primary treatment (clarification of sewage, describe)
Screening and fate of screened material.................................
....

Grinding and fate of ground material.......................................
....

Primary settling and fate of settled materials............................
....

Secondary treatment (processing the liquid from primary, describe)
Filter process (trickling, high rate, etc.).................................
....

Activated sludge process...
....

Final disposal of liquid (Where does it go? Is it chlorinated? What is
its B.O.D.?) ....
....

Treatment of residual sludge from primary and secondary treatments
Digestion ....
....

Gas from digestion (use?)...
....

Drying final residue of sludge (air, vacuum filtering, centrifugation, heat?)
....
....

Final disposal of sludge (how treated for fill, fertilizer, or incineration)....
....

Number of employees and classification..
....
....

Annual budget and breakdown of operating costs...........................
....

Plant deficiencies ....

....

Adequacy of treatment in regard to use of water into which plant discharges ....

....

Recommendations for plant improvement...

....

....

Date.. Analyst....................................

REFERENCES

American Public Health Association. 1936. Standard methods for the examination of water and sewage. New York, Amer. Public Health Assoc. and Amer. Water Works Assoc., 10th ed., xix, 522 p., 57 figs.

Aquatic Life Advisory Committee of the Ohio River Valley Water Sanitation Commission. 1955. Aquatic life water quality criteria. Sewage and Indust. Wastes, 27 (3): 321-331.

Beatty, Robert O. 1948. Wildlife's stake in pollution abatement. Trans. 13th N. Amer. Wildlife Conf., pp. 563-595.

Doudoroff, P., B. G. Anderson, G. E. Burdick, P. S. Galtsoff, W. B. Hart, R. Patrick, E. R. Strong, E. W. Surber, and W. M. Van Horn. 1951. Bio-assay methods for the evaluation of acute toxicity of industrial wastes to fish. Sewage and Indust. Wastes, 23 (11): 1380-1397, 1 fig.

Doudoroff, P., and M. Katz. 1950. Critical review of literature on the toxicity of industrial wastes and their components to fish. I. Alkalies, acids, and inorganic gases. Sewage and Indust. Wastes, 22 (11): 1432-1458.

Doudoroff, P., and M. Katz. 1953. Critical review of literature on the toxicity of industrial wastes and their components to fish. II. The metals, as salts. Sewage and Indust. Wastes, 25 (7): 802-839.

Ellis, M. M. 1936. Effects of pollution on fish. Trans. 1st N. Amer. Wildlife Conf., pp. 564-567.

Ellis, M. M. 1937. Detection and measurement of stream pollution. Bull. U. S. Bur. Fish., 48: 365-437, 22 figs. (Contains extensive bibliography on effects of pollutants as well as classified text summary of same)

Ellis, M. M. 1944. Water purity standards for fresh-water fishes. U. S. Fish and Wildlife Service, Spec. Sci. Rept., 2, 15 p.

Ellis, M. M., B. A. Westfall, and Marion D. Ellis. 1946. Determination of water quality. U. S. Fish and Wildlife Service, Res. Rept. 9, 122 p. (Contains extensive bibliography on methods)

Gaufin, Arden R., and Clarence M. Tarzwell. 1955. Environmental changes in a polluted stream during winter. Amer. Midland Nat., 54 (1): 78-88, 3 figs.

Gaufin, Arden R., and Clarence M. Tarzwell. 1952. Aquatic invertebrates as indicators of stream pollution. U. S. Public Health Service Public Health Rept., 67 (1): 57-64, 1 text-fig.

General Electric Company. 16 mm. sound, color film. Clean Waters. (Accompanied by a substantial, illustrated booklet; domestic sewage treatment)

Hart, W. B., Peter Doudoroff, and John Greenbank. 1945. The evaluation of the toxicity of industrial wastes, chemicals and other substances to fresh-water fishes. Philadelphia, Atlantic Refining Company, 332 p., 43 figs.

Hart, W. B., Roy F. Weston, and J. G. Demann. 1948. An apparatus for oxygenating test solutions in which fish are used as test animals for evaluating toxicity. Trans. Amer. Fish. Soc., 75 (1945): 228-236, 5 figs.

Hasler, Arthur D., and Wilhelm G. Einsele. 1948. Fertilization for increasing productivity of natural inland waters. Trans. 13th N. Amer. Wildlife Conf., pp. 527-555, 1 fig.

Huet, Marcel. 1949. La pollution des eaux. L'analyse biologique des eaux polluées. Bull. Centre Belge d'Etude et de Documentation des Eaux, 1949 (5-6): 1-31, 59 figs. (Damage to fish, index organisms)

Huet, Marcel. 1950. Toxicologie des poissons. Bull. Centre Belge d'Etude et de Documentation des Eaux, 1950 (7): 396-406. (Toxicities of common poisons for fish)

Huet, M., J. A. Timmermans, E. LeClerc, and P. Beaujean. 1955. Recherche des corrélations entre l'analyse biologique et l'analyse physicochimique des eaux polluées par matières organique. Bull. Centre Belge d'Etude et de Documentation des Eaux, 30, 1955 (4): 216-237, 20 figs.

Ingram, William M. 1952. Selected biological references applicable to sewage treatment. U. S. Public Health Service, Ohio-Tennessee Drainage Basins Office, Cincinnati, 26 p., 2 pl.

Ingram, William Marcus, and Peter Doudoroff. 1953. Selected bibliography of publications on industrial wastes relating to fish and oysters. U. S. Public Health Service, Public Health Bibliography Series, 10, 28p.

Ingram, William Marcus, and Clarence M. Tarzwell. 1954. Selected bibliography of publications relating to undesirable effects upon aquatic life by algacides, insecticides, and weedicides. U. S. Public Health Service, Public Health Bibliography Series, 13, 28 p.

Mackenthun, Kenneth M., Elmer F. Herman, and Alfred F. Bartsch. 1948. A heavy mortality of fishes resulting from the decomposition of algae in the Yahara River, Wisconsin. Trans. Amer. Fish. Soc., 75 (1945): 175-180, 3 figs.

Moore, Walter G. 1942. Field studies on the oxygen requirements of certain fresh-water fishes. Ecol., 23: 319-329, 1 fig.

Palmer, C. M., and William Marcus Ingram. 1955. Suggested classification of algae and protozoa in sanitary science. Sewage and Indust. Wastes, 27 (10): 1183-1188, 1 fig.

Raney, Edward C. 1941. Mortality at fish hatchery caused by lightening. Copeia, 1941 (4): 271.

Theroux, Frank R., Edward F. Eldridge, and W. LeRoy Mallmann. 1943. Laboratory manual for chemical and bacterial analysis of water and sewage. New York, McGraw-Hill, 3rd ed., x, 274 p., 4 figs.

Wallen, I. Eugene. 1951. The direct effect of turbidity on fishes. Bull. Okla. Agric. and Mech. Coll., 48 (2), 27 p., 5 figs.

Welch, Paul S. 1948. Limnological methods. Philadelphia, Blakiston, xviii, 381 p., 96 figs.

Chapter XVI

Laws

The best known laws relating to fishing are those that control size of fish, season, and catch, and those that set the kind of gear. Other statutory regulations are concerned with the relations between commercial and sport fisheries, and with trespass, pollution, land acquisition, land easement, riparian rights, public versus private waters, ownership of fish as a natural resource, introduction of exotics, etc. Obviously not all existing laws produce the desired effects; there is room for substantial improvement in their codification, administration, and enforcement, as well as in their use to manage fisheries. Continuing technical investigation of legal restrictions, existing and proposed, is an urgency in the field of fishery biology.

The modern fishery worker is becoming critical of the blanket way in which laws have been used as management tools. Especially in the sport fisheries, evidence is mounting in support of individualized regulations for bodies of water or for restricted localities, in spite of the administrative and policing problems involved. Other evidence is accumulating which suggests that for many waters restriction of size, season, and catch does more harm than good (Hazzard, 1945) or is very wasteful of the fishery resource (Eschmeyer, 1944) (permitting too many fish to die of old age without ever seeing an angler's hook; producing overpopulation and stunting by having only the large fish caught). There is a growing feeling that much of the money spent to create and enforce laws might better be invested to improve the environments on which fish depend for their well being (Langlois, 1944; Hazzard, 1945).

The lines followed by the laws which control fishing may be summarized as follows (adapted from Langlois, 1944):

1. Assertion that all wild fishes are owned by the public and assignment of responsibility for the promotion of their welfare to a branch of government.

2. Concession of the privilege of acquiring ownership in general only to persons who have bought licenses, and denying this privilege to others.

3. Specification of the ways by which the licensee may try to transfer title of fishes from the public to himself, and prohibition of other ways.

4. Indication of the places where fish may be taken legally.

5. Limitation of the time of year, month, and day during which fishing may be done.

6. Restriction of the kinds, sizes, and amounts of fishes which a fisherman may take, if he is expert and fortunate.

Some of the laws most important to the improvement and maintenance of fishing unfortunately are administered by agencies other than those charged with the responsibility for the fisheries (Langlois, 1944). A few selected examples of this condition follow:

1. Some pollution control laws are administered by public health units and are not invoked unless human health is endangered (see preceeding chapter on Pollution).

2. Laws regulating the burning off of lands for agricultural or other purposes, although the practice may have harmful effects in increasing erosion and siltation of waters, are in the hands of agricultural, forestry, or law enforcement departments.

3. Laws encouraging ditching and draining for farming reasons or insect pest control, although both water tables and productive stream courses may be damaged, are assigned to diverse, non-fishery agencies of government.

One of the greatest problems in the legal aspect of fishery management stems from the multiplicity of the laws which deal with the resource. In many regions, even the best informed fisherman cannot help being at times a violator because of this condition and because of the rapid alteration of restrictions which are necessary to keep pace with changing conditions of environment or population. In areas where many kinds of fishes are involved in a fishery another serious difficulty exists, particularly when regulations are pin-pointed on different though closely related and often similar fishes. Commonly, neither the casual angler nor the ordinary enforcement officer, let alone justice-of-the-peace or judge, can distinguish between grass pickerel and pike, between rock bass and warmouth, between green sunfish and bluegill, between cisco and whitefish, between white bass and yellow bass, among common kinds of stream trout (brook, brown, and rainbow), or even among the kinds of black basses.

Additional tedious problems in fishery regulation are posed by boundary waters between states or provinces and between countries. Very often laws of widely different content are in force on the two sides of a boundary stream—a fundamentally ridiculous situation.

In spite of the admittedly pessimistic tenor of the preceding paragraphs, properly conceived and administered laws are most important tools of management. In commercial fisheries of large water areas, legal restrictions and public education are almost the only two management means possible. Consequently it is not surprising that most states and provinces are keenly aware of the continuing need for keeping laws abreast of research findings, and for experimentation with changes in the laws themselves. Furthermore, leaders among such political units are currently making renewed efforts at codification and simplification of existing statutes.

Illustrative of recent advances in legal aspects of fish management are the following:

Preservation of fish habitat. Some states have been able to secure injunctions against marsh owners that have resulted in consent decrees by the terms of which marshes important for the spawning of fish such as northern pike will be preserved.

Preservation of public title in the bottoms of lakes. Owners of certain shore properties on the Great Lakes have recently been compelled not to make fills into the water. These are steps not only to preserve a state's title to the bottom of the water areas in question, but also to preserve shallow shore regions as spawning grounds for fish, and as feeding areas for waterfowl.

Uniformity of fishery regulations on interstate waters. Recently the conservation departments of two northern states (Wisconsin and Michigan) have been authorized by their respective legislatures to bring about uniform regulations in the fisheries of waters that are bisected by the interstate boundary line. The regulations resulting from this agreement supersede those of either state and the fishing licenses of both states are recognized anywhere in the boundary waters concerned.

Interstate cooperation in solving problems of water use. In recent years, many states have worked together successfully to solve use problems of common waters. Examples include New York and New Jersey on the Susquehanna River, and Illinois, Iowa, Missouri, Wisconsin, and Minnesota on the upper Mississippi River. In 1955, the states fronting on the Great Lakes achieved the Great Lakes Basin Compact. The implementing agency is the Great Lakes Commission (located in Ann Arbor), and the pledged purpose is to integrate both research on use and actual use of the Great Lakes.

Unified international action in maintenance of fish production in boundary waters. The need for sea lamprey control and for knowledge on the factors of abundance of fishes in the Great Lakes finally resulted in a treaty between the United States and Canada that was ratified in 1955. The treaty provides for a Great Lakes Fishery Commission to implement sea lamprey control, to formulate and coordinate requisite research, and to recommend to the two governments measures appropriate to the improvement and maintenance of fish production. The record of the International Pacific Salmon Commission has demonstrated the great value of concerted international action in major problems of fish conservation.

Federal aid to sport fishery research and management. The Dingell-Johnson law, passed by the Congress of the United States in 1950, placed an excise tax on fishing tackle. The monies raised from this tax are allotted to the states on the basis of area and sales of fishing licenses. Matched by the state, the funds are used for federally approved projects of fishery research, land acquisition including that for public fishing sites, and lake, stream, and watershed improvement.

Liberalization of laws on certain warmwater game and pan fishes. The years since 1950 have seen an increase in the number of states that have removed all limits from bluegills and other sunfishes and large-mouth bass. These moves resulted from the recognition of the reproductive potential of the species, and of the advantages of increase in rate of population turnover. The result seems to have been consistently an increase in amount and quality of angling enjoyment.

Intensification of laws. Experimental intensification of laws seems to be growing on heavily fished waters, and for the increased protection of predacious game fishes. Included in such programs are "flies only" and larger legal length regulations for more and more miles of trout streams, with the aim to provide more fun but less meat for the angler. Also a part of closer regulation are elevations in legal lengths of such fishes as northern pike, in order to favor their survival and to amplify their impact upon fish species prone to overpopulate and stunt.

Certainly laws can be among the best tools of modern fish management, just as they are the oldest.

STUDY PROGRAM

Read and abstract the views on principles and the facts of fishery regulation as given by Eschmeyer (1944), Langlois (1944), and Hazzard (1945).

Study a copy of the current digest of fishing laws of a state or province and in the light of your readings prepare brief critiques based on each of the following points:

1. Bag limits by number, weight, or length; include discussion of shortcomings.

2. Species categories; consider numerosity of species involved and effects of the limited ability of angler, law enforcement officer, and the law to differentiate among certain kinds of fish.

3. Fixity of seasons; evaluate in consideration of annual variations of climate.

REFERENCES

Eschmeyer, R. W. 1944. Harvesting the fish crop. Trans. 9th North Amer. Wildlife Conf., pp. 202-211.

Fry, F. E. J. 1947. The South Bay experiment. Sylvia, 3 (6): 15-25, illus. (Relations of commercial fisheries to sport fisheries)

Hazzard, A. S. 1945. Fish laws — facts and fancies. Mich. Cons., 14 (10): 6-9, 3 figs.

220   FRESHWATER FISHERY BIOLOGY

Langlois, T. H. 1944. The role of legal restrictions in fish management. Trans. 9th North Amer. Wildlife Conf., pp. 197-202.

Westerman, Fred A., and John Van Oosten. 1939. Report to the Michigan State Senate on the fisheries of Potagannissing Bay, Michigan. Lansing, Mich. Cons. Dept., 82 p., 9 figs. (Conflict of sport and commercial fishery regulations)

Chapter XVII

Fish Culture

One of the most important contributions of successful freshwater fishery management is its ability to secure desirable fishing results by rearing fishes of the kinds and the sizes required and by planting them. American fish culture began with trout, around the middle of the 19th century, and has grown ever since with many improvements and refinements, until today there are more than six hundred state and federal fish cultural stations in the United States alone. Methods have now been developed for propagating most of the common food and game fishes, as well as select forage kinds and species that appeal to aquarium fanciers (Davis, 1953). With this growth in knowledge of fish culture, there has also come an increasing and critical coordination with other management practices (James, et al., 1944). Stocking which appeared to be unnecessary or wasteful, such as the planting of whitefish and lake herring fry in the Great Lakes, has been abandoned generally, though it continues to be tested locally. Introduction of exotic species, on an intercontinental (carp) or interregional basis (western salmons into eastern waters) is no longer highly subjective. In fact, proposed introductions are given most careful scientific scrutiny—and more often than not, they finally do not take place (Dymond, 1955).

The present and future significance of artificial propagation of fishes, in America as almost everywhere in the world, is so great that every fishery worker needs to know its fundamentals. In addition, the opportunities for improvement and development of techniques are many and challenging. Methods being developed now may one day contribute even more importantly to the world's protein food resources.

The principal purposes of stocking with hatchery-reared game and pan fishes are:

(1) to maintain a supply directly for harvest (put-and-take fishing), or indirectly for harvest (addition of potential spawners or of young) where natural spawning is inadequate.

(2) to start a population of desired species-composition in newly created water areas such as farm ponds, or in waters from which the fish have been removed by management procedures such as poisoning or draining or by a catastrophe such as winterkill or pollution.

(3) to change a population by strengthening the numbers of, or starting, a chosen species (e.g., planting pike in waters where bluegills, perch, etc., are overcrowded and giving returns of poor quality).

221

(4) to provide ready stocks for experiment in fish biology and management, and for educational displays.

METHODS OF FISH CULTURE

Basically, four principal kinds of fish culture are practiced in America. They may be classified as trough, jar, pond, and aquarium and are described below.

Trough or Tank Culture

Trough hatching is best exemplified by the method used in salmon and trout culture (Fig. 66). Here the males and females are stripped by hand; the eggs are thus artificially fertilized. Impregnated, water-hardened eggs are then placed, one layer deep, on screens which are stacked in hatchery troughs (formerly wood, now increasingly aluminium or fiber glass) supplied with clear, cool, running water. In about 50 days at 50° F.,

Fig. 66. TROUGH CULTURE. Indoor troughs for hatching and rearing trout.

Fig. 67. REARING RACEWAYS FOR TROUT. Note simple construction, shelter, and rip-rap sides.

Fig. 68. CIRCULAR PONDS FOR TROUT. Note water inlet pipes which give circulating current and concentrate wastes at center outlet.

Fig. 69. ELONGATED PONDS FOR TROUT. Two parallel rearing ponds and a waste channel (at left) are in view.

hatching takes place (details of temperature, time, and incubation period in Embody, 1934, and Davis, 1953). As the yolk sac is absorbed and the young begin to feed, they are given finely ground, meat-base foods, at first several times a day, later less often according to water temperature and size of fish.

As small fingerling sizes are reached, the fish are typically transferred from the indoor hatchery troughs or tanks to outdoor rearing pools (Fig. 67) or raceways (Figs. 68 and 69). Along with this move to nursery waters, some fish and fortified grain meals or manufactured diet pellets are substituted for the costly meat diet. Currently, many trout are reared to lengths of 7 inches or more before stocking, although formerly they were stocked abundantly as fry and somewhat later as fingerlings. Fingerlings are still used in some special situations such as planting reclaimed lakes and tail waters below dams of the Tennessee Valley Authority and elsewhere.

Much of what has been learned about fish diseases and their control (see Chapter XIV) has come about as a result of the growth and development of trout culture in the period since 1850. Concentrating fish at hatcheries and rearing stations for propagational purposes has often resulted in severe health problems and considerable losses. This naturally stimulated investigational work in fish pathology.

Jar Culture

The adhesive eggs of such fish as walleyes and whitefish and other coregonine fishes are adaptable to hatching in the confines of glass jars (Fig. 70), where they can be exposed to relatively strong agitation by water currents (Fig. 71). Suckers, northern pike, and muskellunge, among other species, have also been brought off successfully in jars. The incubation period, of course, varies with temperature; in whitefish 150 days are required at an average of 34° F. and in walleyes, 7 days at 57° F. or 28 days at 40° F. Whitefish are stocked as sac fry or advanced fry because of the presently insurmountable problem of supplying an adequate amount of the required planktonic food for large numbers of young. Walleyes are also stocked as fry, but more recently they are being introduced into nursery ponds at this stage, and later harvested as fingerlings or larger sized individuals for planting in other waters. Artificial feeding is not systematically carried on as in trout culture.

Pond Culture

Whereas trough and jar culture are almost entirely applied to "coldwater" spawners (spawning usually at less than 60° F.), pond culture is the basic method used for "warmwater" spawners. The latter include food fishes, such as catfishes, black basses and other members of the Sunfish Family, and several kinds of bait minnows, carp, and goldfish. A summary of the methods used is given in the accompanying table; the

Fig. 70. JAR CULTURE. Battery of jars used for hatching eggs of such fishes as walleyes and whitefish.

Fig. 71. JAR CULT IN DETAIL. Hatchin shown in Fig. 70. circulation of eggs b trance of water at b of jar through stan connected with tap.

forms included were chosen to illustrate the basic differences and similarities in the fish cultural techniques for various fish groups.

Aquarium Culture

An important part of the pet shop industry rests on the aquarium culture of fishes. A large number of tropical and subtropical forms are hatched, reared, and marketed in the novelty and hobby trade. Included are livebearers such as the guppy (*Lebistes*), and egglayers such as the bubble-nesting Siamese fighting fish (*Betta*). The techniques used are highly specialized and very diverse; they are not described here, but reference to them may be found in such aquarium fanciers' books as those by Innes or Stoye.

FISH TRANSPORT AND STOCKING

For stocking, fish are mostly transported for long distances by tank truck (Fig. 72); for short hauls they are sometimes sent in fish cans (Figs. 73 and 74). Shipping vehicles of advanced design have circulating water, mechanical cooling, filtration, and aeration (often with stand-by tanks of compressed oxygen). Transfer to fishing water is usually made directly from the truck but sometimes it is carried out by scattering the fish in a streamcourse from a boat equipped with a live-well. In remote areas, introductions are made by dropping fish from aircraft or by using pack animals. Eggs of trout are readily transported by packing them in wet moss in insulated containers to which ice has been added; in some regions (e.g., southern France) experiments are in progress on the old question of the practicability of stocking streams with artifically fertilized eggs (now placed in plastic containers from which the hatchlings can escape through slots) (Vibert, 1949).

Fig. 72. FISH TRANSPORT TRUCK. Circulating aerated water feeds into each compartment; partitioning enables simultaneous transport of several kinds and different sizes of fish.

Fig. 73. FISH TRANSPORT CONTAINERS. From left to right: 10-gallon milk can; aluminum Fearnow pail; 20-gallon milk can.

The general attitude toward stocking as a device to improve fishing has changed markedly in the years since 1935 (see References on policy). The general trend has been to subject the value and techniques of fish planting to critical testing, often using plants of marked fish combined with catch censuses in the experiments. For trout this has led to placing catchable fish in many streams during the angling season rather than stocking fry, fingerlings, or legal-sized fish in closed seasons as in the past. Studies of fish populations, reproductive potential, and age, growth, and survival of warmwater fishes under natural conditions, have brought about a substantial reduction in pondfish culture (and liberalization of pertinent fishing laws) in the years since 1940. The numbers of fish to plant in given habitat and population situations remain highly speculative.

STUDY PROGRAM

Visit as many different kinds of fish hatcheries as you can; fish culture is best studied in the field. Make notes on blank forms like those which follow in order to summarize methods, equipment, and results (use one blank for each principal kind of fish). Include in the record as many sketches and photographs of each plant and its equipment as time permits.

Prepare a careful sketch of the ground plan of each hatchery visited; include a profile flow diagram for each unit.

Compare your field observations and experiences with methods and attitudes described in the references, and write a critique of each plant studied and of its operation to indicate where reasonable improvements might be made.

Fig. 74. STOCKING FISH. Note that lip of pail is placed beneath surface of water as a final step in adjusting temperature between contents of pail and pond.

Fig. 75. FISH GRADER. Placed in and filled with fish, smaller indi swim out between grids. Used in se differing grid sizes, heterogeneous of fish may be separated rapidly.

SUMMARY OF BASIC FEATURES OF FISH CULTURAL PRACTICE FOR REPRESENTATIVE FISHES

CULTURAL FEATURE	SALMONS	TROUTS	WHITEFISH	YELLOW WALLEYE	BLACK BASSES	SUNFISHES	CHANNEL CATFISH	FATHEAD MINNOWS	GOLDFISH
Water Supply Cooler than 65° F. requisite	Yes	Yes	Yes	Yes	No	No	No	No	No
Source of Eggs Stripped from females and fertilized	Yes	Yes	Yes	Yes	No	No	No	No	No
Fertile eggs or fry taken from nests	No	No	No	No	Sometimes	Sometimes	Usually	No	Sometimes
Handling of Eggs Placed on trays and hatched in troughs	Yes	Yes	No	No	No	No	Yes	No	No
Placed in jars and hatched	No	No	Yes	Yes	No	No	No	No	No
Left with parents to hatch in natural waters or breeding ponds.	No	No	No	No	Yes	Sometimes	Seldom	Yes	Sometimes
Fry Left in troughs	Yes	Yes	No	No	No	No	Usually	No	No
Stocked	Seldom	Seldom	Yes	Sometimes	Seldom	Seldom	Seldom	No	No
Transferred to nursery ponds	No	No	—	Sometimes	Usually	Usually	Seldom	No	Sometimes
Young Fed ground animal base foods	Yes	Yes	—	No	No	No	Usually	No	No
Left to feed on natural foods (with or without fertilization of water or addition of supplemental live foods)	No	No	—	Yes	Yes	Yes	Seldom	Yes	Yes
Transferred to rearing ponds (or raceways) without grading to size	Usually	Usually	—	Yes	Usually	Yes	Usually	No	No
Graded to size in rearing ponds	Sometimes	Sometimes	—	No	Sometimes	No	No	No	Yes (Fig. 75)
Stocked (or sold)	Usually	Sometimes	—	Yes	Usually	Usually	Usually	Yes	Yes (sold)
Also raised to larger sizes and stocked	Seldom	Sometimes	No	Seldom	Seldom	Seldom	Seldom	—	Yes
Disease Control and prevention a major factor in survival	Yes	Yes	Possible	Possible	Possible	Possible	Possible	Yes	Yes
Selective breeding for improvement of stocks	Rarely	Rarely	No	No	No	No	No	No	Yes

ANALYSIS OF ARTIFICIAL PROPAGATION BY TROUGH CULTURE

Name and location of hatchery..

Superintendent... Date..................................

Authority for following information..

Number of employees.............................. Annual budget............................

Species propagated ....

....

Total output and sizes produced...

....

Nature of water supply: Source..

  Hardness..

	Av. for	Av. for

  Temperature range................. Summer................. Winter.....................

Eggs: Number from brood stock kept on grounds..

  Number purchased and source..

  Cost...

  Method of transportation..

Hatching

  Incubation period of each species...

  ....

  Equipment...

  ....

Care of young

  Nature and preparation of food..

  ....

  Frequency of feeding...

  ....

  Amount of food fed...

  ....

  Numbers of young per trough..

  Mortality...

  ....

Disease: Incidence..

....

    Kinds...

....

    Prevention and cure...

....

Brood stock: Numbers and kinds...

....

    Age at maturity...

....

    Spawning time ....

....

    Problems of simultaneous ripening..

....

Egg yield (by species and size)..

....

Stocking: When...

....

    Where...

....

    How transported...

....

    How to apply for fish...

....

    Sizes of fish...

....

Hatchery maintenance operations...

....

....

....

....

....

ANALYSIS OF ARTIFICIAL PROPAGATION BY JAR CULTURE

Name and location of hatchery...

Superintendent....................................... Date...............................

Authority for following information...

Number of employees...........................Annual budget.........................

Species propagated by this means and total output of various sizes.........
....

Nature of water..
    Source...
    How handled...

Eggs
    Source...
    Percentage fertilized by methods used.......................................

Hatching
    Equipment and its arrangement...
    ....
    Number of eggs per jar...
    ....
    Incubation period and temperature...
    ....

Care of young
    Mortality, etc. ....
    ....

Stocking
    How...
    ....
    When...
    ....
    At what sizes...
    ....
    Where..
    ....

Survival of stocked fish...
....

ANALYSIS OF ARTIFICIAL PROPAGATION BY POND CULTURE

Name and location of hatchery...

Superintendent.. Date............................

Authority for following information...

Number of employees..................................Annual budget.........................

Species propagated ....

Total output and sizes produced...

Nature of water supply..

Acreage under water, and disposition (how many ponds, etc.).....................

Nesting and methods for capture of young..

    Nature of nest materials placed in pond...

    Fate of breeders after nesting...

    Disposition of young taken from nests..

Food for young...

    Artificial feeding...

    Relation of plants to food supply...

    Fertilization...

Stocking: How ....

    When..

    Where..

    At what sizes..

    How to apply for fish..

Plant maintenance operations (by seasons)..

....

REFERENCES

On Methods

Davis, H. S. 1946. Care and diseases of trout. U. S. Fish and Wildlife Service Res. Rept., 12, 98 p., 30 figs.

Davis, H. S. 1953. Culture and diseases of game fishes. Berkeley and Los Angeles, Univ. California Press, x, 332 p., 55 figs.

Dobie, J. R., O. L. Meehean, and G. N. Washburn. 1948. Propagation of minnows and other bait species. U. S. Fish and Wildlife Service Circ., 12, 113 p., 19 figs., 18 text-figs.

Dyche, Lewis L. 1914. Ponds, pond fish, and pond fish culture. Topeka, Kansas Dept. Fish and Game, viii, 208 p., illus.

Dymond, J. R. 1955. The introduction of foreign fishes in Canada. Proc. Int. Assoc. Theoret. and Applied Limnol. 12: 543-553.

Ferris, E. J. (Editor). 1950. The care and breeding of laboratory animals. New York, John Wiley and Sons, Inc., 515 p., illus.

Hagen, William, Jr. 1953. Pacific salmon hatchery propagation and its role in fishery management. U. S. Fish and Wildlife Service, Circ. 24, 56 p., 27 figs.

Huet, Marcel. 1952. Traité de pisciculture. Bruxelles, Éditions la Vie Rustique, xiv, 369 p., 280 figs.

Karrick, Neva. 1948. The nutrition of fish in hatcheries. A literature review. U. S. Fish and Wildlife Service, Fish. Leaflet 325, 23 p., mimeo.

Langlois, T. H. 1935. The production of small-mouth bass under controlled conditions. Prog. Fish-Cult., 7: 1-7.

Lenz, Gerhard. 1947. Propagation of catfish. Outdoor Nebraska, 25 (1): 4-6. Also in: Prog. Fish-Cult., 1947, 9 (4): 231-233.

Morris, A. G. 1939. Propagation of channel catfish. Prog. Fish-Cult., 44: 23-27.

Prather, E. E., J. R. Fielding, M. C. Johnson, and H. S. Swingle. 1953. Production of bait minnows in the southeast. Ala. Polytech. Inst. Agric. Exp. Sta., Circ. 112, 71 p., 33 figs.

Schäperclaus, Wilhelm. 1933. Lehrbuch der Teichwirtschaft (Textbook of pond culture). Berlin, Parey, 279 p., illus.

Surber, Eugene W. 1935. Production of bass fry. Prog. Fish-Cult., 8: 1-7.

Titcomb, John W. 1910. Fish-cultural practice in the United States Bureau of Fisheries. Bull. U. S. Bur. Fish., 28 (1908) (2): 697-757, 26 figs., 13 text-figs.

U. S. Commission of Fish and Fisheries. 1900. A manual of fish culture. Washington, U. S. Gov't. Print. Off., rev. ed., 340 p., illus.

Vibert, Richard. 1949. Du repeuplement en truites et saumons par enfouissement de "boîtes d'alevinage" garnies d'oeufs dans les graviers. Bull. Francaise de Piscicult. 153: 125-150.

Viosca, Percy, Jr. 1937. Pond fish culture. New Orleans, Pelican Publishing Co., xxiii, 260 p.

Vivier, Paul. 1954. La pisciculture. Paris, Presses Universitaires de France, 127 p., 6 figs.

Wiebe, A. H. 1935. The pond culture of black bass. Bull. Texas Game, Fish and Oyster Comm., 8: 1-58, 5 figs.

On Policy

Hazzard, A. S. 1945. Better trout fishing—how? Mich. Cons., 14(8): 6-8.

Hazzard, A. S. 1945. Warm-water fish management. Mich. Cons., 14 (9) 6-9, 5 figs.

James, M. C., O. L. Meehean, and E. J. Douglass. 1944. Fish stocking as related to the management of inland waters. U. S. Fish and Wildlife Service, Cons. Bull. 35: 1-22, 9 figs.

Westerman, F. A. 1945. Changing policies and practices of Fish Division. Mich. Cons., 14(7): 6-7, 4 figs.

Chapter XVIII

Fishery Surveys of Lakes, Ponds, and Impoundments

Fishery surveys, be they of standing or running waters, are inventories of the composition and condition of fish populations and the chemical, physical, and biological factors affecting them. The basic units of study are individual streams, lakes, ponds, or impoundments. Often all of the waters in a geographical region are inventoried; sometimes an entire, extensive watershed is gone over in a season. A fishery survey is to a fishery manager more or less what a "physical examination" is to a medical practitioner.

The purposes of fishery surveys are: (1) to obtain fundamental information on fishery resources and conditions of the environment needed to develop intelligent conservation policies and management practices; (2) to lead to closer integration of research and management programs of the various agencies concerned in fish and wildlife preservation and utilization in the region. Such surveys and related studies contribute information on the kinds and distribution of fishes in an area and on the factors leading to depletion of the fisheries. Properly applied, this information may bring about development on a higher level of water use for fishing and other forms of recreation, and for power, industry, transportation, and domestic consumption.

Data from biological fishery surveys form the basis for fish management plans. Wasteful or harmful stocking is avoided by determining kinds and numbers of fish to plant. The need for aquatic plant introduction or control is identified. Overpopulations are recognized, and sites of pollution become known. Waters lacking in fertility show up and fertilization may be recommended. Soil erosion and related factors that may limit fish production are demonstrated and may be corrected. Situations of overfishing and underfishing are found. Habits of fishes are disclosed, and this knowledge may subsequently be used to increase yield. These and many other features make of fishery surveys in a broad sense a very important tool for the fish manager.

The conduct of fishery surveys involves techniques and specific kinds of information from diverse fields such as hydrology, surveying, geology, chemistry, and limnology. It also calls for special knowledge on the part of the investigator in the aquatic phases of botany, entomology, and invertebrate zoology. In addition it demands that one be thoroughly conversant with principles and techniques peculiar to fish management and that he know the fishes of his region well. Extensive knowledge in all of these fields is difficult for any one individual to attain. Most workers therefore will often find it necessary to seek the help of a specialist. To be a good man, he must have some basic training in each of the subjects listed above, and, before he can lead a field party, he should have considerable practical experience. He should have enough training in each of the subject areas so that he is fully cognizant of the limitations of his knowledge and can recognize when things are going right and when they are going wrong.

PLANNING

Some steps of importance in the preparation and operation of a survey are the following:

1. Apportionment of funds
2. Selection of personnel, temporary and permanent
3. Organization and equipment of field parties
4. Planning, coordination, and integration of field program
5. Provision of base maps
6. Assemblage of basic data already available from literature, and from interviews and conferences
7. Initiation of intensive investigations where needed on problem lakes and streams, on pollution areas, or on the productivity, migrations, and other key life history features of important fish species
8. Compilation of survey results, and relation of findings to the definite objectives sought
9. Publication of results in technical papers and popular reports
10. Organization of supplemental research in a long-range program

The study of a lake or pond is more difficult in many ways than that of a stream, since data cannot be collected as readily and since interpretation is likewise often more tedious. Certain stations are selected on each body of water at which the following data are collected: temperature of the air, temperature of the surface, temperature of the water at various depths, color, turbidity, character of the bottom, water chemistry, depth, aquatic plants, fishes, and, where necessary, counts of invertebrates from dredged samples, and qualitative and quantitative analysis of plankton hauls. The station for each operation is shown by the proper symbol on the hydrographic map (see below).

The number and location of the stations will depend upon the size and character of the body of water in question. One or two stations are usually sufficient for very small lakes or ponds, whereas very large ones may require ten or more. The goal of the inventory is the realization of the best possible cross section of the physical, chemical, and biological conditions of the water area commensurate with the available time. Many important and possible phases of lake survey are often reduced to a minimum or omitted entirely because of lack of time or because of doubtful significance—examples are analyses of plankton and bottom fauna.

In addition to observations made at complete, regular stations, similar data are taken at various points along the shores in order to determine the type of bottom, areas of vegetation, relative abundance of shore foods, presence of fish, potential or actual spawning grounds, etc. It has been the policy in surveys to place the first station rather near the outlet, and, if a large tributary stream enters, another station several hundred yards from its point of entrance. Since a complete picture of aquatic conditions cannot be obtained except through continuous study, a preliminary survey of the nature described on the following pages can do little more than indicate the general character of a particular body of water.

(The center, side, and paragraph headings on the following pages refer mostly to corresponding blanks on the survey forms given in Appendix B at the back of this book.)

NAMING THE BODY OF WATER

The name of the body of water as given on the base map in use should be employed. Follow it in parentheses by any other name which is commonly or locally applied. Under the instructions for designating waters in Chapter XX on stream surveys several systems are described and should be followed here. The importance of accurately designating each lake, pond, or impoundment is obvious.

MAPPING

Sometimes contour maps of the lakes to be surveyed will already be available. They may have been made during the previous winter or they may be the maps of power companies, the U. S. Geological Survey, the U. S. Coast and Geodetic Survey, or other agency. When no hydrographic chart is on hand, one should be made before attempting the other analyses of the inventory. Two methods of plane table mapping are suggested for small bodies of water. Sometimes one, sometimes the other is most desirable. A combination of the two often works out to advantage. A method for mapping ice-covered waters is given by Brown and Clark (1939), and a summary and critique of several methods by Welch (1948). For shore outline, advantage should be taken of aerial photographs where they are available.

The size limits of a map may be set for convenience as follows: minimum length of body of water on map 12 inches; maximum for sheet of paper, 24 by 36 inches. A convenient scale should be adopted for each water area. The worker should be sure to include the scale in miles, also the legend, date, name of body of water, county, and state or province (and Town, Range, and Section number if used in the region) on each finished map, as well as the source of the outline and soundings. Whenever possible, the elevation and the water level (datum plane) should be given, as should be map coordinates such as section lines or latitude and longitude.

Base Line Method for Mapping Small Water Areas

Establishment of a base line. Choose two points A and B as widely separated as is convenient (100 to 300 yards), near the lake shore, from which most of the lake can be seen. Measure the straight-line distance between these points, preferably by means of a steel tape. Locate this line in such a position in relation to the lake that all angles of bearing lines will be as near right angles to the base line as possible. If the angles get small, establish other base lines and tie them in to the first base line or other reference points by back-sighting.

The plane table is set up directly over one end of the base line, the tripod legs spread well apart and firmly planted in the ground with the table approximately waist high. The table is then carefully leveled with a spirit level and oriented so that one side conforms to magnetic north. This procedure is to be followed each time the table is set up anew, in-cluding times when it is moved from place to place on a given body of water.

A convenient point on the paper fastened to the table is marked to represent the locus over which the table is set and is labeled point A. Using point A as a center, sight with the alidade to the other end of the base line and with a sharp, hard (6H) pencil draw a fine line toward point B. With the known length of the distance between points A and B, determine a suitable scale and mark off on the AB line the distance, according to scale, between A and B; label the second point B.

Delineation of shore. From point A now sight around the shore line of the lake from left to right bringing the alidade to bear on each major point and draw a line from A toward each point. Label these lines 1, 2, 3, etc., in order, and record to what each number refers (example: No. 1, dead tree on point; No. 2, large rock on shore, etc.). Complete the circuit of the lake in this manner and then move plane table to point B. Re-orient and level the table at point B and verify by taking a back-sight from point B to point A making sure that the line between A and B corresponds to the edge of the alidade when point A is viewed from B.

From point B now sight around the lake as before to the various objects which were viewed from point A, drawing a line toward each from point B and numbering each line to correspond with the lines from point A. The point at which the lines intersect when extended is the location of the points desired. If the lake is small and the shore line entirely visible from the two base loci, this will be enough. If part of the lake is obscured, however, it will be necessary to proceed to some point already located by the intersection of two lines, to re-orient the plane table correspondingly, and then to set up a new base line and map the part of the lake not visible from the beginning station.

After all of the various points have been located by intersection, the details of the shore line may be filled in by careful free-hand sketching between points. Details may be added from aerial photographs when available.

Determination of bottom contours, etc. Soundings are located on the map as they are made and the location and depth of each is recorded.

Analyze and record distribution of various bottom types, and perhaps vegetation, while making soundings (Fig. 76).

The points at which soundings are made can be located by using as a base one or more of the known stations on the shore line. While one man draws in the points by sighting with the alidade, another stays on shore and keeps the boat in line between two other known points. Keep the soundings numbered in sequence so that they can be located on the map. This work will have to be done on days when there is a minimum amount of wave action – plan the other work accordingly. In northern waters, it is best done when lakes are ice-covered. Echo sounders are also adaptable for use on small boats (Burrows, 1949).

Fig. 76. COMBINATION SOUNDING LEAD AND BOTTOM SAMPLER. Overall length of combination unit is about 9 inches. Note cup at lower end of weight shaft; it is covered by a freely movable washer. The washer rides up on the shaft as the cup goes into the bottom; as the sampler is raised, the washer slides down to keep the bottom materials from washing out of the cup. Also shown are graduated steel cable and hand reel.

Traverse Method for Mapping

The plane table should be set level and carefully oriented as to north and south direction (the weighted end of compass needle points south on tables with built-in compasses). The table is not level if the needle extends above or below the fixed point at either end.

Example. Set plane table over station A (Fig. 78a), orient and level board. Place a small x or a common pin at a point on the paper in a position so that as the map progresses the lines will not run off the board. Place the O mark of the alidade against pin using it (the pin) as a fulcrum. Swing the alidade until station B is sighted. Draw a fine line from pin toward B, measure the distance between stations A and B

Fig. 77. PLANE TABLE SURVEYING. Worker in right foreground is sighting through alidade; the one in right background is setting up surveyor's compass on staff. Station markers are in bundle under arm of rear man and, at left, tape measure is being reeled.

and plot on the board according to the chosen scale. Then set up over station B and draw in the shore line between A and B, being careful to check by measurement any great deviations or irregularities from the straight line between stations.

It is well to take a back-sight on the previous station as a check on your accuracy. This is done by placing the alidade on the line drawn between stations and orienting and leveling the plane table, then sighting the previous station. The line of sight should intersect the former station.

Refer to Fig. 78a; on finishing the traverse, with the table set on station L and properly oriented, and with the alidade placed so that its edge bisects both station L and A on the paper, the line of sight should also bisect station A and the measured distance should correspond to the plotted distance. This is a final check of the accuracy of the map.

Keep the bottom of the alidade clean.

At the first set-up in a survey, draw a north and south line by means of a compass.

One of the most important precautions in all plane table work is to take check sights frequently.

Common sources of error: position of plane table; plane table not level; faulty sighting; faulty adjustment; poor or confused lines; incorrectly plotted distances; contraction and expansion of paper.

Be careful in the choice of scale.

Be sure to lock compass needle while taking table from one station to another.

Be sure to use standard legend.

Symbols to Be Used in Mapping

In general it is well to use standard symbols for designating various features on maps. Sometimes, however, departures are made to fit particular circumstances. The following symbols and practices are in common use. Their inclusion here does not necessarily mean their endorsement.

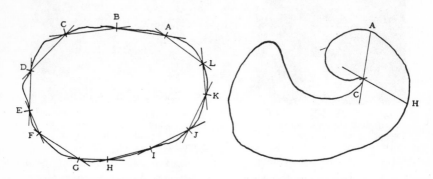

Fig. 78. MAPPING SHORELINE BY TRAVERSE METHOD. a. Serial order of shore stations and sight-lines used in mapping a lake of regular outline by the traverse method.

b. Emendation of serial order of sight-lines by addition of an extra reference bearing (H to C) to locate a major irregularity of the shore.

Should there be a point or irregularity to map while the table is set up at A (see Fig. 78b), draw a line from A toward C. Later when the table is set up at H draw a line toward C. The position of C is at the intersection of these two lines.

Other Plane Table Mapping Suggestions

Take care of the alidade; rough handling can throw it out of adjustment.

Be sure to check your closing error when finishing the traverse.

Verify accuracy often by back-sighting.

In swinging the alidade to the line of sight between stations be extremely careful not to throw ·the plane table out of orientation or level.

Remember a very slight error in the compass adjustment makes a large angular error on the map.

A common or insect pin makes a fine tool to mark the stations and permits the alidade to be adjusted to the station point quickly.

MAP SYMBOLS

Vegetation types

Floating = T   Emergent = ⊥   Submergent = ‾

Bottom types

Pulpy peat = Orange   Gravel = ⦂⦂°

Fibrous peat = Light Blue   Spawning beds = ⸪

Muck = Brown   Brush shelter = ##

Sand = Yellow   Spawning boxes = ☐

Clay = Gray   Snags, deadheads, etc. = ⬭

Marl = Green   Trash = ✕

Outline and contours

Shoreline = ⌒‿   Contours = ‿ 3' ‿

Shore features

Trail = = = = = =   Pasture or cleared land = (P)

Road = ═══   Wooded = (W)

Cottage = ■   Semi-wooded = (PW)

Steep slope = ⸜⸝   Tree = (⌕)

Encroaching shore = ⫯   Permanent inlet = →

Brush shore = ⁂   Intermittent inlet = ⇢

Low brush = ⅄   Outlet = ←

Marsh = ⱶⱷ   Spring = ⌇→

Cultivated land = (C)   Dock = ▨

Stations

Vegetation with Station Number = (1)   Bottom sample = [3]

Temperatures and chemical analyses = △₃   Fish sample = (3)◁

Temperature, chemical, and plankton = △₃   Plankton = △₃

Fig. 79. COMPLETING MAP FROM FIELD SURVEY DATA. Planimeter for measuring area is shown at right.

Use a hard pencil well sharpened. A coarse line makes accurate
work impossible.

Have a good system of keeping track of points and lines and inter-
sections, name them if possible so that those plotted at one station may
be easily identified when the table has been moved to some other station.

Classification of Bottom Types

There follows a reasonably acceptable, although in part subjective,
outline and definition of common homogeneous bottom types (modified
from Roelofs, 1944). Given with each category are symbols usable for
mapping and also for abbreviations in recording field notes (see Chapter
I). Abbreviations, however, are never as acceptable as the word completely written out since the latter can hardly be mistaken. Mixtures
frequently occur and must be described in detail. Record carefully and
enter on map with proper colors, symbols, or letters.

Organic

Detritus — undecomposed woody or herbaceous debris; D

Peat — brownish to greenish, partially decomposed plant remains; P

Fibrous peat — composed of coarser, herbaceous material; parts of plants readily distinguishable; fP (often in shallow water)

Pulpy peat — uniform fine texture; parts of plants not distinguishable; pP (usually in deep water)

Muck — black, completely decomposed organic material; ordinarily found in flooded areas or at mouths of streams; Mk

Inorganic

Bed rock — rock strata in situ; BR

Boulders — rocks over 12 inches; Bo

Rubble — R

Coarse rubble — rocks 6 to 12 inches; cR

Fine rubble — rocks 3 to 6 inches, fR

Gravel — Gr

Coarse gravel — 1 to 3 inches; cGr

Fine gravel — 0.125 to 1.0 inch; fGr

Sand — particles smaller than fine gravel; Sd

Silt — less compact than clay, very slight grittiness; St

Clay — compact, sticky; C

Marl — M

Concretion marl; cM

Shell marl — abundance of shells or shell fragments; sM

Amorphous marl — uniform, relatively pure marl clouding the water when disturbed; aM

Classification of Aquatic Plant Types

There follow a few examples of the three ordinary categories of aquaplant types pertaining to the type mapping symbols previously given.

Floating

Duckweeds (*Lemna, Spirodela, Wolffia*)

Water shield (*Brasenia*)

White water lilies (*Nymphaea*)

Spatterdock or yellow pond lilies (*Nuphar*)

Emergent (leaves mostly emerging from water)

Arrowheads (*Sagittaria*)   Water (arrow) arum (*Peltandra*)

Pickerel weed (*Pontederia*)   Bulrushes (*Scirpus*)

Bur-reeds (*Sparganium*)   Cattails (*Typha*)

Spatterdock or yellow pond lilies (*Nuphar*)

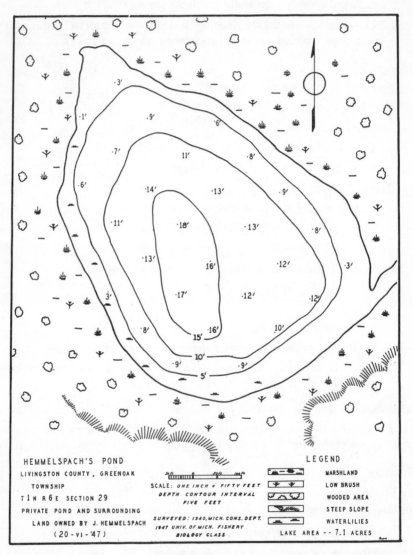

Fig. 80. MAP OF A POND. When needed, supplementary cultural features are shown and explained in the legend.

Submerged (leaves mostly submerged, a few floating leaves present in some)

Pondweeds *(Potamogeton)*

Coontail or hornwort

(Ceratophyllum)

Water milfoil *(Myriophyllum)*

Bushy pondweed *(Najas)*

Wild celery or eel grass

(Vallisneria)

Water buttercup *(Ranunculus)*

Waterweed *(Anacharis = Elodea)*

Completion of Map

The completed map is drafted on tracing cloth or paper of suitable high quality (Figs. 79 and 80). If the scale chosen in the field was not suitable, change it at this time to give a map of the dimensions previously designated (minimum length of body of water, 12 inches; maximum size of sheet, 24 by 36 inches). Ink the map carefully with Higgins eternal ink (or equivalent permanent ink) and include complete legend: name of water area, general and exact location, scale, date of mapping and authority, true and magnetic north, key to symbols (and colors) used, and other pertinent data (study stations, etc.). Additional details of technique, including a method of coloring, are given by Welch (1948).

The area of the body of water should be determined with a planimeter (Fig. 79) or by the cross-section paper (grid) method (see Welch, 1948).

The shore development should be computed and equals actual length of shore line divided by circumference of a circle which would just inclose the area of the lake. In general, the higher the value for shore development the greater the biological productivity of the body of water. To determine the circumference of a circle when the area (A) is known, determine the radius (r); $r =$ the square root of the quotient of A divided by pi ($\pi = 3.1416$), and then the circumference (C), 2 pi times $r = C$.

Significance of Map

Morphometry is a dominant factor in the productivity of lakes, at least of large ones (Rawson, 1955). There is also a tendency for standing crop of fish to decrease with increase in maximum depth in trout lakes, warmwater lakes, and reservoirs (Carlander, 1955).

An accurate hydrographic map of a lake, pond, or impoundment is not only of importance in the selection and location of study stations in a fishery survey, but it is basic to the formulation of the management plan following the survey. Some management procedures that require a map are: (1) fish poisoning — volume of water must be known in order to compute amount of poison to use, and a knowledge of depths is required to enable proper distribution of the poison; (2) stocking — size, depths, and adequacy of spawning grounds (bottom types) are important in determining what species may survive when introduced; (3) regulation of water levels — the desirability and feasibility of permanently raising or lowering water levels may be disclosed partly by the map; in reservoirs, the effects of raising and lowering the water level may be determined in part from a good map; (4) structural improvements — locations for improvement structures (brush shelters, etc.) and numbers of such to use may be judged from a map; (5) fertilization — if fertilizers are to be added to the water its volume must be known in order to calculate amounts to be used; (6) recreational development — both kind and amount of recreational development depend in part on the morphometric characters of a body of water.

Good public relations are fostered by having maps readily available to interested laymen.

MAKING CHEMICAL ANALYSES OF WATER

Chemical water analyses in routine fishery surveys are ordinarily restricted to tests for dissolved oxygen, carbon dioxide, phenolphthalein alkalinity, methyl orange alkalinity, and pH. Certain particular investigations may call for other important determinations such as nitrates, phosphates, etc.

In lakes and ponds, the exact number of chemical stations to be used (location shown by placing chemistry station symbol on map) is left to the discretion of the investigator. On very small lakes a surface and bottom sample at one station might be entirely sufficient. It is urgent to determine in all cases whether or not stagnation occurs in lakes. Analyses on larger lakes will therefore have to cover all major depressions. It is also urgent that analyses be made in the mouths of the larger inlet streams. The chemistry record sheet is adapted for recording chemical data of more than one series at a station (Appendix B). Impounded waters are treated in the same manner as natural lakes and ponds. In streams, one complete series of analyses should be made for each station.

Reagents

Make sure that you have a complete set of glassware and chemicals (Fig. 81) as well as an adequate extra supply of reagents before entering the field. Anticipate your need for replacements since it may take considerable time for more materials to reach you. You can take all reagents ready-made. Reagents in the following list concerned with determination of dissolved oxygen are for the Alsterberg (Azide) modification of the Winkler method, although the choice of the exact routine to be followed must depend on the nature of the sample and the interferences present, as described in the tenth edition of "Standard Methods for the examination of water . . ." (1955, pp. 250-251).

Among the advantages of the Alsterberg method in routine surveys in unpolluted waters are:

a. It is rapid (comparable to the unmodified Winkler method).
b. It effectively eliminates nitrite interference which is the most common source of interference in surface waters and incubated B.O.D. samples ("Standard Methods . . ." loc. cit.).
c. It is applicable even in the presence of 100 to 200 mg/1 of ferric iron if 1.0 cc. of fluoride solution is added, as described below.

LIST OF CHEMICALS FOR WATER ANALYSES
IN ROUTINE SURVEYS

Reagent and Specifications	Amount
Concentrated H_2SO_4. Specific gravity 1.83-1.84	One 250-cc. bottle, glass stoppered
Manganous sulphate solution. 480 g. of $MnSO_4$ or 400 g. $MnSO_4$. $2H_2O$ or 364 g. $MnSO_4$. H_2O dissolved in distilled water, filtered and made up to 1 liter	500 cc.
Alkaline-iodide reagent. 500 g. NaOH or 700 g. KOH, and 135 g. NaI, or 150 g. KI dissolved in distilled water and diluted to 1 liter. Potassium and sodium salts may be used interchangeably	1,000 to 2,000 cc.
Alkaline-iodide sodium azide reagent. 10 g. NaN_3 in 40 cc. distilled water. Add this solution with constant stirring to 950 cc. of the alkaline-iodide reagent prepared as above	1,000 cc.
Potassium fluoride solution. Dissolve 40 g. KF. $2H_2O$ in distilled water and make up to 100 cc.	250 cc. in wax-lined glass or in polyethylene bottle
Sodium thiosulphate "Acculate" vials or ampules. Each vial or ampule contains $Na_2S_2O_3.5H_2O$ in solution to make 1.0 liter of 0.1N strength	6 ampules
Soluble starch	2 oz.
Chloroform	25 cc.
Phenolphthalein indicator. Dissolve 2 g. of a good quality phenolphthalein in 400 cc. of 50 per cent alcohol. Neutralize with N/50 sodium hydroxide. The alcohol should be diluted with boiled distilled water	50 cc.
Methyl orange indicator. Dissolve 0.2 g. of a good grade of methyl orange in 400 cc. of distilled water	50 cc.
N/44 NaOH	250 cc.
N/50 H_2SO_4	3, 1-liter bottles
Distilled water	3, 1-liter bottles
Requisite pH indicator solutions	2, 25-cc. bottles ea.

If standardization of sodium thiosulphate solutions is contemplated, add the following to the list of reagents above: (1) 12 ampules of KI, 2.5 g. each, free from iodate, each to be dissolved in 50 to 75 cc. of distilled water for use; (2) 250 cc. of 0.025 N potassium dichromate solution made up with 1.225 g. of $K_2Cr_2O_7$ in distilled water to make 1 liter.

Small quantities of these reagents may be carried in convenient field kits (Fig. 81).

Preparation of sodium thiosulphate solution.

1. Using "Acculate" or equivalent sealed standard volumetric solution in polyethylene vials with a concentration to give 0.1 N final solution, wash contents into a 1-liter volumetric flask.
2. Add distilled water to prepare exactly one liter.
3. Store this stock solution in a cool place in the dark or in a brown glass bottle, tightly stoppered. Properly handled, this stock solution will give satisfactory results for a month or longer.
4. For use in dissolved oxygen titrations, dilute the stock solution by adding distilled water in an amount of 3 parts of water to 1 part of stock solution, accurately measured, to obtain a .025 N solution.

Should it be desired to use a thiosulphate solution of less than .025 N (which may be done for greater accuracy), the following formula may be applied to make 1 liter of solution of the new normality:

$$\text{cc. of stock solution required for dilution} = \frac{1,000 \times \text{desired normality}}{\text{normality of stock solution}}$$

5. The solution from a given preparation may be used for a period of a week or longer when stored, tightly stoppered, in its brown bottle, in a cool, dark place. If old thiosulphate must be used, or if its normality is in doubt, it may be standardized according to procedures given in "Standard Methods . . . ," or as follows:

Standardization of sodium thiosulphate solution. The potassium biiodate method is the simplest method of standardizing thiosulphate solutions of questionable normality for use in dissolved oxygen titrations:

1. Empty an ampule containing approximately 2.5 grams of KI into a 250-cc. Erlenmeyer flask or beaker and add 50 to 75 cc. of distilled water to dissolve.
2. Add 0.5 cc. of concentrated sulphuric acid.
3. Add 20 cc. of .025 N potassium dichromate solution from a burette.
4. Cover the mixture with an opaque cloth, or place it in a dark place, for 5 minutes.
5. Titrate with the sodium thiosulphate to be standardized, using a few drops of starch solution as the indicator.

If the thiosulphate is of the normality desired, exactly 20 cc. will be required in the titration. If more or less than 20 cc. is used, obtain a cor-

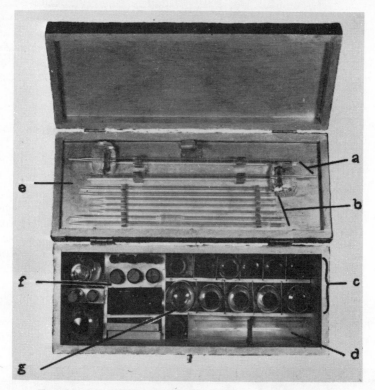

Fig. 81. WATER CHEMISTRY KIT. Convenient kit for chemical water analysis in the field: (a) burettes; (b) pipettes; (c) reagents; (d) Nessler tubes; (e) removable rack; (f) pH outfit; (g) concentrated sulphuric acid in glass-stoppered bottle.

rection factor by the method given below, but use the volumes of thiosulphate which you obtained rather than those given in the example.

  a. If in the standardization exactly 20 cc. of the sodium thiosulphate were used then the thiosulphate is exactly 0.025 N.

    If the sodium thiosulphate is exactly 0.025 N then the titration value (cc.) in the oxygen determination is equal to oxygen in parts per million (ppm.).

  b. If the amount used in the standardization varies on either side of 20 cc. a correction factor must be made.

    (1) Variation I:

      (a) If 22 cc. were used in the titration, the solution is less than 0.025 N. Therefore the titration value in the oxygen determination will be too high. The correction factor, therefore, should be less than 1.

(b) 20 divided by 22 equals 0.91. 0.91 is now the factor in this case. Multiply the titration value in the oxygen determinations by the factor in order to get the oxygen in ppm. Example: if the titration value in an oxygen determination is 12 cc. multiply this by 0.91 to get a corrected value 10.9 ppm. for oxygen.

(2) Variation II:

(a) If 18 cc. were used in the standardization, the sodium thiosulphate is more concentrated than 0.025 N. Therefore the titration value in the oxygen determination will be too low. The factor, therefore, should be more than 1.

(b) 20 divided by 18 equals 1.11, 1.11 being the factor in this case. Multiply the titration value in the oxygen determination by the factor in order to get the oxygen in ppm. If the titration value in the oxygen determination is 8 cc., multiply this by 1.11 which equals 8.88 ppm. of oxygen for the corrected value.

Dissolved Oxygen (O_2)

There are several methods for determining dissolved oxygen content of water (as in: Welch, 1948; Ellis, Westfall, and Ellis, 1946; Standard

Fig. 82. WATER SAMPLING DEVICE. The instrument is a brass cylinder with a movable rubber stopper at each end, designed to secure about two liters of water from any desired depth. It is lowered with the stoppers open: at the depth from which a sample is wanted, a weighted messenger is sent down the line to trip a mechanism which causes the stoppers to close. (Stoppers are in open position in this figure.)

Fig. 83. FILLING WATER-SAMPLE BOT Rubber delivery tube from sampler is run t tom of bottle to avoid undue agitation o water.

Methods for the Examination of Water and Sewage, tenth edition, etc. The Alsterberg (Azide) modification of the Winkler method is among those reasonably well suited for use in ordinary, inland fresh waters (see references just cited for limitations and p. 246, above, for advantages of method). As indicated previously, no one method is best suited for all occasions. The procedure for the Alsterberg (Azide) method follows:

1. Collect water sample with a suitable device, such as a Kemmerer Water Sampler (Figs. 82 and 83), and record station, depth, water temperature at the given depth, etc., on blank record form. (See Appendix B.)

   a. Sampler should be equipped with a rubber delivery tube (Figs. 83 and 90) long enough to reach the bottom of the water sample bottle (250 cc. capacity, glass-stoppered).

   b. If the sampler shows leakage, discard the water; otherwise, insert delivery tube to bottom of sample bottle and start water transfer; avoid undue agitation of contents of sampler and sample bottle.

   c. 250-cc. bottle should be overflowed two times its capacity (Fig. 83) (20 seconds after bottle is filled).

2. Unless the presence of 5 or more mg/1 of ferric iron is suspected in the sample, proceed with step 3. Where large amounts of ferric iron are suspected add 1 cc. of potassium fluoride solution (KF . $2H_2O$), using a separate pipette for this and all other reagents. Pipettes must be dipped below the surface of the sample.

3. Restopper and mix. Be sure to exclude air bubbles.

4. Add 2 cc. of manganous sulphate ($MnSO_4$) and 2 cc. of alkaline-iodide sodium azide reagent using separate pipettes for each reagent as outlined in step 1 above. If the sample bottle is of less than 250 cc. capacity, 1 cc. of each of the above reagents, and 1 cc. of H_2SO_4 in step 5 below are sufficient, provided the sample is thoroughly mixed after addition of each reagent.

5. Restopper and mix. Exclude air bubbles. When the precipitate settles leaving a clear supernatant liquid above, repeat the mixing a second time.

6. When the second settling has produced at least 100 cc. of clear supernatant, carefully remove the stopper of the sample bottle and add 2 cc. of conc. H_2SO_4, allowing the acid to run down the neck of the bottle. Restopper and mix until solution is complete.

7. At this point titration may be delayed several hours without appreciable change in oxygen content. However, where either ferrous or ferric iron is suspected, the titration should be made without delay.

Fig. 84. ANALYZING
WATER   CHEMIS-
TRY.   Titration for
amount of dissolved
oxygen is in progress.

8. Titration (Fig. 84).
   a. Remove excess liquid over 200 cc. from sample bottle, or trans-
       fer 200 cc. of the sample with a volumetric pipette to an Erlen-
       meyer flask.
   b. Titrate 200 cc. of sample with 0.025 N sodium thiosulphate.
       Rotate bottle or flask during addition of sodium thiosulphate
       until sample becomes a pale yellow.
   c. When sample becomes a pale yellow, add 1.0 cc. of starch
       solution; the resulting mixture will ordinarily be dark blue.
   d. Continue titration carefully until blue color first disappears.
   e. Record amount of sodium thiosulphate used during titration.
9. Results: Number of cc. of 0.025 N sodium thiosulphate used in
   the titration equals dissolved oxygen in ppm.   Use correction
   factor obtained from standardization of thiosulphate to obtain corrected value for dissolved oxygen when normality of thiosulphate
   is not 0.025. Record results on blank form.

As an alternative procedure for determining the amount of dissolved
oxygen, the unmodified Winkler method may be employed. When used
on unpolluted and unfertilized waters, this method will give results as
valid as those obtained by the Alsterberg modification just described.
Ordinarily, natural waters low in dissolved oxygen and with a pH less
than 7.0 will yield incorrect values by the shorter routine if they contain
large quantities of nitrite. Well-aerated waters with pH greater than 7.0
can be analyzed satisfactorily by the unmodified technique. The procedure for the Winkler method is the same as that for its modification

except for the following: omit steps 2 and 3, and in step 4 substitute 2 cc. of alkaline-iodide for 2 cc. of alkaline-iodide sodium azide solution, re-stopper and mix; proceed with steps 6 and 7, unchanged, and then titrate (step 8).

On completion of dissolved oxygen analysis, consider whether or not your results are reasonable before proceeding with other steps in the survey. A few simple observations will illustrate this point. If duplicate samples are run, they should give results which agree to 0.05 ppm. when the quantity of dissolved oxygen present is greater than 2.0 ppm. Ordinarily, dissolved oxygen values will not exceed those for saturation at any

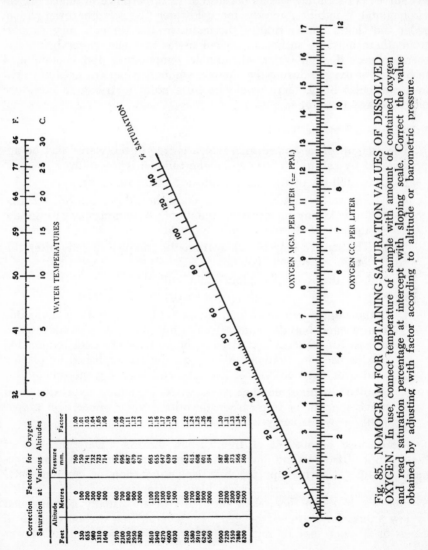

Fig. 85. NOMOGRAM FOR OBTAINING SATURATION VALUES OF DISSOLVED OXYGEN. In use, connect temperature of sample with amount of contained oxygen and read saturation percentage at intercept with sloping scale. Correct the value obtained by adjusting with factor according to altitude or barometric pressure.

given temperature. Check Fig. 85 to see if your sample is within the limits of saturation as indicated there. If your results indicate super-saturation, employ the following test for verification: repeat the analysis, but immediately after placing the water sample in the sample bottle, agitate it violently. If the amount of dissolved oxygen is reduced by this procedure, it is likely that a condition of supersaturation was originally encountered. If not, check solutions and routine to find cause of error.

Significance of a knowledge of amount of dissolved oxygen. The amount of dissolved oxygen present at various times is determined in fishery surveys of standing waters because of its importance in indicating environmental suitability, mostly for coldwater fishes. For example, in order that lakes which stratify thermally in the summer may support trout, there must be sufficient oxygen in the stagnant water below the thermocline. If such water (of suitable temperature and containing 4 to 5 ppm. of oxygen during the summer stagnation period) does not exist in a particular body, there would be little point in trying to introduce or encourage trout in it.

Free Carbon Dioxide (CO_2)

The amount of carbon dioxide which is free in the water may be approximated by carefully carrying out the following procedure.

1. Draw 100 cc. of the sample into a Nessler tube.
   a. The water should be flowed along the side of the Nessler tube to avoid any unnecessary agitation. Agitation may change the amount of dissolved carbon dioxide.
   b. The sample may be taken from the sampler directly after collection of oxygen sample.
2. Add 10 drops of phenolphthalein indicator.
3. If the sample turns pink record as 0.0 on blank form.
4. If the sample remains clear, titrate with N/44 sodium hydroxide from a hand burette, until a weak pink (pink color should remain at least for 30 seconds). Record the number of cc. of sodium hydroxide used in titration. Mixing can be accomplished by placing hand over open end of Nessler tube and inverting the tube.
5. Results: 10 times number of cc. of N/44 sodium hydroxide used equals amount of free carbon dioxide in ppm. Record in proper blank on water analysis form.

Significance of amount of free carbon dioxide. Determination of the amount of free carbon dioxide in water is important in fish management because it is perhaps the best single criterion of environmental suitability for fishes. Furthermore, high concentrations of free carbon dioxide which are in themselves toxic to fish are usually accompanied by low values for dissolved oxygen. In general, free carbon dioxide in excess of 20 ppm. may be regarded as harmful to fishes, although lower values may be equally harmful in waters of low oxygen content (less than 3 to 5 ppm.).

pH

An acceptable field method for determining pH values of water is by means of the Hellige glass comparator (Fig. 86). To give best results, the indicator solutions and corresponding comparator disks should have a substantial overlap in series (Fig. 87).

Fig. 86.   DETERMINING pH OF WATER.   Field use of Hellige comparator block and color wheels.

1. Draw 10 cc. of the sample into each of two pH tubes. This analysis can be made on water from part of the same sample used for O_2 and CO_2.

2. Add the required amount of indicator (indicated on bottle) to one of the tubes. The other is used untreated to correct for natural color of the water.

3. Place both tubes in comparator.

4. Compare colors by revolving disk corresponding to indicator solution used (Fig. 86).

5. Result: Read pH directly from disk when colors match, and record.

6. Verify with indicator of overlapping range, if possible.

7. Cautions. Be sure to keep indicator solutions away from heat, cold, and light as much as possible. Use a separate pipette for each indicator; void excess solutions in pipettes on ground, do not return to bottle; do not take indicator up into bulb of pipette. Mix by rotating test tube, do not contaminate contents by placing them in contact with skin of fingers.

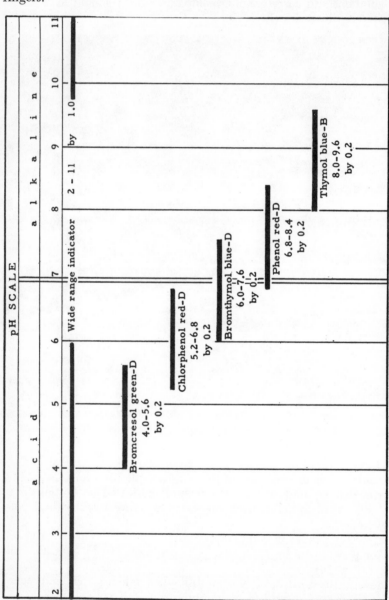

Fig. 87. RANGE OF pH INDICATORS. A selection of Hellige pH indicators and comparator wheels showing effective range, interval, and overlap required for verification of readings in ordinary fresh-water work.

Pause to determine whether or not your pH values are within the limits of normal expectation, about 6.5 to 8.5 in ordinary lakes. Now consider them in relation to the amount of free CO_2 present in the same water. Ordinarily, if pH values are less than 8.0, some free CO_2 should also be present in the water sample. If pH is greater than 8.2, CO_2 does not exist free in the same water. Later, when you have determined phenolphthalein alkalinity ("ph-th alkalinity") reconsider your values for free CO_2 and pH to see if they are consistent with the following generalization: Phenolphthalein alkalinity is not indicated in samples where free CO_2 is present. In other words, if your sample was pink with phenolphthalein indicator, you found no free CO_2 but instead you had an indication of the presence of carbonates the amount of which is determined by titration with 0.02 N sulphuric acid with methyl orange as the indicator.

Significance of pH values. Determinations of pH are mostly valuable for detecting pollution (e.g., possible source of pollution or other unusual explanation is sought when values are outside the 6.5 to 8.5 range). Most fishes tolerate both wide ranges and rapid changes of acidity and alkalinity as expressed on the pH scale.

Alkalinity

1. From the water in the sampler, draw 100 cc. into a volumetric pipette and transfer them to a 250-cc. Erlenmeyer flask.
2. Add 4 drops of phenolphthalein indicator to the sample while holding it before a white background.
3. If the sample remains clear, record it as 0.0 ppm. ph-th.
4. If the sample becomes pink, titrate it with 0.02 N. sulphuric acid, from a burette, until it becomes clear. The flask should be rotated during the addition of the acid. Record the amount of acid used in the ph-th titration.
5. To the same sample add 2-4 drops of methyl orange indicator.
6. Titrate with 0.02 N sulphuric acid, from a burette, until it turns pink-orange. The flask should be rotated during the addition of the acid. Record the amount of acid used in the methyl orange titration. In order to identify the delicate end point of this reaction, it is helpful to set up a comparative sample in another flask which is not to be titrated but which can be used for color references.
7. Results.
   a. 10 times the cc. of 0.02 N sulphuric acid in the ph-th titration equals **ph-th alkalinity in ppm. as calcium carbonate.** Record on form.
   b. 10 times the cc. of acid used while making the methyl orange titration after the ph-th titration equals **methyl orange alkalinity in ppm. as calcium carbonate.**

c. Total alkalinity is the sum of a. and b., when both have values to contribute to the sum.

Reconsider the values recorded for free CO_2 and for pH from point of view of those obtained here, in the manner previously indicated. If they do not seem logical, repeat your analyses and determine cause of departures, if possible, before proceeding.

Significance of total alkalinity in fish management. Total alkalinity in water depends on the geology of the region. In mid-continental United States ordinary fresh waters may have as much as 350 ppm. total alkalinity expressed as calcium carbonate, although most values will be between 45 and 200 ppm. (Ellis, Westfall, and Ellis, 1946), with little direct effect on fishes. Indirectly, however, the well-being of fish may be affected by total alkalinity, because waters with low values are generally biologically less productive than those with high values. A significant increase in standing crop per acre is found with increase in carbonate content in trout lakes, in warmwater lakes, and in Midwestern reservoirs (Carlander, 1955). This knowledge has led to attempts to classify waters on the basis of total alkalinity; the results demonstrate regional individuality and bespeak a need for localized rather than general treatment.

STUDY PROGRAM

Study published reports of biological fishery surveys, and compile a comprehensive list of objectives, procedures, findings, and applications, (see References) before participating in a survey yourself. Using this information and that in succeeding chapters, make a plan for the survey of certain local waters.

REFERENCES

References cited in this chapter, other than those given below, are listed at the end of the next chapter.

Carlander, Kenneth E. 1955. The standing crop of fish in lakes. Jour. Fish. Res. Bd. Canad., 12 (4): 543-570, 7 figs.

Cooper, Gerald P., et al. 1939-1946. (Fish survey reports 1-7 based on work in Maine. Augusta, Maine Dept. Inland Fish. and Game)

Harmic, Jay L. 1952. Fresh water fisheries survey. Delaware Bd. Game and Fish Comm., Fish. Publ. 1, 154 p., illus.

Hoover, Earl E., et al. 1937-1939. (Biological surveys of New Hampshire, by watersheds, 1936-39. Published as survey reports 1-4 by the New Hampshire Fish and Game Dept.)

Kemmerer, George, J. F. Bovard, and W. R. Boorman. 1923. Northwestern lakes of the United States: biological and chemical studies with reference to possibilities in production of fish. Bull. U. S. Bur. Fish., 39 (1923-24): 51-140, 22 figs.

Moore, Emmeline, et al. 1927-1940. (Biological surveys of New York, by watersheds, conducted in the years 1926-39, and published yearly as Supplements to the Annual Report of the State of New York Conservation Dept.)

Rawson, D. S. 1955. Morphometry as a dominant factor in the productivity of large lakes. Proc. Int. Assoc. Theoret. and Applied Limnol., 12: 164-175, 5 figs.

Shepard, M. P. 1955. Resistance and tolerance of young speckled trout (*Salvelinus fontinalis*) to oxygen lack, with special reference to low oxygen acclimation. Jour. Fish. Res. Bd. Canad., 12 (3): 387-446, 24 figs.

Chapter XIX

Fishery Surveys of Lakes, Ponds, and Impoundments (Continued)

MAKING PHYSICAL ANALYSES OF WATER

Turbidity and Color

Field measurements of turbidity are conventionally made with a Secchi disk (Fig. 88). This instrument is submerged on a graduated line over the side of the boat away from the sun. The depth at which it disappears from view as it is slowly lowered is noted, as is the depth at which it reappears when it is raised. The average of these two depths in feet is recorded as the Secchi disk reading (see space on water analysis form in Appendix). Where necessary, fine evaluations of turbidity are possible with the use of special instruments called turbidimeters (Figs. 89 and 90), (Welch, 1948); by their use, waters with a turbidity of 25 ppm. or less may be classified as clear.

Fig. 88. MEASURING WATER TRANSPARENCY. Secchi disk in use in the field.

Turbidity should not be confused with true water color which is due to solution of a coloring substance in the water. If the water has a color (a shade of brown may be encountered commonly in bog lakes), it should be mentioned in the record of the Secchi disk reading. Color, like turbidity, influences light penetration. Although coloration may be measured rather accurately by a photoelectric colorimeter or by other means,

89. JACKSON TURBIDIMETER. Note the wing parts: standard candle for light source; d; graduated cylinder surrounded by metal th (sheath has a center opening in bottom igh which light from candle may pass upward igh cylinder), portable "darkroom" case in h the instrument is placed when readings made. A modern improvement of this in- ient is a submersible photoelectric cell, suit- calibrated.

Fig. 90. FILLING JACKSON TURBIDIMETER. Water may be added to the graduated cylinder of the turbidimeter from a conventional sampler as shown. Additions are made until the flame of the candle is visually extinct when viewed in darkness through the length of the glass cylinder. Graduations on the latter give turbidity in terms of parts per million when read to the meniscus of the fluid contained; instrument not useful for "clear" waters having less than 25 ppm. of turbidity.

in the field it is recorded as seen in a colorless glass container against a white background. On this basis the broad terms most often assigned are: colorless, light brown, and dark brown.

Significance of turbidity and color. Secchi disk readings are quite subjective and are influenced by a number of things besides turbidity. They are therefore of limited value in technical fishery investigations. However, if the limitations are understood, such measurements may be used to indicate roughly the amounts of material suspended in water. In this way they can express relative densities of plankton populations or amounts of suspensoids such as clay and certain pollutants. They may also afford crude appraisals of the effects of fertilization or of other chemical treatment of water.

Natural inorganic agents causing turbidity may harm fish directly if present in high concentrations. Perhaps a more important though less obvious effect of turbidity is the manner in which it reduces the photosynthetic zone of a lake and thereby lowers its overall productivity. Artificially

Fig. 91. MEASURING WATER TEMPERATURE. Reversing thermometer in use in the field. A messenger trips the instrument in its case (shown tripped in this figure) at any desired depth; this reversal breaks the mercury column and thereby gives a record of temperature at that depth.

induced turbidity (also artificial staining of the water) may be used to control rooted aquatic plants (see Chapter XX).

Temperature of Air and Water

Air temperature has an important influence on the temperature of the water; in survey procedure one is seldom measured without the other. Air temperatures are taken in the shade, over the water, with a thoroughly dried thermometer. A record to the nearest degree Fahrenheit is satisfactory for most purposes.

Water temperatures are obtained with calibrated reversing thermometers (Fig. 91), or with electrical resistance instruments (Fig. 92). In most surveys, temperature profiles, as well as those of water chemistry, are required (Fig. 93). These profiles should be made from surface to bottom at stations over all major depressions of the lake basin, and involve the recording of temperatures at intervals as short as 3 feet (or 1 meter) (at least in non-isothermal strata), from top to bottom. If typical thermal stratification is extant (Fig. 93), the temperature decline in the upper layer (epilimnion) will be less than 0.548° F. per foot (1° C. per meter); in the middle layer (thermocline) it drops at the rate of 0.548° F. per foot or faster; in the bottom layer (hypolimnion) it again falls less than 0.548° per foot and may level off, with increasing depth in deeper waters, at about 39.2° F. (4° C.). Thus the temperature is relatively uniform in both the epilimnion and hypolimnion, but it falls rapidly with relatively slight increases in depth within the thermocline.

Fig. 92. ELECTRICAL RESISTANCE THERMOMETER. Such an instrument gives a direct and almost instantaneous reading of the temperature at any depth. Parts labelled are: (A) Alignment and reading switch; (B) Alignment vernier for zeroing instrument prior to each occasion of use; (C) Selector for the 20-degree temperature interval (°F.) within which reading falls; (D) Off-on switch; (E) Thermocouple attached to rubber insulated wire which is coiled on combination reel and battery case. The dial on this Whitney instrument is graduated by 0.5° F.

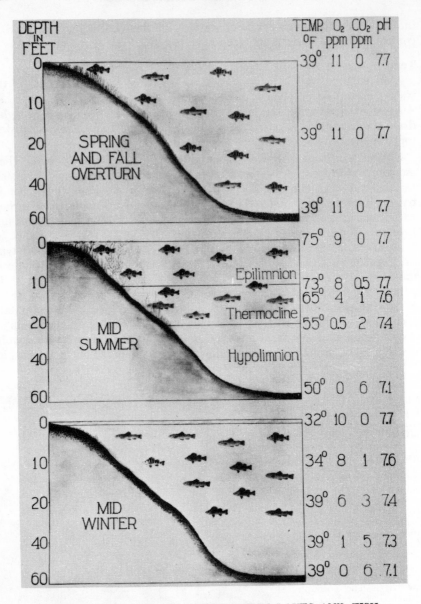

Fig. 93. ECOLOGICAL CONDITIONS IN LAKES AND FISH
DISTRIBUTION. Conditions for the four seasons in lakes which
become ice-covered in the winter. Note effect of thermal and chemical features on fish distribution. These effects are particularly evident during the midsummer period of stagnation in which the coldwater fish are essentially confined to the thermocline and the warmwater fish to the epilimnion. Warmwater fish are represented by
perch type with dark, vertical bars; the other fish shown are trout.

Significance of water temperatures. If lakes stratify thermally to separate the epilimnion from the hypolimnion by a thermocline, and if there is adequate oxygen in solution below the thermocline, they may be expected to support trout and other coldwater fishes. Other factors, however, may determine whether or not such fishes can reproduce. All told, temperature profiles and associated water chemistries are of great use in survey identification of potential lacustrine trout waters in the temperate zones. Knowledge of location of the thermocline is in itself of value in both sport fishing and survey fish sampling. In angling for trout and certain other fishes in stratified lakes, for example, one may expect to find them in the thermocline (Fig. 93) or below it. In technical collecting, samples of fish should be taken from all layers of such lakes to assure qualitative adequacy. When these waters are not stratified, but are more or less isothermal as in the spring and fall periods of overturn, these same fishes may be near the surface or distributed at all depths (Fig. 93).

The location of temperature stations by the appropriate, numbered symbol is a part of the survey map.

SAMPLING PLANKTON

In certain routine surveys, plankton samples may be omitted, although information of considerable value can be gathered from them by competent observers. In the western Great Lakes area, for example, there are correlations of productivity and algal components with the following lake types: (1) hard-water drainage lakes; (2) hard-water seepage lakes; (3) soft-water drainage lakes; (4) soft-water seepage lakes; (5) acid bog lakes; (6) alkaline bog lakes (Prescott, 1951). Survey plankton collections are unlikely to be quantitative, but plankton swarms or absence of plankton should be noted. If samples are taken, their location should be plotted on the map with identifying, numbered symbol.

Care of Plankton Net

A survey plankton net (Fig. 94) is made of exceedingly fine (No. 20) silk mesh (other meshes are used in special studies). Care must be taken to maintain it in a condition of maximum efficiency. Repair any holes by touching a very small drop of Duco household cement to each break; allow to dry 15 minutes before using. The mouth of a conventional net is 11.2 cm. in inside diameter.

Before collection of plankton at each station detach bucket and carefully wash net by drawing it through water. Similarly wash bucket (Fig. 94) but take care not to lose the stopper pin which is loose in the bottom of it.

Collect plankton on opposite side of boat from that on which net is washed.

On completion of sample collection again wash net and bucket.

Each night shake out net and dry thoroughly, replacing net and bucket in separate pockets of the bag or other container which is provided.

Collection of Plankton Samples

1. Anchor boat at station.
2. Have plankton analysis form handy for recording data (see in Appendix B).

Fig. 94. SAMPLING PLANKTON. Plankton net with removable bucket at bottom about to be lowered for a vertical haul.

3. Take sounding to determine depth.
4. Permit boat to drift two or three yards away from region of any bottom disturbance.
5. After net is washed on opposite side of boat, use the following procedure for collecting the sample.
6. Subtract 5 feet (or other approximate length of bucket and net) from the depth at the station and lower the net to this point. Draw net to the surface at the rate of approximately 1 foot per second. Be certain that the bucket does not touch the bottom as silt will ruin planktonic volume determinations. In lakes shallower than 6 feet take a measured horizontal haul.
7. After the haul is made permit all water to drain into bucket with about 10 cc. of water remaining in the bucket.

8. Place centrifuge tube under bucket and drain water with a slight rotary motion into it.

9. Rinse bucket by permitting water to come in through sides (not over top).

10. Again drain remaining 5 cc. of water into tube.

11. Add 1/2 cc. formalin to each 10 cc. of plankton and water.

12. Place plankton sample in tube at once and label with data giving name of lake, station number, length of haul, date, and collector's name. Cork the tube carefully and allow each plankton sample to settle for approximately 24 hours; then read the volume to the nearest hundredth of a cc. and record on the field blank under the proper station number. Also record the number of cc. per cubic meter which may be approximated by the following formula:

$$\frac{\text{volume in cc. of plankton}}{.00985 \text{ sq. m. (the area of net mouth having} \times \dfrac{\text{length of haul in ft.}}{3.28}} = \text{cc. per cubic meter}$$

Note: If diameter of upper end of net is not 11.2 cm., substitute proper area determined from the diameter.

For nets of diameter 11.2 cm. the following simplified formula is given:

$$\frac{\text{cc. of sample} \times 333.3}{\text{length of haul in feet}} = \text{cc. per cubic meter}$$

The formula for a net with diameter 10.2 cm. is:

$$\frac{\text{cc. of sample} \times 401.6}{\text{length of haul in feet}} = \text{cc. per cubic meter}$$

Merely substitute the volume of plankton and length of haul in feet and determine the result. Apply a correction factor for efficiency of net mesh (net coefficient; Welch, 1948) when obtainable.

Transfer sample and label to a vial and store carefully for future qualitative detailed analysis if this is requisite.

Weight of plankton per unit volume of water may be more convenient and meaningful for fishery workers than volumetric data in certain studies. Where centrifuge, balance, dessicators, and ovens are available, gravimetric values may be obtained in terms of the difference between dry weight and incinerated weight.

The problems of realizing truly quantitative samples of plankton are many. Use of a closing net, plankton trap, water-sample bottles, or the Clarke-Bumpus sampler adds improved quantitative features to the method described above (Welch, 1948).

SAMPLING BOTTOM FOOD

The number of Ekman or other dredge samples (Figs. 95 through 98) to be taken in each body of water will depend on its size, the suitability

Fig. 95. SAMPLING BOTTOM ORGANISMS. Removing bottom sample from 6×6-inch Ekman dredge. Sample is run onto screen and washed prior to sorting out the fish food organisms.

Fig. 96.   DEEPWATER BOTTOM SAM-
PLING. Winch, swinging crane, depth recording pulley, and Peterson dredge for sampling
firm bottom and contained food organisms.
A winch is requisite when the Peterson dredge
is used, particularly in deep waters, because
it is heavy.

Fig. 97. PETERSON DREDGE. [
showing extra weights which may be a
to obtain samples from very firm bottom.
white scale bar between the jaws is 6 i
long.

of the bottom for sampling, and the time available for the care of samples. All indentifications and measurements should be made in the field, unless other arrangements are in order. The total volume (by water displacement in a centrifuge tube) is recorded, as is the number and, if obtainable, the weight of each kind of organism present. The sample should be made as representative as possible and a complete record should be made on the appropriate form (see Appendix). Shoal sampling may be limited to qualitative observations. Specimens not broken in the counting and measuring process may be preserved in 80% ethyl alcohol for finer identification if this is desired or necessary in detailed surveys or special studies.

In ordinary practice, only enough samples need be taken to give an idea of kinds and relative abundance of organisms present. If there is evidence of stunting in the fish population, or if there is some other special reason, detailed bottom food analyses throughout the seasons may be necessary. Investigational requirements determine the size of the mesh in screen used for washing the dredged sample (Figs. 95 and 98); a common mesh has 30 grids to the inch.

ANALYZING AQUATIC VEGETATION

Because of the difficulties involved in the classification of aquatic plants it may be necessary to make extensive collections. Both a plant hook (Fig. 98) and a rake should be available for use. Besides conforming with conventional botanical collection methods, the following procedure should be followed.

One label should be filled out for each different plant collected at each station. The first line should have the collection number followed by symbol for abundance (S – Sparse; M – Medium; D – Dense), or by an actual quantitative value per unit of area (number of plants, dry weight, etc.) as required in the particular investigation. Following this should be given the area or extent of the plant, e.g., about 1/4 acre or strip 100 ft. wide by 100 ft. in length, etc. Record the number of the station corresponding to the numbered symbol placed on the map.

Give depth of water as the approximate depth at the point where the specimen was collected. Follow this with the range in depth for the species in question for the particular vegetation station. Under type of bottom should be included the approximate classification.

Vegetation stations should be sufficiently numerous to give a good cross section of the plants in the lake or stream. The exact number will have to be determined according to the best judgment of the individual worker. Record observations and corresponding station numbers on the aquatic vegetation analysis form (see Appendix).

A description of the preparation of plant collections follows. Plant collections that are meant to serve as records of the survey, enabling doubtful identifications to be verified whenever necessary in the future, must conform to certain standard requirements.

Fig. 98. PLANT SAMPLING. Plant hook, bottom and top views of screens used in washing fish food organisms from aquatic plants, and Ekman dredge which may be used for obtaining plant samples. Note cross wires on bottom screens which reinforce and protect the mesh.

Since herbarium specimens are preserved on paper sheets 11.5 by 16.5 inches in size, the amount of plant material of any species collected from any given locality should be sufficient to fill at least one herbarium sheet without undue overlapping of parts. If the plant species seems to be rare and is in excellent condition (with flower or fruit), a few extra specimens (full herbarium sheets) should be collected. Only one sheet of each species from a given station is necessary for record purposes, unless the species shows much variation, in which case a series of specimens illustrating each marked variation should be secured.

Although a full herbarium sheet is ideally the least amount of material that should be taken, it is important that collectors always preserve rarities or unique specimens of which only very limited amounts are available.

The specimens selected should consist in general of complete plants, so that all morphological parts are represented. When a complete plant is too large to come within the size limitations of an herbarium sheet even by folding or bending, only representative portions of the plant need be collected, or the plant may be divided into suitably sized consecutive parts which are considered as serial portions of the collection. The latter are to be labelled in order "a", "b", "c", etc. In the case of water lilies, for example, a representative set would consist of two leaves (or portions thereof) so that the upper and lower surface can be seen when they are correctly mounted, two or more flowers, a fruit (split open), and a split portion of the rhizome. In general, aquatics can be collected as complete plants. When they are longer than 15 inches, they are best bent into long N's or M's, and should not cover an area larger than 10 by 15 inches. Most pond-weed collections should have mature fruit rather than flowers, if, as is often true, both cannot be obtained. It is true of aquatics in general that fruiting specimens are easier to identify than flowering ones, although both should be secured when possible. Moreover, whether collecting a single sheet or several sheets of small species, it is well to include extra clusters of fruit or of flowers, whichever may be available. These add greatly to the permanent reference value of the material, since they permit it to be studied repeatedly without being destroyed.

Field collections may be made in folded newspapers; be sure that each is labelled. Repeated changing of blotters in the plant press is necessary to keep specimens from molding.

MAKING FISH AUTOPSY

An autopsy or host examination should be made for each important game and forage fish in each lake. Follow the procedure given in Chapter XIV on fish pathology and use autopsy record form given there.

99. GILL-NET COLLECTING. Shown ᵼe manner in which gill nets capture fish and ᵼhod of hanging such nets to dry (after re- ᵼ of the catch.)

Fig. 100. HOOP NETS. The basic hoop net plan is modified slightly here by the substitution of square frames at the front of each net as a means of improving efficiency of operation.

MISCELLANEOUS COLLECTING

Crdinarily there will be very little time for making extensive collections of insects, but party members may collect series of adult as well as immature aquatic food organisms to build up reference collections. These should be preserved in 80% alcohol and be labelled as to exact location, date, and collector. A large series will prove desirable if collected when readily available, as during emergences.

FISH SAMPLING

Although it is urgent to secure a complete cross section of the fish population, this must be done in a reasonable length of time. The methods used will be determined by the nature of the water to be studied (Chapter I). Night seining is often desirable and may yield many more

Fig. 101. TENDING A HOOP NET. Shown here is the method of under-running a trap net by boat in order to remove the catch.

fish (both numbers and kinds) for a given amount of seining effort than seining in the daytime. In lakes and impounded waters, seining should be supplemented by gill-net (Fig. 99) sets, by the use of hoop (Figs. 100 and 101) or trap nets (Figs. 121 and 122), and by examinations of anglers' catches. The collecting program should be carefully planned to cover all possible habitats, including various depths, and to sample as many sizes of each fish species as possible.

Fish collecting stations should be indicated on the map by the proper numbered symbol and should be accompanied by complete records on a fish collection form (see Appendix B).

Seines should include at least one 25-foot seine 6 feet deep with a trailing bag ("bag-seine") of 1/4-inch square mesh. This is the best all-purpose net for shore seining in inland waters (Chapter I).

Certain identifications may be made in the field, but only for species readily recognized. Where any doubt arises, specimens should be preserved for later identification. Specimens of identifiable species need not be saved, but measurements and counts should be made on those discarded. When large series of fishes not identified are collected, only a good representative sample, 25-50 specimens, should be saved. This information should appear on the fish collection sheet.

Obtain good series of paired lengths and weights for as many species as possible. All length measurements should be consistent and accurate and of a kind using conventional, accepted criteria (Chapter IX). All weights should be made on an accurate balance in pounds and hundredths thereof, or in ounces and tenths of ounces (except for smaller fish which may be weighed in grams for greater accuracy).

Fish collections should be properly labelled with a serial number corresponding to that placed on the fish collection blank. The label should also have the name of the lake or stream, and the date. For labels, use only a stout variety resistant to the preservative. Use a soft lead pencil, typewriter, or Higgins eternal ink and write legibly. When collections consist of small fish, these with the completed label may be tied securely but loosely in a piece of cheese cloth and saved together in a large container. Larger specimens should be individually labelled with metal tags. All fish over 5 inches long should be slit an inch or so on the right side to insure proper preservation.

All fish collections should be preserved in 10 percent formalin. Two-quart jars and 10-gallon milk cans are most useful for these collections. Be sure that all containers have a label securely tied to the outside as well as one inside. Labels on large containers should give a list of the collection numbers included as well as the water from which these collections came.

SCALE SAMPLING

Substantial series of scale samples should be secured for all important game and food fishes (Fig. 102). Particular attention should be given to getting good representation in the largest and smallest sizes. Follow instructions given in Chapter IX, section on scale sampling. Be sure to record complete data for each sample.

Fig. 102. SCALE SAMPLING. Note placement of scales in folded paper insert to facilitate their subsequent removal from scale sample envelope. Also shown are fish measuring board and 500-gram capacity diet scale used for weighing smaller fish.

SEARCHING FOR HISTORICAL DATA

Fishing History

If available, include a summary of catch records, sport and commercial. Also interview persons who fish the lake, but regard with caution their subjective views on the quality of fishing.

Previous Stocking Record

Bring together records of previous stocking which should include year and number and kinds of fish planted. Valuable information may be gained from these records on the success or failure of stocked fish.

SUMMARIZING FINDINGS

Most of the items on the survey summary blank (see Appendix) may be answered directly from the other data forms. However, the summary sheet should be filled out before leaving the lake that has been investigated. No attempt should be made to include all of the data from the other reports; instead, give a brief, well-worded abstract.

REPORTING RESULTS

After completing the necessary laboratory studies to supplement field work, a running account of the survey should be written, perhaps using the following outline as a guide. The writer ought to be sure to add a brief statement as to the significance of each point of information for formulating management plans. In so doing, he may give a brief explanation of how each environmental factor studied might limit the fish production.

INTRODUCTION
Location and accessibility
>   Town, range, section
>   Township
>   County
>   Near what other geographical features
>>   Mountains
>>   Other lakes
>   Drainage affinities
>   Accessibility to general public
>   Roads
>   Trails
>   Railroads

Map and survey
>   Map—include a black-line map on tracing cloth suitable for blue-printing
>   Source of map
>   Biological survey
>   Personnel
>   Time of survey
>   Purpose or instigation

History and recreational development
>   Amount of recreational development
>   Amount and nature of industrial development

History of fishing
    Past
    Present, including creel census records and angling pressure
Boat liveries
Hotels
Resorts
Importance as a public fishing water
    Summer
    Winter
Importance other than as fishing water
Desirability of maintaining or altering present state of development

PHYSICAL CHARACTERS
General physical characters
Shape of basin
Area of surface
Length of shoreline
Compass direction of main axis
Depth
    Regular
    Irregular (describe depressions, etc.)
Shoreline development, give figure and state its significance and
    how computed
Dropoff, presence, absence, location
Shoal areas
Widths around lake
Percentage of surface area of lake made up by such
Bottom types and extent of types
Water color
Transparency
Secchi disk readings; sources of turbidity if turbid

GEOLOGIC ORIGIN OF THE LAKE AND PRESENT STAGE OF EVOLUTION
DRAINAGE OF THE LAKE
Extent of drainage basin of the lake itself in square miles
Nature of the drainage basin
    Soil
    Ground cover
    Woods
    Marginal vegetation

Fluctuations of water level
Inlets
    Size
    Flow
    Dimensions
    Characteristics
    Points of entrance
    Differences among inlets
    Use by lake fishes for spawning, etc.
Outlets (as for inlets)
Dams in drainage system

TEMPERATURE AND CHEMICAL CHARACTERS
Significance
Water temperatures
Surface, time, air temperature at same time
Bottom, at what depth
Thermocline

Oxygen
Epilimnion
Thermocline
Hypolimnion

Other chemical characters
Carbon dioxide
Alkalinity
pH
Pollution

Biological Characters
Vegetation (include summary table composed of species list, relative abundance, and bathymetric distribution)
Fish foods
Plankton
    Dominant forms
    Relative abundance
Bottom foods
    Dominant forms
    Relative abundance
        Qualitatively
        Quantitatively

Food of the fish
Compare with available forms

Fishes present
Game species — kinds, sizes, relative abundance
Coarse fishes — kinds, sizes, relative abundance
Forage fishes — kinds, sizes, relative abundance, significance in food of game species
Obnoxious fishes
Growth rate and condition for game fishes of the lake; compare with regional averages — explain differences
Adequacy of spawning facilities and natural propagation
Previous management history including stocking and fate of introduced species

Management Suggestions
See next Chapter on lake, pond, and impoundment improvement, with references.

State what is wrong with fish, fishing, or environment and how it may be improved.

Give cost estimates and exact procedures to back up suggestions where pertinent.

Designate lake as trout or non-trout.

Make stocking recommendations.

Indicate further studies needed; describe how and why they should be conducted.

STUDY PROGRAM

Conduct a fishery survey of a body of standing water and, in doing so, obtain practice in as many of the foregoing techniques as possible. Do not lose sight of the objectives of your survey: to determine what may be done to improve fishing and to gain new information on the biology of fish. As each step of the procedure is executed, consider the bearing of the information gained on the management of the water area for fish production. Throughout your study, be cognizant of the limitations of the methods and results; see if you can suggest improved ways for gaining needed data and if you can add information other than that called for in the routines or associated record forms.

Prepare a report of the results of the survey and draft a management plan for the body of water studied. Before making your management recommendations, you should read the next Chapter on improving natural and artificial lakes and ponds for fishing.

REFERENCES

American Public Health Association, et al. 1955. Standard methods for the examination of water and sewage. 10th ed. New York, Amer. Public Health Assoc., xix, 522 p., 8 figs.

Brown, C. J. D. 1942. Fisheries lake survey. Mich. Cons., 11 (11): 6-7, 6 figs.

Brown, C. J. D., and O. H. Clark. 1939. Winter lake mapping. Mich. Cons., 8 (6): 10-11.

Burrows, Charles R. 1949. An echo sounder for small boats. Prog. Fish-Cult., 11 (4): 199-201, 2 text-figs.

Coker, Robert E. 1954. Streams lakes ponds. Chapel Hill, Univ. North Carolina Press, xviii, 327 p., 28 figs., 23 pl.

Cooper, Gerald P., et al. 1939-1946. (Biological surveys of Maine lakes and ponds. Augusta, Maine Dept. Inland Fish. and Game, Fish Survey Repts. 1-7)

Davis, H. S. 1938. Instructions for conducting stream and lake surveys. U. S. Bur. Fish., Fish. Circ., 26, 55 p., 11 figs.

Ellis, M. M. 1937. Some fishery problems in impounded waters. Trans. Amer. Fish. Soc., 66 (1936): 63-75.

Ellis, M. M., B. A. Westfall, and Marion D. Ellis. 1946. Determination of water quality. U. S. Fish and Wildlife Serv. Res. Rept., 9, 122 p., 3 figs.

Evermann, B. W., and H. W. Clark. 1920. Lake Maxinkuckee. A physical and biological survey. Indianapolis, Indiana Dept. Cons., 2 vols., illus.

Eyles, Don E., J. Lynne Robertson, Jr., and Garnet W. Jex. 1944. A guide and key to the aquatic plants of the southeastern United States. U. S. Public Health Service, Public Health Bull., 286, iv, 151 p., many figs.

Fassett, Norman C. 1940. A manual of aquatic plants. New York, Mc Graw-Hill, vii, 382 p., many figs.

Hubbs, Carl L., and R. W. Eschmeyer. 1938. The improvement of lakes for fishing. Bull. Mich. Inst. Fish. Res., 2, 233 p.

Ingram, William M., and C. Marvin Palmer. 1952. Simplified procedures for collecting, examining, and recording plankton in water. Jour. Amer. Water Works Assoc., 44 (7): 617-624, 1 fig.

[McCabe, Britton C., et al.] 1946. Fisheries report for lakes of central Massachusetts 1944-1945. Springfield, Mass. Dept. Cons., 254 p., 95 figs.

McMurray, K. C., R. W. Eschmeyer, and C. M. Davis. 1933. Objectives and methods in the lake inventory in Michigan. Pap. Mich. Acad. Sci., Arts, and Lett., 18 (1932): 259-276, 2 pl.

Muenscher, Walter C. 1944. Aquatic plants of the United States. Ithaca, Comstock, x, 374 p., 154 figs., 400 maps.

Prescott, G. W. 1951. Algae of the Western Great Lakes Area. Bull. Cranbrook Inst. Sci., 31, xiii, 946 p., 136 pl.

Roelofs, Eugene W. 1944. Water soils in relation to lake productivity. Mich. St. Coll. Agric. Exp. Sta. Tech. Bull., 190, 31 p., illus.

Ruttner, Franz. 1953. Fundamentals of Limnology. (Trans. by Frey and Fry) Toronto, Univ. Toronto Press, xi, 242 p., 51 figs.

Theroux, F. R., E. W. Eldridge, and W. LeRoy Mallmann. 1943. Laboratory manual for chemical and bacterial analysis of water and sewage. New York, McGraw-Hill, x, 274 p., 4 figs.

Thorpe, L. M., et al. 1942. A fishery survey of important Connecticut lakes. Bull. Conn. Geol. and Nat. Hist. Surv., 63, 339 p., 15 figs.

Welch, Paul S. 1952. Limnology. New York and London, McGraw-Hill, xi, 538 p., 50 figs.

Welch, Paul S. 1948. Limnological methods. Philadelphia, Blakiston, xviii, 381 p., 97 figs.

Wisconsin Department Agriculture Division of Land Economic Survey. 1942. Inventory of northern Wisconsin lakes. Wis. Dept. Agric. Bull. 228, 104 p.

Chapter XX

Improvement of Lakes, Ponds, and Impoundments

The improvement of standing waters has as its major objective the maximum sustained production of preferred species. The method for achieving this objective is manipulation of the environment, the fish population, or both. The need for improvement is discovered by fishery surveys, often in very intensive ones.

Some of the factors known or suspected to affect fish production in lakes, ponds, and impoundments are listed in what follows. All are subject to improvement by physical, chemical, or biological means. For each of the factors there is given a note on its significance in fish production and exemplary methods of improvement. Some key references are included: Hubbs and Eschmeyer (1938) also give information on these points, although some of it is out of date.

SHELTER

Shelter (other than aquatic plants) is seldom too abundant in natural waters. In general it favors survival by providing escapement, and tends

Fig. 103. BRUSH SHELTERS FOR FISH. Experimental improvement of a lake for fishing is here exemplified by the brush shelters which have been installed more or less along the edge of the drop-off. The shelters show as dark spots in this figure.

to increase the substratum for fish food production. Shelter may also serve to concentrate fish of catchable size. Often there is need for more such cover; it can be provided by the introduction of brush shelters (Rodeheffer, 1945) (Figs. 103-105), and by other means.

Fig. 104.   NATURAL SHELTER FOR FISH. Brushy shelter made by anchoring a natural windfall with steel cable and stakes.

Fig. 105.   CONSTRUCTING A SHEL' Shelter being constructed on ice cover of a note sacks of gravel which will cause brush bⱳ to sink automatically during spring thaw.

AQUATIC VEGETATION

Management of aquatic plant communities in inland waters is still in the experimental stage. There are no universally applicable routines for increasing or decreasing quantities of vegetation in lakes, ponds, and streams. Not only do the depth and chemical composition of the water and its drainage basin offer variables, but the species of plants and their growth characteristics also call for individual consideration. The practices employed are of three kinds: chemical, mechanical, and biological. Of these, chemical means seem to hold most promise of control, but some of the materials which may be used are toxic to fish, man, and the animals. It is possible, however, to develop specific herbicides for aquatic nuisance plants. Mechanical management is very laborious and hence applicable only to very small areas, or in regions where labor is cheap. Biological manipulation, such as by use of carp to control rooted aquatics, seems to be the least promising.

Water plants, especially seed-bearing ones, may be too abundant. They may be filling the body of water too rapidly, or favoring survival of fish to such an extent that there is overpopulation and stunting. Plants may be controlled chemically, as, for example, by poisoning (Bauman, 1947; Swingle and Smith, 1941b; Surber, 1931; Speirs, 1948; Timmermans, 1955). Aquatic control by chemicals has been achieved experimentally as follows:

Algae—copper sulphate, sodium arsenite;

Submerged plants—copper sulphate, sodium arsenite, nigrosine analine dye, "Benochlor," sodium chlorate (on dried pond bottom), trichloroacetate of sodium = T.C.A.;

Floating and emergent plants—2-4-D amine + T.C.A., fuel oil, ammate, "Benochlor," "Dow contact herbicide," sodium chlorate, "Agroxone 30," "Herbiselamine," "Herbisel," "Brushkiller," "Debrousol";

Shore plants—ammate, "Benochlor," "Dow contact herbicide".

Mechanical control, though feasible, may be very tedious (Brown, 1940; Clark, 1944; Swingle and Smith, 1941b; Speirs, 1948). In reservoirs, water level fluctuation may be used to retard aquatic plant growth. However, there are no really good or generally applicable techniques for coping with the problem of excess vegetation.

If aquatic vegetation is judged to be too sparse, introductions of seeds (Sharp, 1939), tubers, or whole plants may be made, or fertilization may be tried (Roelofs, 1944). It should be remembered that since fertilizers also increase plankton they are useful for controlling rooted aquatics by reducing light penetration through the water.

SPAWNING FACILITIES

Facilities for spawning may be so good that too many young are produced, resulting in overpopulation. This may be controlled by nest or spawn destruction or by covering parts of the spawning grounds with unfavorable materials. In impoundments, water levels may be altered, during spawning seasons to decrease the spawning area (or to increase it if required).

If spawning facilities are inadequate, they may be augmented by placing suitable nesting materials in proper locations (Hubbs and Eschmeyer, 1937). Low dikes have been used to flood marshes in order to favor reproduction of northern pike. Legislation has also been enacted to prevent filling or draining of marshland used by pike for spawning (Chapter XVI). For stream-dwelling species of trout, which may live in lakes for part of their life cycle, access to flowing water with suitable substrate for spawning is important.

WATER LEVEL AND DEPTH

Elevating the water level of a lake or pond will sometimes increase its fish producing capacity; low dams are useful for this purpose. At other times, lowering the water level, possibly to increase the amount of shoal area for fish food production, may be beneficial. In impoundments, it may be desirable to minimize fluctuations in water level, particularly during spawning seasons (Cahn, 1937) so that nests or spawning grounds are not alternately stranded and drowned.

SALINITY

Salinity may depress freshwater fish production in sea-side lagoons and river-mouth lakes. Barriers to saltwater tidal encroachment may be installed but effects on anadromous fishes should also be considered (Paul and Pelgen, 1955).

NATURAL FOOD

Food supply is basic in fish production. It is perhaps never too abundant. Plankton and insects may be increased by fertilization. Other foods of game fishes, such as minnows, may be introduced successfully (Hubbs, 1936), particularly if care is taken to ensure adequate spawning and escapement facilities for them.

EROSION, SILTING, AND TURBIDITY

Erosion and silting are two of the most important natural agencies tending to fill standing bodies of water, and are of particular concern in impoundments. Generally, control is desirable. Very often this control involves planning and work in an entire watershed and may start with recommendations for contour plowing and soil stabilization in a farmer's field miles away from the body of water in question. Eroding bluffs along shores may be stabilized by terracing (as in Fig. 116), by planting soil-binding woody and herbaceous plants, or by the use of floating log booms (as in Fig. 117) to dissipate wave action.

Turbidity due to colloidal clay may be reduced by causing liberation of hydrogen ions in the water. Green or dried hay, added to the water, will have this effect during its decomposition. In Oklahoma ponds, the addition of three times the weight of the clay suspended in the body of water in terms of green vegetation, or two times the weight of the clay in the form of dried vegetation, will clear the water without critically depleting oxygen (Irwin, 1951).

High turbidity may sometimes be due to the abundant presence of a fish species, such as the carp, which disturbs the bottom in its feeding activity. Control of the fish may reduce the cloudiness of the water.

POLLUTION

Pollution is seldom a problem in inland standing waters, except in impoundments. In small quantities, certain types of non-toxic organic pollutants increase fertility. However, if the water is also used for human consumption or for bathing, even the smallest sources of pathogen-bearing pollution (e.g., domestic sewage) should be arrested. Substances of known toxicity to fishes should forever be excluded from inland waters, particularly if they may produce toxic effects by accumulation (e.g., substances containing metallic ions such as copper ions) (Ellis, 1944; see also Chapter XV on pollution).

SEASONAL ANAEROBIOSIS

Complete oxygen depletion, leading to catastrophic fish mortality, may occur during several seasons of the year; all such situations cannot be alleviated. Flash mortalities resulting from sudden, temporary spread of oxygen deficient waters at the time of spring or fall overturn in northern waters are apparently without remedy. Suffocation or poisoning of fishes resulting from sudden decomposition of large quantities of algae (plankton algae and mat algae) or from protozoans is also difficult to combat.

In small, shallow bodies of water, algal mats may be raked aside. Large algal blooms may also be chemically controlled (Brown, 1940), but the chemicals required (e.g., sodium arsenite) are toxic to fish, if not in the quantity used in a single application, then in the accumulation resulting from repeated doses. The hazard of winterkill resulting from oxygen depletion under the ice and other causes (Greenbank, 1945; Moore, 1942) may be reduced and sometimes warded off by removing snow cover from the ice, and perhaps by mechanical aeration. In general these operations are costly and are applied only where the existing fish population is in particularly good balance and especially prized.

TEMPERATURE

Shallow bodies of water may become so warm that preferred game fishes will not bite or even live in them. Sometimes this condition may be improved by planting water or pond lilies which afford shade. In impoundments, stagnation may occur in the depths owing to the surfacing of warm tributary waters. Such a condition may be overcome by drawing water from the bottom of the dam, rather than over the top of a spillway. Such drainage may be used to extend significantly the habitable waters for particular fish species, both within the impoundment and downstream from the dam retaining it.

FISH SPECIES PRESENT

Recent experimental work has re-emphasized the generally known fact that certain fish species in combination may produce more fishing of a desired quality than other species combinations (Swingle and Smith, 1942; Bennett, 1942). Some voids in fish production in individual bodies of water may be filled by introducing a new kind of fish after environmental suitability has been established. In other instances, it may be necessary to remove the entire existing fish population and to start with a chosen, limited combination of forms. Impoundments may be drawn down to

106. ERADICATING UNDESIRABLE
. Towing a sack containing a fish poison
d a motor boat in order to disperse the
nt.

Fig. 107. SPRAYING A FISH POISON. An aqueous suspension of powdered *Derris* root being sprayed by use of a centrifugal pump to kill undesirable fish.

do this; natural waters may be poisoned with rotenone. Poisoning (Figs. 106 and 107) may be partial, total, (Reynolds, 1948) or even selective (e.g., for gizzard shad, Bowers, 1956; for sea lamprey larvae, Sawyer MS).

Introductions of fish which extend their natural geographic ranges should be practiced with caution. Exotic species may not be as desirable in the long run as they would at first appear to be. Witness the history of the carp in North America.

OVERPOPULATION

It is a normal characteristic of fish populations in smaller inland waters to be composed of more fish than could realize optimum growth on the basis of available food. It has furthermore long been known that a body of water can support only a certain number of pounds of fish at one time; it obviously follows that if the fish are exceedingly numerous they will be of smaller average size than otherwise. In the absence of an adequate number of predators or fishermen (Bennett, 1947), over-population leads to stunting, often severe. Stunting is identified by a substantial lag in rate of growth within a population as compared with the average growth rate for the region. Rock bass, bluegills, and yellow perch are three commonly stunting species. Some remedial measures are partial poisoning (removal of fish in individual bays, coves, or arms) (Beckman, 1941 and 1943; Reynolds, 1948), selective poisoning, or other technical means of fish control; discontinuation of stocking of the unbalanced species; nest and spawn destruction; introduction of predatory fish species; augmentation of fishing pressure; and liberalization or removal of fishing regulations (Westerman and Hazzard, 1945).

PREDATORS AND COMPETITORS

In some situations, predator control may produce an increased yield of preferred species (Foerster and Ricker, 1941). Seemingly, however, this is the exception rather than the rule in inland waters, in spite of the popularity of such control with fishermen in general. Furthermore, it should be recognized that predators may be beneficial (as in population balance) as well as harmful (Lagler, 1944).

Competition has many ramified bearings on fish production. Largely on the basis of Thompson's and Bennett's works in Illinois, it has become known that if a large poundage of coarse fishes is present in a body of water, the total weight of predacious game fishes present at the same time is likely to be smaller than it would be were the poundage of coarse fishes less. Coarse fish removal may be indicated in some waters.

DISEASES AND PARASITES

The role of diseases and parasites in fish production in natural waters is essentially unknown. However, fishes which are noticeably diseased or parasitized are revolting to most fishermen and to persons eating fish. At present, there are no measures for combatting such conditions that could be recommended with complete confidence. As one preventive means, fish with contagious diseases, such as furunculosis, should not be stocked.

BASIC FERTILITY

Ordinary agricultural fertilizers have been used successfully for increasing fish production, at least temporarily (e.g., Swingle and Smith, 1939). However, there are no reliable formulas for determining exactly the kind and amount of fertilizer to be used for this purpose. Furthermore, the detrimental effects which fertilizers may have on higher aquatic plants demand caution. If fertilization seems desirable in a body of water, analysis should be made of available nutrients in the bottom and in the water (Roelofs, 1940), and the kinds and amounts of fertilizer to be used planned from there. In general, repeated small doses would seem to be a better approach to fertilization than single large applications (except where control of submerged aquatics is sought). Any fertilization program should be considered as experimental and should be supervised and followed carefully.

FISHING PRESSURE

Fishing pressure is, in a sense, an environmental factor which may be manipulated to increase both fish production and yield. The pressure may be either too great or too small, in relation to the productive capacity of a body of water, to give maximum yield or annual crop. In many lakes, ponds, and impoundments, it would appear that both the fishing pressure and the way it is regulated permit inadequate harvesting of the fish crop (Eschmeyer, 1944b, 1947). This is not only wasteful but may lead to the survival of less desirable species, and contribute directly to overpopulation and stunting. In general, it is best to manipulate and regulate the fishing pressure individually for each body of water, changing the rules to obtain greatest possible sustained yield as the population changes. Often this will be impossible because of existing laws (which resist change) or public sentiment (which also resists change), and concessions will be necessary and expeditious.

PRECAUTIONS

Hubbs and Eschmeyer (1938: 54-56) suggest the following precautions when environmental lake improvement is contemplated. (I have made a few changes or comments in light of more recent findings.)

(1) Consider the lake as an aquatic farm, with game fish as the desired crop. Apply common sense and planning such as is required in farm operation. Think of the seed, fertilizer, crop, and harvest.

(2) Determine the principal factors which appear to be limiting fish production.

(3) Plan the improvement so as to meet the particular needs of the body of water in question, and, if feasible, conduct detailed "before and after" studies to determine the effectiveness of what you have done.

(4) Treat each lake as a separate management problem; i.e., avoid overstandardization of work.

(5) Balance the environment for fish life by building up those conditions which, because of their deficient development, are retarding fish production.

(6) Anticipate future needs.

(7) Concentrate the work along one section of the shore line at a time, for the sake of efficiency.

(8) Conduct the operations when conditions are most favorable. Some work is best done when the ice cover may be used for facile movement of structural materials (Fig. 105).

(9) When construction work is required, do it on dry lake bottom where feasible, as in new impoundments

(10) Make improvements where maximum results may be expected.

(11) Do not destroy beneficial situations while making improvements.

(12) Use material available in or along lake.

(13) Retard siltation from surrounding lands.

(14) When desirable, minimize fluctuations in water level, particularly during spawning season.

(15) Build for permanence.

(16) Build for natural appearance.

(17) Integrate improvement practices with other uses of the water.

STUDY PROGRAM

Include an improvement plan with the lake survey report called for at the end of Chapter XIX, and give reasons for each point in your plan and state probable or desired effect. Document the reason for your expectations by literature references insofar as possible.

Visit lake improvement sites and describe the improvements made and their apparent effects. If technical reports are available on these, determine whether or not the actual results conform with the expected or desired ones.

From readings in the general references, in the special references arranged by topics, and elsewhere, extend the information which has been given to show further how each of the factors previously cited as affecting fish production in standing waters may be improved.

GENERAL REFERENCES

Eschmeyer, R. W. 1936. Essential considerations for fish management in lakes. Proc. 1st N. Amer. Wildlife Conf., pp. 332-339.

Hubbs, Carl L., and R. W. Eschmeyer. 1938. The improvement of lakes for fishing. Bull. Inst. Fish. Res., 2: 1-233.

Westerman, F. A., and A. S. Hazzard. 1945. For better fishing. Lansing, Mich. Cons. Dept., 14 p., illus.

SPECIAL REFERENCES ARRANGED BY TOPICS

Shelter

Rodeheffer, Immanuel A. 1945. Fish populations in and around brush shelters of different sizes placed at varying depths and distances apart in Douglas Lake, Michigan. Pap. Mich. Acad. Sci., Arts, and Lett., 30 (1944): 321-345.

Aquatic Vegetation

Bauman, Aden C. 1947. The effects of ammonium sulfamate on emergent aquatic vegetation. Trans. 12th N. Amer. Wildlife Conf., pp. 346-355, 3 figs.

Brown, C. J. D. 1940. Water weeds — their value and control. Mich. Cons., 9(10): 6, 7, 11.

Clark, Clarence F. 1944. Lotus and cattail control. Ohio Cons. Bull., 8(8): 18-19.

Clark, Wilson F. 1954. Controlling weeds and algae in farm ponds. Cornell Ext. Bull., 910, 15 p., illus.

Domogalla, Bernard. 1941. Scientific studies and chemical treatment of the Madison lakes. [In] A Symposium on Hydrobiology. Madison, Univ. Wis. Press, pp. 303-310.

Eicher, G. 1947. Aniline dye in aquatic weed control. Jour. Wildlife Mgt., 11 (3): 193-197.

Luethy, Don R. 1955. Noxious vegetation control a Federal aid project. Bull. Fla. Game and Fresh Water Fish Comm., 2, 22p., illus.

Lynch, J. J., et al. 1947. Effect of aquatic weed infestations on the fish and wildlife of the Gulf States. U. S. Fish and Wildlife Service, Spec. Sci. Rept., 39, 71 p.

Roach, Lee S., and E. L. Wickliff. 1935. Relationship of aquatic plants to oxygen supply, and their bearing on fish life. Trans. Amer. Fish. Soc., 64(1934): 370-378. (Includes description of mechanical control.)

Roelofs, Eugene W. 1944. Water soils in relation to lake productivity. Mich. State College Agric. Exp. Sta. Tech. Bull., 190, 31 p., 6 figs., 12 maps.

Sharp, Ward M. 1939. Propagation of Potomogeton and Sagittaria from seeds. Trans. 4th N. Amer. Wildlife Conf., pp. 351-358, 4 figs.

Smith, E. V., and H. S. Swingle. 1941a. Control of spatterdock (Nuphar advena Ait.) in ponds. Trans. Amer. Fish. Soc., 70(1940): 363-368. (Mechanical control.)

Smith, E. V., and H. S. Swingle. 1941b. The use of fertilizer for controlling the pondweed, *Najas guadalupensis*. Trans. 6th N. Amer. Wildlife Conf., pp. 245-250, 2 figs.

Speirs, J. Murray. 1948. Summary of literature on aquatic weed control. Canad. Fish Cult., 3 (4): 20-32.

Steenis, John H. 1939. Marsh management on the Great Plains Waterfowl Refuges. Trans. 4th N. Amer. Wildlife Conf., pp. 400-405.

Surber, Eugene W. 1932. Sodium arsenite for controlling submerged vegetation in fish ponds. Trans. Amer. Fish. Soc., 61(1931): 143-149.

Timmermans, J. A. 1955. Essais sur le contrôle de la végétation aquatique à l'aide d'herbicides. Station de Recherches de Groenendaal, Trav.-Ser. D, 17, 37 p., 5 pl.

Zimmerman, F. R. 1946. Propagating aquatic vegetation. Wis. Cons. Bull., 5(6): 3-5.

Spawning Facilities

Hubbs, Carl L., and R. W. Eschmeyer. 1937. Providing shelter, food and spawning facilities for the game fishes of our inland lakes. Trans. 2nd N. Amer. Wildlife Conf., pp. 613-619.

Water Level and Depth

Cahn, A. R. 1937. The management of impounded waters. Trans. 2nd N. Amer. Wildlife Conf., pp. 417-423.

Salinity

Paul, Robert M., and David E. Pelgen. 1955. Feasibility of construction by the state of barriers in the San Francisco Bay System. Calif. Dept. Public Wks., Rept. Water Proj. Auth., App. C, 53 p., 6 pl.

Natural Food

Hubbs, Carl L. 1936. Planting food for fish. Proc. N. Amer. Wildlife Conf., pp. 460-464.

Rawson, D. S. 1930. The bottom fauna of Lake Simcoe and its role in the ecology of the lake. Publ. Ont. Fish. Res. Lab., 40, 183 p., 5 pl.

Erosion, Silting, and Turbidity

Aitken, W. W. 1937. Management of impounded water in Iowa. Trans. 2nd N. Amer. Wildlife Conf., pp. 424-427.

Irwin, W. H., and James H. Stevenson. 1951. Physiochemical nature of clay turbidity with special reference to clarification and productivity of impounded waters. Bull. Okla. Agric. and Mech. Coll., 48 (4), 54 p.

Wickliff, E. L., and Lee S. Roach. 1937. Management of impounded waters in Ohio. Trans. 2nd N. Amer. Wildlife Conf., pp. 428-437.

Pollution

Ellis, M. M. 1944. Water purity standards for fresh-water fishes. U. S. Fish and Wildlife Service, Spec. Sci. Rept., 2, 16 p.

Huet, Marcel. 1949. La pollution des eaux et l'analyse biologique des eaux pollués. Bull. Centre Belge d'Etude et de Documentation des Eaux, 5 and 6:1-31.

(See also, References for Chapter XV)

Seasonal Anaerobiosis

Black, Edgar C., F. E. J. Fry, and Virginia S. Black. 1954. The influence of carbon dioxide on the utilization of oxygen by some fresh-water fish. Canad. Jour. Zool., 32: 408-420, 7 figs.

Greenbank, John. 1945. Limnological conditions in ice-covered lakes, especially as related to winter-kill of fish. Ecol. Monogr., 15: 343-392, 34 figs.

Moore, Walter G. 1942. Field studies on the oxygen requirements of certain fresh-water fishes. Ecol., 23(3): 319-329. (Summer-kill and winter-kill)

Temperature

Brett, J. R. 1944. Some lethal temperature relations of Algonquin Park fishes. Publ. Ont. Fish. Res. Lab., 52, 49 p., 11 figs.

Fish Species

Bowers, Charles C. 1955. Selective poisoning of gizzard shad with rotenone. Prog. Fish-Cult., 17 (3): 134-135.

Black, Edgar C. 1953. Upper lethal temperatures of some British Columbia freshwater fishes. Jour. Fish. Res. Bd. Canad., 10 (4): 196-210, 14 figs.

Dymond, J. R. 1955. The introduction of foreign fishes in Canada. Proc. Int. Assoc. Theoret. and Applied Limnol., 12: 543-553.

James, M. C., et al. 1944. Fish stocking as related to the management of inland waters. U. S. Fish and Wildlife Service, Cons. Bull., 35, 22 p., 9 figs.

Needham, Paul R., and Frank K. Sumner. 1942. Fish management problems of high western lakes with returns from marked trout planted in Upper Angora Lake, California. Trans. Amer. Fish. Soc., 71 (1941): 249-269.

Reynolds, H. J. 1948. The chemical eradication of undesirable fish. Sumner, Wash., [Published by the author?], 12 p.

Swingle, H. S., E. E. Prather, and J. M. Lawrence. 1953. Partial poisoning of overcrowded fish populations. Circ. Agric. Exp. Sta., Ala. Polytech. Inst., 113, 15 p.

Overpopulation

Beckman, William C. 1941. Increased growth rate of rock bass, *Ambloplites rupestris* (Rafinesque) following reduction in the density of the population. Trans. Amer. Fish. Soc., 70(1940): 143-148.

Beckman, William C. 1943. Further studies on the increased growth rate of the rock bass, *Ambloplites rupestris* (Rafinesque), following the reduction in density of the population. Trans. Amer. Fish. Soc., 72 (1942): 72-78.

Bennett, George W. 1947. Fish Management—a substitute for natural predation. Trans. 12th N. Amer. Wildlife Conf., pp. 276-286.

Eschmeyer, R. W. 1937. Some characteristics of a population of stunted perch. Pap. Mich. Acad. Sci., Arts, and Lett., 22(1936): 613-628, 2 pl.

Eschmeyer, R. W. 1938. Further studies of perch populations. Pap. Mich. Acad. Sci., Arts, and Lett., 23(1937): 611-631.

Swingle, H. S., and E. V. Smith. 1942. The management of ponds with stunted fish populations. Trans. Amer. Fish. Soc., 71(1941): 102-105.

Yoshihara, Tomokichi. 1952. Effect of population-density and pond area on the growth of fish. Jour. Tokyo Univ. Fish., 39 (1): 47-61, 2 figs.

Predators and Competitors

Bennett, George W. 1947. Fish management — a substitute for natural predation. Trans. 12th N. Amer. Wildlife Conf., pp. 276-286.

Foerster, R. E., and W. E. Ricker. 1941. The effect of reduction of predaceous fish on survival of young sockeye salmon at Cultus Lake. Jour. Fish. Res. Bd. Canad., 5(4): 315-336, 5 figs.

Hubbs, Carl L. 1940. Predator control in relation to fish management in Alaska. Trans. 5th N. Amer. Wildlife Conf., pp. 153-162.

Lagler, Karl F. 1944. Problems of competition and predation. Trans. 9th N. Amer. Wildlife Conf., pp. 212-219.

Diseases and Parasites

Pratt, H. S. 1929. Parasites of fresh-water fishes. U. S. Bur. Fish. Econ. Circ., 42, 10 p., 11 figs.

Basic Fertility

Maciolek, John A. 1954. Artificial fertilization of lakes and ponds. A review of the literature. U. S. Fish and Wildlife Service, Spec. Sci. Rept.: Fish., 113, 41 p.

Mortimer, C. H., and C. F. Hickling. 1954. Fertilizers in fish ponds. London, Colonial Off. Fish. Publ., 5, iv, 155 p., illus. (Outstanding review of subject.)

Roelofs, Eugene W. 1940. Available plant nutrients in lake soils. Mich. Agric. Exp. Sta. Quart. Bull., 22(4): 247-254.

Swingle, H. S., and E. V. Smith. 1939. Fertilizers for increasing the natural food for fish in ponds. Trans. Amer. Fish. Soc., 68(1938): 126-134.

Thomas, R. P.   1954.   Fertilizer food for plants.   Chicago, International Minerals and Chemical Corporation, 45 p., illus.

Weatherly, A., and A. G. Nicholls.   1955.   The effects of artifical enrichment of a lake.   Australian Jour. Marine and Freshwater Res., 6 (3): 443-468, 10 figs., 2 pl.

Fishing Pressure

Eschmeyer, R. W.   1944a.   Norris Lake fishing, 1944.   Tenn. Dept. Cons., 18 p.

Eschmeyer, R. W.   1944b.   Harvesting the fish crop.   Trans. 9th N. Amer. Wildlife Conf., pp. 202-211.

Eschmeyer, R. W.   1947.   Have we overregulated our sport fishery? (Talk given to Int. Assoc. Game, Fish, and Cons. Comm., 11 p., mimeo.)

Hazzard, A. S.   1945.   Fish laws — facts and fancies.   Mich. Cons., 14(10): 6-9.   (Also in: Westerman and Hazzard, 1945, see Gen. Ref.)

Chapter XXI

Stream Surveys

Biological fishery surveys of streams have the broad objective of measuring fish producing resources in running waters and determining how they may be managed to secure the best, continuing yield for fishermen.

Prior to entering the field, the survey leader and his assistants should study carefully the maps available for the area in which work is to be carried out. A tentative schedule for the work should be drawn up in advance, even though numerous changes may be necessary later. The importance of proper planning cannot be overemphasized.

Each day, before starting into the field, the work for that day should be outlined and should be divided among the workers. This is essential in order to avoid duplication of effort and excessive and unnecessary travel.

Blank forms, such as those given in Appendix B, are useful for recording field observations. Such record sheets help systematize operations and ensure that critical points of information will not be overlooked. After completing the forms, however, many workers are prone to ignore the addition of original data on items which are often important and peculiar to an immediate situation and for which there is no specific provision on the blanks. The careful worker will guard against developing this habit. (See Chapter I.)

Many of the headings in the following outline of procedure for stream surveys refer directly to corresponding blank spaces on the forms which are given in Appendix B.

DESCRIBING THE GENERAL STUDY AREA

Care should be taken to give precise names of waters and their exact locations. The stream survey form indicates the data desired for each section.

Main Drainage

Indicate the name of the principal drainage system in which the stream is found.

Name of Stream

Give the name of the stream under immediate investigation.

Tributary Relationship

Record the name of the stream, lake, or other water area into which the last mentioned stream runs.

Stream Section

Give the exact boundaries of the stream section under consideration. The length of this section can be obtained from the maps by using a map measurer or by the pin and string method.

County, Township, Range, Section, etc.

Full geographic reference data should be entered carefully for each stream section when available. At least give accurate distance and compass direction from nearest city or village.

Dredging

Give extent and date of completed or planned dredgings for drainage or navigation purposes. Such operations often seriously impair fish habitats.

Tributaries

List the names of tributaries entering the stream in the section under consideration. Do this in order progressing upstream. Make only a very general statement regarding the fish in these streams. There is no need to mention fish here at all if these tributaries are to be investigated also.

Water Supply

Indicate the source of the water supply such as spring, run-off, seepage, etc. Information on present water level and degree of flooding can be secured from local residents; power companies often have accurate records; flood evidence such as high-water erosion marks and drift materials caught on fences are good indicators. In some studies it may be desirable to measure ground water contributions as against those from surface run-off.

Pollution

Describe the nature and extent of pollution. Make comprehensive reports when information is available, including name and address of polluting agency. (See Chapter XV). In coastal streams and/or their mouths, salinity may limit production of desired fishes. Watch for it.

Dams

Locate all dams or obstructions as accurately as possible, and describe as to nature, height, and state, whether or not the particular structure constitutes a barrier or other hazard to fish movements and migrations. If fish ways, ladders, or by-passes have been installed in the past, determine whether or not they are functional as desired and if not, be prepared to suggest remedial measures in your report.

Immediate Shore

Describe the stream banks as to cover, nature and composition, height, erosion, etc.

Surrounding Country

Is the adjacent country wooded, cultivated, hilly, level, swampy, etc.?

Use of Water

Describe uses for industrial, recreational, or other purposes.

Fishing

Is public fishing allowed? Is the stream free from brush so that it can be fly fished? Describe the accessibility of the section. The general fishing reputation and history may be secured from land owners and fishermen. Is it used as a minnow stream by bait dealers or fishermen? Does it have possibilities as a minnow stream?

Previous records of stocking can be secured from governmental agencies and from local individuals or clubs. Make statements as specific as possible, giving numbers and kinds of fish planted, dates of stocking, and results.

Species of Fish

Fill out proper fish collection blank for each section. Collections should be made in all habitats and by proper means, to ensure complete listing of species. Give the number taken at a given station, then the species, and then the range of size as total length in inches, and other data on spawning activities, occurrence of various life history stages, etc.

Take scale samples with complete data for game species when stream has management possibilities; follow procedure described in Chapter IX.

For fish names use technical names or standard common ones as given in Special Publication No. 1 of the American Fisheries Society or in Appendix F of this book.

For classification of fishes as to game, coarse, obnoxious, or forage, follow system prevailing in the region where you are working or use that given in Appendix F. There is no standard grouping.

Spawning Grounds

It is highly important to make observations on the spawning grounds of all game fishes. It will be possible in certain seasons to see the spawning activity of important species; make and record detailed observations. Give an estimate of the extent of suitable spawning grounds and their adequacy for population maintenance.

Predators

List the predatory species encountered or reported, and indicate their relative abundance. Watch for seemingly abnormal concentrations.

Beaver

Give the relative abundance and the extent of beaver cutting and damming, age of dams where known, effects of impoundment on temperature, cover, and fish production.

Remarks
Describe fishing effort spent in the collection of fish. Report fry and fingerlings of game fishes seen but not collected and any other pertinent information not entered elsewhere. Take the opportunity here to express any obvious inadequacies of your analysis or of the methods or equipment employed.

Sketches
A separate sheet should be attached to the report for each section studied. This should have a careful sketch of the stream section, including the important recognizable objects which will help subsequent observers to find your stations. Also include tributaries, dams, diversions, extent of private and public ownership, etc. If a careful map seems justified it may be prepared by the traverse method (see p. 194) or other methods given by Welch, 1948. Advantage should be taken of aerial photographs where they are available.

DESCRIBING A SPECIFIC STUDY STATION

Location of Station
Station refers to the exact points on the upper, middle, or lower portions of the stream where readings are taken. Each may be marked on the map or sketch by a circle with a cross in it. The station should be indicated on the written sheet by reference to some definite point such as "main highway crossing," "bench mark," or by giving the distance from the mouth of a tributary stream. The exact location of every station is of the utmost importance, and no report is acceptable which does not clearly indicate where the readings were taken.

Average Width and Depth
Average width and depth should be determined by a series of measurements at the widest and narrowest points of the stream and by considering in the average both pools and riffles. At least three measurements of width should be taken at each station. At each of these points the depth should be determined halfway between one shore and the middle of the stream, at the middle, and midway between the middle and the opposite side. Obviously the width and depth will vary depending on the height of the water. The condition of the stream in this respect should be indicated in the proper place. The average depth is determined by adding readings and dividing by 1 more than the number of readings. This is to allow for 0 depth at each side.

Volume of Flow
Record volume of flow in cfs. (cubic feet per second) where it is one or greater. Streams with a flow of less than one cubic foot per second should be described in gallons per minute. One cubic foot per second is

equal to approximately 450 gallons per minute. Embody (1927) gives the following formula for approximating volume of flow of a stream:

$$R = \frac{W \, Da \, L}{T}$$

in which R is equal to the volume of flow in cfs.; W is average width; D is average depth in feet; L is the length of the section measured; a is a constant for correction of stream velocity; and T is the average time in seconds required for a float to traverse the distance L.

If the bottom is rough and strewn with rocks and coarse gravel, the constant, a, should be taken as 0.8; if the bottom is smooth (of mud, sand, hardpan, or bedrock), 0.9 is used.

If no mechanical current meter is on hand (e.g., Fig. 108), measure 100 feet of a straight section of the stream where there are few, if any, obstructions to the current. Then measure and average both width and

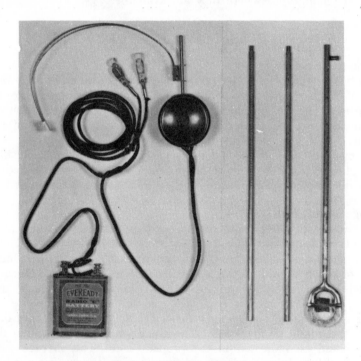

Fig. 108. SONIC CURRENT METER. Device for measuring current velocity. In use, the propellor is placed in the stream on the joined extension rod and headphone is attached to battery, to rod, and to terminal on rod. Rotations of propellor are heard as clicks on the earphone, their number counted, and number of clicks per minute converted into velocity in feet per second from calibration data provided by manufacturer.

depth at each end of the section and at the middle. Drop a float into the water at the upper end of the section and time its run in seconds to the lower end. Average of three trials should be substituted in the previous formula for T.

Robins and Crawford (1954) obtained excellent flow measurements by the following method.

(1) Divide a neat cross section of the stream into three equal width segments, each a third of the bank to bank measurement.

(2) Take a depth reading in the middle of each segment.

(3) At the same midpoint, also measure the surface velocity (V) by dropping a small fisherman's float fastened to exactly 5 feet of limp monofilament line (less than .01-inch in diameter) onto the surface and determining accurately (by stopwatch) the interval required for the float to run its five-foot downstream travel.

(4) Average the times and compute velocity in feet per second.

(5) Calculate volume of flow, R, in the formula $R = W D a V$, (V equals surface velocity in feet per second; for other explanation see above).

Velocity

Velocity is described as sluggish, rapid, or torrential. Where the current is very slight and the flow is less than 1/2 foot per second, the velocity is considered sluggish. A stream is considered rapid if its velocity is greater than 1/2 foot per second, and there is a regular succession of pools and riffles. Torrential streams are those which descend steep gradients and have few, if any, pools in their course.

Color and Turbidity

Color is often loosely described in the terms colorless, light brown, and dark brown. The majority of waters are colorless, although streams draining boggy areas often show a more or less marked brown color. Turbidity is also loosely described in the terms clear, slightly turbid, and turbid; clear, if bottom is distinctly seen through 4 or more feet of water; slightly turbid, if the bottom is indistinct at from 1 to 4 feet; and turbid, if the bottom is visible only at less than 1 foot. In larger streams with sluggish current a Secchi disk may be used. Electrical devices exist for determining color (photoelectric colorimeters) and turbidity (turbidimeters, e.g., Fig. 89) in special studies (Welch, 1948).

Determinations of color and turbidity in streams are of particular value in the detection and measurement of certain kinds of pollution.

Temperatures

Temperature of the air may be taken while standing in the stream with back to the sun, holding an ordinary mercury thermometer at forearm's length at the level of the waist with the bulb in the shade of the body. The instrument may require four or five minutes to register the temperature of the air; the observer should be certain that the thermometer bulb is dry. Water temperature is taken by inserting the bulb below the surface and reading the temperature in this position; this usually requires only a minute. The Fahrenheit scale has more meaning for American workers than the Centigrade one.

The hour and sky condition when temperatures are taken should be recorded. The terms clear, partly cloudy, and overcast are used to express the condition of the sky. Also note if temperatures were taken after an unusually hot or cold night, following rain, or in relation to other things which might affect them markedly.

For special studies, electrical (e.g., Fig. 92) and/or recording thermometers may be used.

Pools and Shelter

Pools are judged subjectively in routine surveys by their size, type, and frequency. The following classification of pools is adapted with only slight modification from Embody (1927).

A good fish pool is generally deeper and wider than the average width and depth of the stream, the current within it is appreciably slower than that upstream or downstream from it, and hiding places for the fish are more extensive in it than in adjacent parts of the stream.

Not all pools, however, are equally attractive to fish. A type frequently occurring in narrow, deep gorges is one scoured out during heavy rains. It generally has a bottom of smooth bedrock or hardpan and the forage is scant. A shallow exposed pool, without shelter or food, is a detriment to a trout stream.

There is not much specific information to guide us in evaluating pools and hence only a tentative outline of study can be suggested here.

Near each station pace off about 200 yards of shore length and study the size, type, and frequency of the pools. Which of the following numbered conditions prevail under each of the three headings?

Size

1. Pools having an average width or length much greater than the average width of the stream.
2. Pools having a width or length equal to the average width of the stream.
3. Pools much narrower or shorter than the average stream width.

Type

1. Deep (2 feet or more), exposed pools containing a great luxuriance of aquatic plants harboring a rich fauna; or deep pools with abundant shelter (overhanging banks, logs, roots, boulders), much drift or detritus, and shaded by forest cover or shrubs.
2. Pools intermediate in depth, shelter, plant abundance, etc.
3. Shallow exposed pools without shelter and without plants; scouring basins.

Frequency

1. More or less continuous pools – about 75% to 25% ratio of pools to riffles.

2. Rather close succession of pools and rapids – approximately 50% to 50% relation.

3. Pools infrequent with long stretches of swift, shallow water between – pools making up 25% or less of the total stream area.

If we let S refer to size, T to type, and F to frequency, then it is evident that a combination of $S_1 - T_1 - F_1$ would receive the highest rating and $S_3 - T_3 - F_3$, the lowest. Likewise various other combinations may be roughly recorded as intermediate, although they are not necessarily of equal value. However, a more detailed evaluation would be too complicated for the purpose for which this outline is intended.

In case of heavily fished streams which may be studied intensively, it is a good practice to make an actual count of the pools per mile of stream, classifying them as to size and type. Such a count and classification may explain the high or low productivity of the stream, and may indicate definitely the amount of stream improvement needed.

State the factors responsible for pools at each station, i.e., whether caused by the boulders, undercut banks, log jams, or whether simply open pools caused by the digging action of the current. Under shelter, indicate the abundance of water plants, rocks, sunken logs, or whatever form of protection for fish is afforded in the pools. An open pool absolutely devoid of hiding places is not necessarily attractive to fish even though the water may be fairly deep.

Bottom

Describe pool and riffle bottom separately in the spaces provided on the survey form. Estimate the percentages of mud, silt, sand, clay, detritus, gravel (coarse or fine), rubble, boulders, or bedrock. The type of bottom of the stream is of greatest importance for a number of reasons. Needham, and later Pate, have shown the following types of bottoms productive in decreasing order as listed: silt, small rubble, coarse gravel, fine gravel, and sand. In his 1932 results, Pate found rubble to be more productive even than silt bottom. In his summary of food studies for a four-year period, Pate records the following wet-weight yield in grams per square foot for different types of bottom: silt, 3.07; rubble, 2.47; (large rubble, 1.55, small rubble, 3.53); coarse gravel, 1.51; fine gravel, 0.93; and sand, 0.1.

Apparently the same silty soil type which produces such luxuriant crops in river valleys is also most productive of water plants such as algae, water cress, and various pond weeds. As a result, this soil supports the heaviest populations of fish food, since most of these organisms are directly dependent upon the aquatic plants for their food and shelter.

Detritus in streams is composed more or less of leaves, twigs, bark, and remains of water plants. Detritus is frequently found on the pool bottoms or in the shelter of any obstruction to the current. It appears to provide excellent harbor or food for many stream organisms such as midges, stick caddis worms, nymphs of dragonflies and certain stoneflies.

"Hardpan" consists of hard deposits of clay which have been exposed by water action. Hardpan and bedrock appear to be almost as unproductive as sand bottoms. However, of the three, bedrock should probably be placed first, hardpan second, and sand at the bottom of the list. It is easy to understand why sand should be so low in productivity. Its shifting nature and finely divided particles offer little shelter or attachment for plants and animals.

The type of bottom is also important when conditions for natural spawning are considered, since many fish such as stream trouts and salmons require gravel beds in which to deposit their spawn successfully.

An irregular bottom, such as that made up of rubble and boulders, provides shelter for young fish as well as old. This is not the case in bottoms of fine gravel, hardpan, or sand.

Shade

The stream should be described as densely shaded if overhanging brush and trees render it unfishable, partly shaded if approximately half of the water is shaded, and open if no shade whatever exists. State cause of shade, i.e., size and kind of trees or shrubs.

Chemical Analyses

Methods for water analyses are given in Chapter XVIII on lake surveys. It is usually not necessary to make chemical water analyses in streams unless there is evidence of pollution, or for other particular reasons. Dissolved oxygen is usually at or near saturation in streams, and pH most often between 6.8 and 8.5.

Aquatic Vegetation

Notes should be made on the types and abundance of water plants which are observed. As mentioned above, this vegetation is of the greatest importance not only in providing food for the organisms upon which the stream fish live, but also in providing shelter for these organisms and for young fish as well. This vegetation should be described as to occurrence of (1) higher plants, (2) algae, and (3) mosses. If aquatic vegetation is noticeable upon practically every rock, or if it margins the stream, it should be indicated as dense; if observed on approximately half of the rocks and in patches here and there in the stream, it should be recorded as medium. If seldom observed in a stretch of stream, aquatic vegetation should be recorded as sparse. Collections and records of aquatic vegetation should be made according to instructions under lake survey methods (Chapter XIX).

Fig. 109. ESTIMATING RELATIVE ABUNDANCE
OF BOTTOM FOOD ORGANISMS. Gross inspection
method in use for subjective appraisal.

Fish Food (See also, Chapter VIII)

The most important natural fish foods are those which have a part or all of their life histories in the water itself (Fig. 109) (See also, Chapter VIII). These include: the mayflies, stoneflies, caddisflies, and various forms of two-winged flies (Diptera); crustaceans such as freshwater shrimp, crayfish, and sowbugs; molluscs, in the form of snails and clams; small fishes and freshwater earthworms (oligochaetes). In addition to these primarily aquatic organisms, a considerable source of food is found in the terrestrial organisms which fall into the stream by accident, such as earthworms, grasshoppers, ants, bees, wasps, beetles, flies, moths, etc. The quantity of this latter class of food is very difficult to estimate but in general, those streams which are partially shaded by trees and brush seem to receive the greatest quantity of land forms.

Estimates of the bottom fauna of shallow streams are often based on square-foot samples made with a frame and net (Fig. 110) (Welch, 1948). At every station where a reading is taken, at least two samples of fish food should be secured, one taken in the middle of the stream

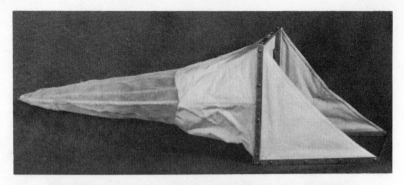

Fig. 110. BOTTOM FOOD SAMPLER FOR STREAMS. Square metal frame at right is 12 inches on a side. When the sampler is placed on the stream bottom, all materials falling within the frame are washed by hand, downstream, into bagging net. Standing crop of organisms per square foot of substratum is then determined by sorting. Some limitations of sampling are given by Needham and Usinger, 1956.

and one midway between the center and a bank. The sampler is to be set up in position and all of the stones included in a square foot area are to be turned over and washed off in front of the net and into it. The bottom within this square foot is then to be stirred vigorously in order to dislodge the deeper lying forms such as the cranefly larvae and others. After this area has been completely worked over, the net with its contents is thoroughly washed in the current and the contents dumped into a counting pan. Large stones, sticks and other trash are washed off and removed, leaving only the finer material and bottom organisms for sorting.

If the sample contains a large number of very active organisms such as stoneflies and mayflies, a few cc. of formalin should be added to quiet them. The count is then made in a random number of squares depending on the richness of the sample and the quantity of trash. Unless the count contains a large number of midge larvae or other small forms, it will usually be possible to count the total number of each order in a very few minutes. As an aid in sorting some forms of life from associated debris, salt solution may be added in strengths to take advantage of the differences in specific gravity of the items to be separated. Records should be inserted in the proper places on the appropriate blank form.

Where the stream sampling net is not suitable for taking quantitative sections of the bottom, use Ekman or Peterson dredges (Figs. 95 and 97).

Experience has shown that numbers alone do not give a complete picture of the food supply. Samples containing three or four hundred mayfly nymphs may measure less than 0.5 cc. in volume whereas other samples composed of only thirty or forty organisms, some of which are large stonefly nymphs or tipulid larvae, may displace 4 or 5 cc. of water. Graded on the basis of numbers alone, the former would be considered rich; the latter poor. However, the total volume of the food supply of the latter would presumably produce more fish and would require much less energy on the part of fishes in obtaining it. On the other hand, samples containing a very few large organisms obviously could feed only a few fish since fish are not given to sharing their meals. Therefore, standards of richness have been tentatively proposed to aid in a preliminary classification of streams as to food supply. These have been derived from studies of square foot samples made in various parts of the country and are as follows.

Food Grade 1. (Exceptional richness) volume greater than 2 cc. or 2 grams, number greater than 50.

Food Grade 2. (Average richness) volume from 1 to 2 cc. (1 to 2 grams), more than 50 organisms.

Food Grade 3. (Poor in food) volume less than 1 cc (1 gram) and (or) fewer than 50 organisms.

Studies of the specific gravity of the principal fish food organisms have shown them to be slightly heavier than water, so that volumetric determinations by displacement are feasible.

In order to qualify in any grade, both the numerical and volumetric requirements must be met by the average square foot sample. For example, a sample containing 30 organisms having a volume of 3 cc. would be graded 3. Likewise a sample having 200 organisms but with a total volume of less than 1 cc. would be placed in class 3.

The method to be followed in determining volume is as follows: the organisms from at least one square-foot sample from each station should be picked out as the count is made and placed in a partly folded sheet of paper. In this way the excess water can be drained off and the organisms are protected from the wind. Remove all large caddis fly worms from their cases (discard cases). Allow the excess moisture to drain off and evaporate. When the mass will drop from the paper (about 5 minutes are required) tranfer the organisms to a graduated centrifuge tube containing a known quantity of water. With the sample completely submerged read the new volume to the nearest 1/10 of a cc. The difference between the two volumes is the total volume of the sample. Record this together with the numbers of individuals of each kind in the spaces provided on the fish food record form.

Totally dessicated weights or other forms of analysis may be used in special studies.

SUMMARY

On stream summary blank, bring together data from all stations. Also write up recommendations for the management of the stream and attach photographs to illustrate all points possible. Do not lose sight of the fact that better management is the objective of the survey. See next Chapter on stream improvement. Use it and its reference materials in connection with this report. If stocking is required, plan it from pool and food grades and, for trout, use Embody's stocking table (Chapter XXII).

STUDY PROGRAM

After reading published accounts of stream surveys and resulting management plans, plan and conduct a fishery survey of a stream.

Following study of the next Chapter on stream improvement, add recommendations for management to the report of your survey.

REFERENCES

Allen, K. Radway. 1951. The Horokiwi Stream, a study of a trout population. Fish. Bull. N. Z. Mar. Dept., 10, [x], 238 p., illus.

Dence, Wilford. 1928. A preliminary report on the trout streams of southwestern Cattaraugus Co., N. Y. Roosevelt Wild Life Bull., 5(1): 145-210, 24 figs.

Embody, G. C. 1927. An outline of stream study and the development of a stocking policy. Contr. Aquicult. Lab., Cornell Univ., 21 p., blank forms.

Hoover, Earl E., et al. 1937-1939. (Biological surveys of New Hampshire, by watersheds, 1936-39. Published as survey reports 1-4 by the New Hampshire Fish and Game Dept.)

Moore, Emmeline, et al. 1927-1940. (Biological surveys of New York, by watersheds, conducted in the years 1926-39, and published yearly as Supplements to the Annual Report of the State of New York Cons. Dept.)

Needham, Paul R. Trout streams . . . Ithaca, Comstock, x, 233 p., front., 74 figs.

Needham, Paul R., and Robert L. Usinger. 1956. Variability in the macrofauna of a single riffle in Prosser Creek, California, as indicated by the Surber sampler. Hilgardia, 24 (1): 383-409, 22 figs.

Robins, C. Richard, and Ronald W. Crawford. 1954. A short accurate method for estimating the volume of stream flow. Jour. Wildlife Mgt., 18 (3): 366-369.

Smith, Lloyd L., Jr., and John B. Moyle. 1944. A biological survey and fishery management plan for the streams of the Lake Superior north shore watershed. Minn. Dept. Cons., Div. Game and Fish., Tech. Bull., 1, 228 p., 40 figs.

Swartz, Albert H. 1942. Fisheries survey report. Mass. Dept. Cons., Div. of Fish and Game, xi, 181 p., many figs.

Tarzwell, Clarence M. 1938. Factors influencing fish food and fish production in southwestern streams. Trans. Amer. Fish. Soc., 67 (1937): 246-255.

Welch, Paul S. 1948. Limnological methods. Philadelphia, Blakiston, xviii, 381 p., 97 figs.

Chapter XXII

Stream Improvement

The improvement of streams may be defined as the control of environmental conditions to augment the production of desired fish species. Detection of the need for improvement comes through careful fishery surveys which should be as objective as possible; too often they are highly subjective and based on rule-of-thumb procedures. Theoretically, actual alterations may be made of chemical, physical, and biological factors affecting fish production. At present, most of such work must be regarded as experimental and should be accompanied by "before" and "after" measurements to determine effect. The principle of improving entire watersheds is gaining wider application than it has had heretofore.

Chemical improvement of streams, except by the removal of harmful pollutants, has not progressed very far. Huntsman (1948) has reported some success in the use of fertilizers. Direct biological improvement is perhaps limited to such things as elimination of "weed" fishes, control of predators, introduction of desired species, and special regulation of angling to suit local needs. Most kinds of biological amelioration are effected indirectly by changing physical conditions. Some of the factors influencing fish production in streams which are subject to intentional change are (1) shelter and feeding range; (2) food supply; (3) spawning and survival facilities; (4) predation pressure; (5) angling; (6) water supply and pollution; (7) erosion.

Fig. 111. DEFLECTOR AND SUBMERGED DIGGER LOG. Together these structures speed the current which results in a deeper channel.

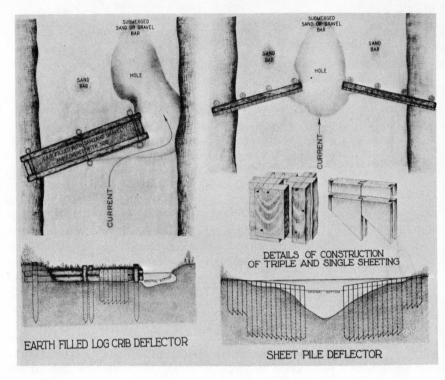

Fig. 112. USING DEFLECTORS FOR CHANNEL AND BANK IM-
PROVEMENT. Note both structural details and effects.

SHELTER

Both shelter and feeding range in shallow streams can be extended
by the creation of pools, introduction of streamside shrubs and trees, and
installation of table shelters in midstream. Pools can be caused to form
in soft-bottomed running water by the use of digging logs and deflectors
(Figs. 111, 112 and 113). On hard bottoms, low dams of natural or artificial materials may be employed to raise water levels for pool formation
upstream and to create a plunge basin with marginal feeding shelter
downstream (Fig. 114, C-C).

FOOD

Food supply in streams may be augmented temporarily by placing
porous sacks of agricultural fertilizer in upstream waters (Huntsman,
1948). In sandy streams, production may be stepped up by the judicious
use of deflectors. A silt bank and weed bed, which are good substrata
for food organisms, build up behind properly located and devised de-

flectors. Besides, the speeding of the water at the channel end of such a structure may wash the sand off of underlying gravel and rubble (Fig. 112) to help the food picture.

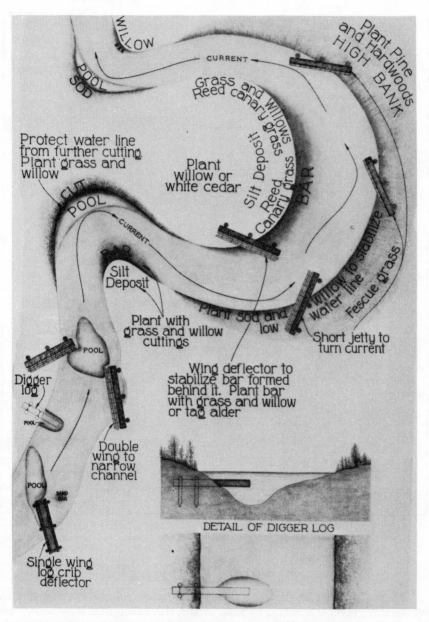

Fig. 113. RELATED EFFECTS OF IMPROVEMENT STRUCTURES.

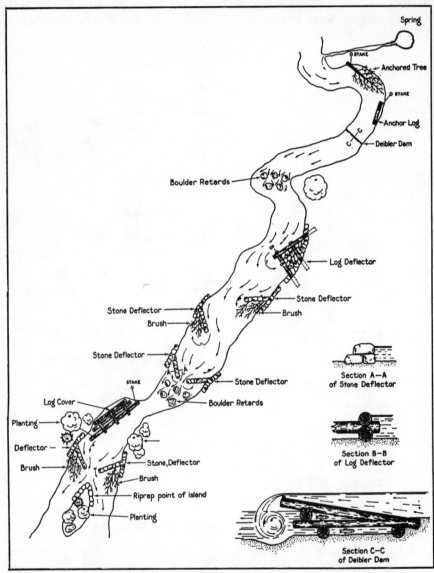

Fig. 114. SCHEMATIC SUMMARY OF SOME STREAM IMPROVE-
MENT TECHNIQUES. Emphasized here is the localized approach in
improvement which involves the stream and its immediate banks.

SPAWNING FACILITIES

Where key fish species are dependent on gravel for spawning, and
where this gravel is overlaid by sand or silt, these materials may be moved
by the engagement of current speeding devices (Figs. 112 and 114).

Among those which have been found useful for this purpose are deflectors, digger logs, and bank fillers to constrict the channel. Also applicable are erosion control, both on a local and on a watershed basis. Sometimes the installation of fishways (as at Hell's Gate), or the blasting out of barriers to spawning migration (such as natural falls or high beaver dams), may be of value.

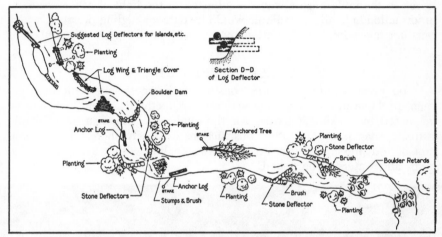

Fig. 115. SCHEMATIC SUMMARY OF SOME STREAM IMPROVEMENT TECHNIQUES. The need for many of the structures shown in Figs. 114 and 115 might be obviated if good land management was practiced throughout the surrounding watershed.

SURVIVAL

Survival of young fish in streams may be encouraged by the installation of stone piles, log jams, or other structures having many interstices (Fig. 115). In a general way, the creation of food-rich, slackwater areas behind deflectors also appears to favor survival (at least if one may judge from the small fishes which are often concentrated in these locations). Survival of older fish is favored by any means which makes them harder to catch, either by anglers or by natural predators. Streamside plantings which ultimately form a canopy over the water, addition of log covers (Fig. 114), and the installation of unfishable, snaggy retreats (Fig. 115, "anchored tree") are three primary means of prolonging the lives of fish.

PREDATION

Predation may be reduced by the means indicated in the previous paragraph. It may also be lessened by predator control. The control of predators by decimating their numbers, however, is more easily undertaken than justified under most circumstances. Clearly, it should never be employed, unless based on a sound scientific basis. In its worst form, it exists in the bounty system. Sometimes barrier dams will reduce predation pressure, as in barring pike or other undesirable fish from migration into headwater trout reaches of streams.

Some adjustment for losses due to angling and to predators can be made by stocking. The accompanying table for stocking trout streams is a guide with the help of which the number of fish to be planted per unit of length and character of streams has been approximated. Values given in the table must always be adjusted in the light of other pertinent information in hand; an example would be data on angling pressure, which was not taken into consideration by Embody (1927) when the table was prepared.

ANGLING PRESSURE

Too much angling pressure constitutes the most important management problem in many running waters. Indirectly, this condition may be regulated by making it harder for the angler to catch fish. Unfishable retreats, snag piles, and other obstructions are useful here. Direct control of rod pressure is exercised by laws dealing with season, size, bag, gear, and waters to be fished.

Fig. 116. TERRACING A SLIDING BANK. Supplementary planting of soil-binding vegetation will complete the corrective measure.

WATER SUPPLY

The need of fish for clean water, and means of pollution control, have been discussed in Chapter XV.

Stabilization of water supply and control of erosion go hand in hand in stream improvement (Figs. 113-115). Work to improve conditions of flood, drought, bank cutting, and silt load is not by any means confined to the immediate stream-side. Rather, and ideally, it begins in careful planning of land use on a watershed basis and encompasses public education as well as the installation of the needed controls. In agricultural areas, headwater control may take the direction of contour plowing, cover planting, strip cropping, and the fencing of watercourses. Downstream, springs may be cleaned, eroding banks stabilized (Fig. 116), etc. In both areas, road cuts and drainage ditches may need special attention. Protection of ground water supplies is important in stream improvement.

In trout streams, reduction of summer water temperatures is sometimes desirable. For some spots, this may be achieved by streamside plantings

STOCKING TABLE FOR TROUT STREAMS[1]

Stream Width (Feet)	Number of Three-Inch Fingerling Trout to Plant									Stream Width (Feet)
	Pool Grade A[2]			Pool Grade B			Pool Grade C			
	Food Grade[2]			Food Grade			Food Grade			
	1	2	3	1	2	3	1	2	3	
1	144	117	90	117	90	63	90	63	36	1
2	288	234	180	234	180	126	180	126	72	2
3	432	351	270	351	270	189	270	189	108	3
4	576	468	360	468	360	252	360	252	142	4
5	720	585	450	585	450	315	450	315	180	5
6	864	702	540	702	540	378	540	378	216	6
7	1008	819	630	819	630	441	630	441	252	7
8	1152	936	720	936	720	504	720	504	284	8
9	1296	1053	810	1053	810	567	810	567	324	9
10	1440	1170	900	1170	900	630	900	630	360	10
11	1584	1287	990	1287	990	693	990	693	396	11
12	1728	1404	1080	1404	1080	756	1080	756	432	12
13	1872	1521	1170	1521	1170	819	1170	819	468	13
14	2016	1638	1260	1638	1260	882	1260	882	504	14
15	2160	1755	1350	1755	1350	945	1350	945	540	15
16	2304	1872	1440	1872	1440	1008	1440	1008	576	16
17	2376	1930	1485	1930	1485	1039	1485	1039	594	17
18	2448	1989	1530	1989	1530	1071	1530	1071	612	18
19	2520	2047	1575	2047	1575	1102	1575	1102	630	19
20	2592	2106	1620	2106	1620	1134	1620	1134	648	20

For streams over 20 feet in width use formula $1/2 \, N_1 W + 8N_1 = X$ where N_1 = number of fingerlings for stream 1 ft. wide, w = average width, and X = number to be stocked per mile.
The above table refers to 3" fingerlings only. To find the number of other sizes multiply the number of fish given for the stream width in question by the following factors (dependent on size)

Length in inches	1"	3"	4"	6"	10"
	Fry	Fing.	Fing.	Half-grown	Adult
Factor	12	1	0.75	0.6	0.3

for shade. In other locations, restriction of the watercourse and augmentation of channel velocity will turn the trick. In still other places, it may be necessary to remove obstructions such as beaver dams in order to speed the water through a stretch in which it is becoming excessively

[1]From: Embody, George C. 1927. Stocking policy for the Genesee River system. In: A biological survey of the Genesee River system. Suppl. 16th Ann. Rept., 1926, N.Y. St. Cons. Dept., pp. 12-28.

warmed. And in yet others, it may be feasible to store water in the ground at headwaters during cold, wet seasons to insure flow of desired quality downstream during hot, dry seasons.

STREAM IMPROVEMENT ANALYSIS

Location of site or structure..

....

Kind of structure..

Date of construction........................... Builder..

Dimensions, etc. (include a sketch)..

Materials used ....

    Where obtained ....

    Approximate cost...

Labor cost for planning..

Labor cost for construction...

Estimated longevity ....

Observed points of structural failure...

....

Probable points of structural failure..

....

Estimated annual cost of maintenance...

....

Manner in which need for structure was determined...

....

Apparent desired effects..

....

Actual gross and obvious effects to date..

    At structure...

    Upstream ....

    One bank..

    Other bank ....

    Downstream ....

Biological effects (if known)..

....

Related effects at other water levels..

....

....

....

Esthetic qualities...

Relation to other water uses at the site..

Criticisms and recommendations..

....

....

....

....

....

Sketch (give plan, front, and side views and scale)

Analyst.. Date...................................

STUDY PROGRAM

Study references and make sketches and descriptive notes on as many specific items as you can for each major category of improvement device.

Study Figs. 114 and 115; number all structures from headwaters downstream, and make a brief statement as to the probable reason for use of each.

Visit as many sites of stream improvement as possible; record as a minimum for each site or structure the information called for on the accompanying blank form. Evaluate the improvement from point of view of the multiple uses of the water at and about the location as well as its effectiveness in improving fishing.

REFERENCES

Hazzard, A. S. 1937. Results of stream and lake improvement in Michigan. Trans. 2nd N. Amer. Wildlife Conf., pp. 620-624.

Hubbs, Carl L., J. R. Greeley, and C. M. Tarzwell. 1932. Methods for the improvement of Michigan trout streams. Bull. Mich. Cons. Dept. Inst. Fish Res., 1, 54 p., 18 figs.

Huntsman, A. G. 1948. Fertility and fertilization of streams. Jour. Fish. Res. Bd. Canada, 7(5): 248-253, 1 fig.

Pennsylvania Board of Fish Commissioners. [1938]. Stream improvement suggestions. 8 p., 6 text-figs., 1 chart.

Tarzwell, C. M. 1935. Progress in lake and stream improvement. Trans. 21st Amer. Game Conf., pp. 119-134.

Tarzwell, C. M. 1937. Experimental evidence on the value of trout stream improvement in Michigan. Trans. Amer. Fish. Soc., 66(1936): 177-187.

Tarzwell, C. M. 1938. An evaluation of the methods and results of stream improvement in the southwest. Trans. 3rd N. Amer. Wildlife Conf., pp. 339-364.

U. S. Bureau of Fisheries. 1935. Methods for the improvement of streams. U. S. Bur. Fish. Memo. I-133, 27 p., many text-figs.

U. S. Soil Conservation Service. 1954. A manual on conservation of soil and water . . . U. S. Dept. Agric., Agric. Handbook 61, 208 p., 175 figs,

Chapter XXIII

Creation of New Fishing Waters

The impounding of stream water or of surface runoff is an age-old human art. It has resulted in the creation of many water areas useful for fish production. Impoundments are of two kinds as regards primary intent, those built for fish production and those constructed for water storage. They range in size from a tenth of an acre or less to several thousands of acres. In general it is among the smaller ones that we find those constructed for the purpose of producing fish crops. The larger bodies are mostly concerned with other water uses such as human consumption, navigation, flood control, and power, but they also provide fishing and other forms of recreation.

SMALL PONDS

In addition to the artificial ponds built for private or public production of fish, there are many small impoundments which were originally constructed for watering livestock ("stock tanks") and for controlling erosion. Most of these can yield good fish crops if they are created and managed according to the following basic tenets:

1. The soil must be of a kind that will hold water in the impoundments and not let it seep away too rapidly; soil classifications on this basis have been prepared for most parts of the United States by the U. S. Soil Conservation Service.

2. The water supply — springs, surface runoffs (area of drainage basin), tributaries — must be of sufficient magnitude to offset losses by evaporation, seepage, etc., and by planned uses (livestock, irrigation, etc.).

3. Associated erosion hazards must be minimized, usually by planting suitable vegetation, to retard filling by silt, and to protect the dam from washing out (Fig. 117) and other banks from slipping as a result of wave action. Sometimes fencing will be required (Fig. 118).

4. Some marsh and aquatic plants may be introduced if they favor rather than compete with the uses to which the pond is to be put. Planting of aquatics is illegal in some states and is to be discouraged where establishment of water weed beds might increase production of malarial mosquitoes.

5. Stocking with fish should be conservative and should be carried out with the thought in mind that short food chains are beneficial to fish growth.

Fig. 117. PROTECTING AN EARTHEN DAM. Log boom
and plantings guard this low, earthen dam against erosion.

6. If at all possible, the dam should contain a well-built control structure of adequate size to pass flood waters. A means of draining the pond to control excessive plant growth or overpopulation by fish is desirable (Fig. 118).

7. Opportunity for use of such ponds by waterfowl, furbearers, and other wildlife should be considered.

8. Fertilizer may be applied in areas where research has shown it to be beneficial. Kind, amount, and frequency of fertilizing are local matters. It may be considered in non-muddy ponds when the bottom can be seen clearly in more than a few feet of water.

9. Best fishing is likely to ensue if the cropping by angling, seining, or predatory fish is heavy enough to prevent overpopulation or excessive competition without resultant stunting of the fish.

10. Owners or builders of farm ponds should consult freely with fish managers or other qualified persons to avoid costly blunders made because of ignorance.

If summer water temperatures do not exceed 65° F. at least in a substantial part of the impoundment, brook, brown or rainbow trout may be stocked. The number will vary according to size of the fish and available food supply per acre of water. Ordinarily, trout may not be expected to do well in a small body of water if competing or warm-water fishes are present. If the pond has surface water temperature of 80° F. or more in the summer, and game fish are desired in it, largemouth bass or spotted bass may be used. They may be planted alone or in various combinations with other fishes upon which they may feed.

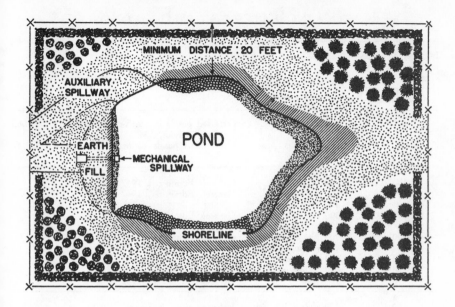

LEGEND

FOR "ALL-PURPOSE" PONDS ONLY

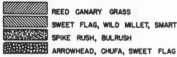 REED CANARY GRASS
SWEET FLAG, WILD MILLET, SMART WEED
SPIKE RUSH, BULRUSH
ARROWHEAD, CHUFA, SWEET FLAG

FOR ALL PONDS

LIVING FENCE
CONIFERS
HARDWOODS AND SHRUBS
GRASSES AND LEGUMES
REED CANARY GRASS

Fig. 118. DEVELOPING A SMALL POND. Basic features of construction and protection for small ponds as recommended by the U. S. Soil Conservation Service. In the southeastern United States, introduction of aquatics is barred by health regulations dictated by the malaria problem.

Kinds which are suitably combined with bass, if properly managed, are: bluegills, redear sunfish, or hybrid sunfishes (bluegill X redear; bluegill X pumpkinseed); crappies; rock bass; warmouth; and catfishes. Several of the minnows, such as golden shiner and fathead minnow, may be used as bass forage if sunfishes or other fishes are not employed (see following table).

Stocking rates claimed to be successful are far from uniform in small American impoundments. They vary according to species and size of fish to be stocked, basic fertility of the water area, geographical location, and individual worker. A selection of these rates in an accompaying table illustrates their variation.

STOCKING RATES FOR SMALL PONDS

Number of large-mouth bass fingerlings to be stocked per surface acre	Number and kind of other fingerlings to be stocked per surface acre	Region and authority
100	1000 bluegills	Fertilized ponds in north-central states; U. S. Soil Cons. Service, 1945
50	500 bluegills	Unfertilized ponds in north-central states; U. S. Soil Cons. Service, 1945
100	1000 bluegills	General, Edminster, 1947
100	800 bluegills and 200 crappies	General, Edminster, 1947
100	800 bluegills and 200 rock bass	General, Edminster, 1947
100	1000 bluegills and 75 channel catfish	General, Edminster, 1947
100	400 bullheads	General, Edminster, 1947
100	400 yellow perch	General, Edminster, 1947
0	300 trout	General, Edminster, 1947
100	100 redear sunfish	Indiana ponds; Krumholz, 1950
0	200 rock bass	Indiana ponds; Krumholz, 1950
0	500 hybrid sunfish	Indiana ponds; Krumholz, 1950
0	200 channel catfish	Indiana ponds; Krumholz, 1950
100	50 bluegills and 100 rock bass	Indiana ponds; Krumholz, 1950
100	50 bluegills and 100 crappies	Indiana ponds; Krumholz, 1950
100	748-1500 bluegills	Fertilized ponds in southeastern states; Swingle and Smith, 1942; Swingle, 1951.
30	400 bluegills	Unfertilized ponds in southeastern states; Swingle and Smith, 1942.
100	1500 bluegills and 25 white crappies	Fertilized ponds; Swingle and Smith, 1949.
20	400 bluegills and 10 white crappies	Unfertilized ponds; Swingle and Smith, 1942.
100	1200 bluegills and 75 bullheads	Fertilized ponds; Swingle and Smith, 1942.
30	300 bluegills and 25 bullheads	Unfertilized ponds; Swingle and Smith, 1942.
50	500 bluegills	New ponds in Oklahoma; Aldrich, 1946
25	300 bluegills and 50 crappies	New ponds in Oklahoma; Aldrich, 1946
50	100 bluegills and 50 channel catfish	New ponds in Oklahoma; Aldrich, 1946
25	300 bluegills 25 crappies and 50 channel catfish	New ponds in Oklahoma; Aldrich, 1946
0	750 bluegills and 100 channel catfish	New ponds in Oklahoma; Aldrich, 1946
0	500 bluegills 50 channel catfish and 50 crappies	New ponds in Oklahoma; Aldrich, 1946

LARGE IMPOUNDMENTS

Many large impoundments or artificial lakes, brought into being essentially for purposes other than fish production, are now yielding tremendous fish crops. Among these are the reservoirs of such cities as New York, Tulsa, and Los Angeles, and the power and navigation impoundments of the Tennessee Valley Authority. The basic features of fish productivity in such extensive water areas are not unlike those of comparable natural waters, and they are measured and managed in practically the same way (see Chapters XVIII through XX). Certain problems, however, are peculiar to the large artificial lakes. Since the impounding of such waters makes profound changes in local geography, important social and economic considerations arise. Furthermore, dams may be physical barriers to the migration of fishes and consequently pose serious ecological problems. For example, almost any dam in the lower reaches of a major stream in the Columbia River System is bound to affect adversely the future of the Pacific salmons which use the watershed for their remarkable spawning migrations. This remains true even when fishways are installed to encourage negotiation of the obstacles by migrating fish. It is thought by many fishery workers that dams were the most important of the agencies which combined practically to exterminate the Atlantic salmon and its fishery from New England. In an opposite situation, there is general agreement that high dams have no such basically undesirable effects in the region of the Tennessee Valley Authority's influence.

STUDY PROGRAM

Visit a farm fish pond or a small artificial lake and fill in the questionnaire at the end of this chapter. Secure information from the owner and builder, if possible. Determine what consideration has been given to the basic tenets previously listed, and the results of the application of or failure to employ these principles in the development of the project. Finally, using the references and other information, make the best fish management proposals that you can; insofar as possible, keep them compatible with the non-angling uses made of the pond.

REFERENCES

Allen, Philip F., and Cecil N. Davis. 1941. Ponds for wildlife. U. S. Dept. Agric., Farmer's Bull., 1879, 46 p.

Authors, various. Symposium of Farm Fish Pond Management. Jour. Wildlife Mgt., 16 (3): 233-287.

Bennett, George W. 1943. Management of small artificial lakes. Bull. Ill. Nat. Hist. Surv., 22(3): 357-376, 7 text-figs., front.

Clark, Wilson F. 1954. Controlling weeds and algae in farm ponds. Cornell Ext. Bull. 910, 15 p., illus.

Compton, Lawrence. 1943. Techniques of fishpond management. U. S. Dept. Agric. Misc. Publ. 528, 22 p. 4 figs.

Davison, Verne E. 1953. Homemade Fishing . . . Harrisburg, Pa., The Stackpole Company, 205 p., illus.

Davison, Verne E. 1955. Managing farm fishponds for bass and bluegills. U. S. Dept. Agric. Farmers' Bull. 2094, 18 p.

Edminster, Frank C. 1947. Fish ponds for the farm. New York, Scribners, xii, 114 p., 12 figs., 30 pl.

Embody, G. C. 1916. A small trout producing plant for the farm. Cornell Countryman, 14: 27-30, 97-100.

Krumholz, Louis A. 1950. Indiana ponds, their construction and management for fishing. Indianapolis, Ind. Lake and Stream Surv., 35 p., 8 figs.

Lawrence, J. M. 1949. Construction of farm fish ponds. Agric. Exp. Sta. Ala. Polytech. Inst., Circ. 95, 55 p., 36 figs.

Missouri Conservation Commission. 1943. Multiple purpose farm ponds. Bull. 15, 16 p.

Pistilli, August D. 1952. Farm ponds. Cornell Ext. Bull. 771, 14 p., 18 figs.

Prather, E. E., et al. 1953. Production of bait minnows in the southeast. Agric. Exp. Sta. Ala. Polytech. Inst., Circ. 112, 71 p., 33 figs.

Swingle, H. S. 1947. Experiments on pond fertilization. Ala. Polytech. Inst. Agric. Exp. Sta., Bull. 264, 34 p.

Swingle, H. S. 1949. Some recent developments in pond management. Trans. 14th N. Amer. Wildlife Conf., 295-312.

Swingle, H. S. 1951. Experiments with various rates of stocking bluegills, *Lepomis macrochirus* Rafinesque, and largemouth bass, *Micropteus salmoides* (Lacépède) in ponds. Trans. Amer. Fish. Soc., 80 (1950): 218-230.

Swingle, H. S., and E. V. Smith. 1942. Management of farm fish ponds. Ala. Polytech. Inst. Agric. Exp. Sta., Bull. 254, 23 p., 15 figs.

U. S. Soil Conservation Service. 1945. Pond Management. [In] Biology Handbook, pp. 37-46.

U. S. Soil Conservation Service. 1953. Books, booklets, bulletins on soil and water. Agric. Info. Bull. 63, 30 p.

Westerman, F. A. 1943. Michigan "creates" trout lakes. Mich. Cons., 12(6): 8-9.

EVALUATION OF A FARM FISH POND OR SMALL ARTIFICIAL LAKE

Location ....

Owner.................................... Construction date........................

Date of first filling...

Dates and durations of draw-downs...

Kind of dam..

Height of dam..

Control structure ....

Effect of dam on fish movements...

Water supply: Source..

    Adequacy ....

    Silt load...

    Pollution ....

Bottom soil..................................... Fertilization...............................

Surrounding soil.. Fertilization...............................

Immediate shore..

Surrounding land..

Area......................... Max. depth.......................... Av. depth............................

Color........................ Turbidity............... M. O. Alk. .... pH................

Vegetation ....

Fish food...

Spawning facilities and success...

....

Temperature: S................ B.............. Thermal stratification.......................

Winterkill history... Summerkill history..................

Fish diseases and parasites..

Fish species present..

....

....

Stocking history ....

Fishing intensity...

Annual fish harvest in lbs. by species..

Recommendations (and other observations)...

....

....

Observer.. Date..

Chapter XXIV

Freshwater Commercial Fisheries

Commercial fisheries of American fresh waters are most important in the Great Lakes, the Mississippi Valley, and the larger coastal streams. In the marine commercial fisheries, many organisms other than fish enter the catch. Among them are whales, seals, turtles, shellfish (both crustaceans and molluscs), sponges, and aquatic plants. In fresh waters, the largest proportion of the total take is composed of fish; turtles, frogs, shellfish, mayfly nymphs and aquatic young of other insects, and aquatic plants make up only a small fraction of the harvest. In both fisheries, however, a large number of species of organisms are involved, and consequently many different fishing methods are employed.

METHODS

Seines

Drag nets of various lengths, depths, and mesh sizes are used for taking bait minnows for sale, and for seining coarse fishes from quiet back waters, sloughs, and flood ponds (Fig. 2). They are no longer utilized to any significant extent for food fishes in the Great Lakes, although they are employed for coarse fishes, especially the carp, and for bait minnows. Seines are used for commercial harvest in smaller inland waters. Sometimes seines are hauled parallel to shore and at other times they are pulled from deeper waters to the beach or bank. Long nets are effectively laid parallel to shore from a boat and then drawn in by means of a rope of appropriate length at each end. Between uses the nets are cleaned and dried to prevent decay. Preservatives such as tanbark, oleate, or naphthenate are employed to lengthen the life of the twine.

Trawl Nets

Trawl nets, like those of the oceanic otter and beam trawl fisheries, are not used in inland waters. The future, however, may find them or modifications of them employed in such waters as the Great Lakes. The basic shape of a trawl net is more or less conical. The net mouth is held open and the depth of fishing regulated by frames, blades, or depressors. Habitats to be fished by these means are the bottom and various levels of midwater. In operation a trawl is towed through the water at slow speed. Mesh size varies according to the size of fish desired. Tanbark is a commonly used preservative for the twine.

Gill Nets

Gill nets (Figs. 99, 119, 120) are usually made of relatively light-weight thread of cotton, linen, or nylon. They are typically weighted to fish on

Fig. 119. CARING FOR GILL NETS. Two methods of reeling gill nets to dry; at right, already on reel, by stretching; at left, in hands of operator, by roping.

the bottom although some are used as "floaters" or experimentally to fish through all depths from the bottom to the surface. Net length, depth, and mesh size vary according to the capital and opinion of the operator, the law, and the fishery. In the Great Lakes and large Canadian lakes, gill nets are used extensively for taking lake trout and whitefish among other species; in the Great Lakes they are the most important item of commercial fishing gear. Gill nets normally capture fish by "gilling" them, that is, by having the fish pass its head through a mesh too small to permit either passage of the rest of its body or withdrawal of the head once the posterior margin of the gill covers has been passed by the mesh (Fig. 99). The use of anchored gill nets is limited to relatively quiet water since in flowing waters they would be destroyed or carried away by accumulating debris. However, in some fisheries, such as the estuarine ones for Pacific salmons, the nets are permitted to drift suspended from the surface with one end attached to a buoy and the other fixed to the fishing boat. In the winter, gill nets are threaded under the ice in some Great Lakes bays and in larger lakes of Canada. They are periodically washed in soap, treated with preservatives, and dried between sets (Fig. 119) to lengthen life.

Trammel Nets

A trammel net (or "bar net") is made up of three nets hung together from a single float line to a single lead line. The two outer meshes are larger; the loosely hung inner mesh is smaller. Fishes trap themselves in pockets of the fine webbing pushed through the heavier twine. This type of gear has been abandoned in most states but may still be seen in use in the Mississippi Valley and in Lake Erie. Tanbark and copper naphthenate are preservatives.

Impounding Nets

Impounding nets (particularly trap and pound nets) are the second most important kind of gear in the Great Lakes' commercial fishery, and perhaps the primary kind in that of the Mississippi Valley.

Hoop nets (Figs. 100 and 101) are more or less conical fish traps typically made of twine mesh hung on round frames and having two funnel shaped throats in series. The hoops are usually made of willow, number six or seven, and range in size from a diameter of about 5 feet for the entry hoop to 2 feet for the hoop nearest the cod end or pot. In moving waters, the entrance is directed downstream and the cod is staked upstream. Used in quiet water, the hoop net becomes a fyke net when wings 6 feet deep by 30 or more feet long are added to the mouth; sometimes a leader of 100 or more feet in length is employed to bisect the angles of the wings and guide fish into the mouth. In standing waters, net sets are either parallel or at various angles to the shore in order to intersect most effectively the routes of fish movement (as in Fig. 122). Tar or tanbark are common preservatives.

Fig. 120. GILL NETTER. Vessel used on the Great Lakes. Gill nets are paid out of trays in the stern and taken in, with help of a mechanical reel, at one side or the other of the bow (port hatch just below and in front of wheelhouse on this figure).

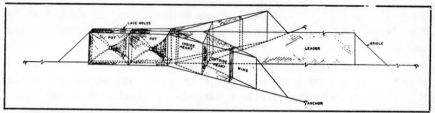

Fig. 121. TRAP NET. Used both in commercial fisheries (in various sizes, to very large) and in population studies in inland waters (smaller editions).

Trap nets are really modifications of fyke nets in which rectangular shape, floats, sinkers, and spreaders have been substituted for hoops

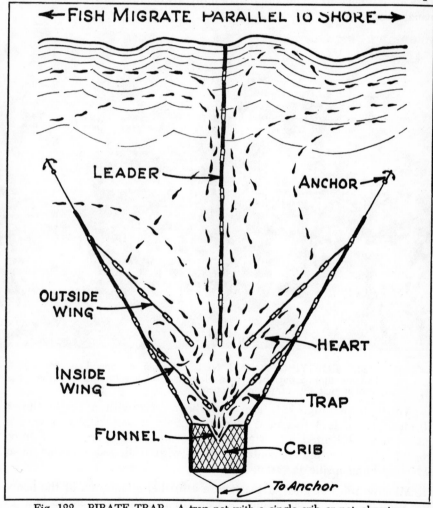

Fig. 122. PIRATE TRAP. A trap net with a single crib or pot, showing response of fish to leader and wings.

(Figs. 121 and 122). They are adaptable for fishing in deeper waters than hoop nets. A "deep trap" may have a pot 40 or more feet tall; one or two pots may be present (Figs. 121 and 122).

Pound nets (Fig. 123) are traps in which the top is not closed with mesh. They extend from the bottom to a few feet above the surface and are composed of a leader, a somewhat heart-shaped pound, and a rectangular bowl, crib, or pot. A pound net is usually staked out in water between 30 and 50 feet in depth; rarely as deep as 90 feet. This type of impounding device is used in the inshore fisheries of all of the Great Lakes to take a wide variety of fish. Since the top is open, trapped fish are subject to some depredation by fish-eating birds. Tar is the usual preservative.

Fig. 123. EMPTYING POUND NET. Bottom of pound is raised and fish are dipped out; basic plan of gear is similar to trap net (Fig. 121) except that top of pound is open.

Turtle traps (Fig. 124) are small hoop nets with a single throat. Typical length is 4 feet, and diameter 1.5 to 2 feet. Chicken wire is sometimes substituted for twine in the covering. The turtles are lured to enter by a perforated container filled with fresh fish or other meat which is hung inside the trap.

Minnow traps of glass or plastic are a further adaptation of the hoop-net principle. Such capturing devices are usually between 12 and 18 inches long and 9 to 12 inches in diameter. They are baited with corn

Fig. 124. TURTLE TRAP. Side view at left (note bait container within); front view at right (note shape of opening in throat).

meal or cracker crumbs and have a removable end for taking out the catch.

Crayfish traps also employ the funnel shaped entrance and are made of hardware cloth, or of wood like lobster pots. They are used in the crayfish fishery of northern waters, and also as catfish traps in a number of other areas. There is a small market for crayfish both for human consumption and for use as bait in sport fishing.

Weirs

Weirs are stationary fish traps which act as barriers to fish movements and lead fish into pots. In Atlantic coastal streams they are used for taking eels on downstream migration. In the Great Lakes region they are employed in tributaries to arrest upstream spawning runs of the sea lamprey (Figs. 3 and 4). They are also used commonly for studying fish movements.

Lines

There are no extensive commercial line fisheries in American fresh waters, except locally for lake trout in lakes Michigan and Superior. Handlining for smelt, lake trout, and other fishes contributes to the livelihood of many more or less solitary fishermen in the Mississippi Valley, in the Great Lakes region, and in central Canada. Considerable handlining for smelt and trout is done in northern waters through the ice in

Fig. 125.   FISHING WITH DIP NETS.   Famous dip net fishery for salmons by American Indians at Celilo Falls on the Columbia River, Oregon.

winter.   In the Mississippi Valley long trot lines or set lines with many baited hooks at intervals of a few feet are used to take such fishes as catfishes, suckers, and drum.   Single baited hooks on short lines attached to springy willow poles sometimes serve the same purpose and are also used to capture snapping turtles.   Trolling baited hooks or other lures is a minor form of commercial fishing, although the yield of lake trout by this means in Lake Superior is considerable.

Dip Nets

Small dip nets are used for taking such fish as smelt on their spawning runs, by hand dipping.   Larger, square nets are worked from the ends of counterbalanced poles to dip fishes such as suckers and catfishes from larger streams. Such dipping is usually done near the downstream side of a dam or falls where fish are barred from upstream movement. A famous dip-net fishery is that practiced by the Indians at Celilo Falls, at the Dalles of the Columbia River (Fig. 125). These fisheries are seasonal, local, and relatively unimportant.

Spears

Spearing is not a productive method of commercial fishing in inland waters. It is, however, used to take such fishes as pike and sturgeon through holes chopped in the ice. It is also employed in getting suckers on their spawning runs in small, shallow streams, and in the control of rough or obnoxious fishes. In southern waters, spears and spring-clamp gigs are commonly used for catching frogs.

Rakes and Tongs

Rakes or tongs are used in the mussel fisheries of the upper Mississippi Valley and in a few of the tributaries of the Great Lakes. The shells were formerly important in the manufacture of pearl buttons, but they are largely being superseded by plastics. Rakes are also the tools for gathering aquatic plants for the aquarium trade.

Sieves

Long handled sieves are used in dredging operations in several northern lakes to secure "wigglers," the burrowing nymphs of certain mayflies. These are sold to ice fishermen for panfish bait.

MARKETING

Much of the product of the inland fisheries is marketed locally, often directly from fisherman to consumer. From the larger fisheries of the Great Lakes and of the Canadian lakes, however, the fish are often sent great distances. If the journey is to be of short duration, the carcasses are iced and boxed; for holding and for shipments over longer distances, they are sharp frozen. Live transfers are rare, although certain markets still merchandise live fish such as carp and suckers for a particular trade. Many shipments, particularly of frozen fish, are made in the round. Dressed fish are usually shipped in crushed ice. Only the smaller shippers and retailers still remove scales by hand; larger operators use machines which can scale a fish in a few seconds. Some freshwater fishes are smoked (e.g., ciscoes), and a small amount of caviar is still prepared— however, the roe is now from whitefish whereas formerly it was from sturgeons.

The principal means of transporting fish to the markets are truck and rail, although for greater distances air express is sometimes used.

The relatively recent advent and growth in popularity of packaged frozen fish has considerablly expanded the number of retail outlets for fish and is doing away with the fish peddler and retail fish markets except in the proximity of unloading docks.

Fig. 126. THE CISCO. Research vessel of the U. S. Fish and Wildlife Service on the Great Lakes; length is about 64 feet over-all.

LICENSES

Most inland commercial fisheries require operators or units of gear to be licensed. The revenue thus gained by state or provincial governments is not great and is usually used for law enforcement.

CONSERVATION

Conservation of the freshwater commercial fishery resources is now largely a matter of restriction of season and gear (see Chapter XVI). In

Fig. 127. THE INVESTIGATOR. Research vessel Investigator in the foreground and 60-foot laboratory barge for commercial fishery research on larger, inland waters of Canada. Operated by the Fisheries Research Board of Canada.

the upper Great Lakes, however, control of the parasitic sea lamprey is an important measure. Research on the commercial fisheries of inland waters is conducted mostly by state or provincial governments, although the U. S. Fish and Wildlife Service (Fig. 126), the Tennessee Valley Authority, the Fisheries Research Institute (Seattle), and the Fishery Research Board of Canada (Fig. 127) are engaged in many important studies, some of them of a long-term nature. The results of these investigations are reported in several professional journals and are described in trade magazines and other educational media (Elliott, 1950).

STUDY PROGRAM

Using references, movies, and field trips, study as many inland commercial fisheries as possible. For each fishery, or for each kind of organism pursued, summarize your information on an outline form such as the one that follows.

INLAND COMMERCIAL FISHERIES

Species caught ....

Location of fishery..

....

Method of fishing..

....

Specifications of gear..

    Care ....

    Method of preservation..

    Durability.. Cost per unit......................................

Vessel: Size....................................Weight....................Power....................

    Special qualifications and apparatus..

....

....

Seasons of fishing: Closed........................Open....................:Best................

Catch per unit of effort: Give unit..

    Maximum........................ Minimum........................ Average................

License cost and requirements..

Habitat where pursued (Depths, currents, etc.)......................................

....

....

Frequency of tending gear..

....

Crew (titles, wages, assignments)..

....

Operational costs..

Preparation of fish for market..

....

Storage and holding..

....

Marketing ....

Prices ....

Records kept...Where published............................

Chief difficulties encountered in the fishery and steps being taken to alleviate them..

....

....

....

Indications of depletion..

....

....

....

Sketches of gear, vessels, and special apparatus (on additional sheets).

Date.. Observer ....

REFERENCES

Carlander, Harriet Bell. 1954. History of fish and fishing in the Upper Mississippi River. Upper Mississippi River Cons. Comm., 96 p., 22 figs.

Carson, R. L. 1943. Fishes of the Middle West. U. S. Fish and Wildlife Service, Cons. Bull. 34, 44 p.

Elliott, R. Paul. 1950. Information sources for students of commercial fisheries. U. S. Fish and Wildlife Service, Fish. Leaflet, 362, 20 p.

Forbes, S. A., and R. E. Richardson. 1920. The fishes of Illinois. (Second ed.) Ill. Nat. Hist. Surv., vol. 3, Text, cxxi, 357 p.; Atlas, 103 maps.

Goode, G. B., et al. 1884-1887. The fisheries and fishery industries of the United States. U. S. Comm. Fish and Fisheries (see p. 81 for complete citation; Sect. V is particularly pertinent on methods).

Gowanloch, J. N. 1933. Fishes and fishing in Louisiana. La. Dept. Cons., Bull. 23, 638 p., illus.

Harlan, James R., and Everett B. Speaker. 1956. Iowa fish and fishing. Des Moines, Iowa State Cons. Comm., [vi], 377 p., illus. (incl. many col. pl.).

Illinois State Department of Conservation. 1942. Illinois game and food fish. 36 p.

International Board of Inquiry for the Great Lakes Fisheries. 1943. Report and supplement. U. S. Gov't. Printing Office, 213 p.

Koelz, Walter. 1926. Fishing industry of the Great Lakes. Rept. U. S. Comm. Fish., 1925, App. XI, pp. 552-617.

Rawson, D. S. 1949. Estimating the fish production of Great Slave Lake. Trans. Amer. Fish. Soc., 77 (1947): 81-92, 4 figs.

Rounsefell, George A., and W. Harry Everhart. 1953. Fishery science its methods and applications. New York, John Wiley and Sons, Inc., xii, 444 p., illus.

Starrett, William C., and Paul G. Barnickol. 1955. Efficiency and selectivity of commercial fishing devices used on the Mississippi River. Bull. Ill. Nat. Hist. Surv., 26 (4): 325-366, 17 figs.

Taylor, Harden F., et al. 1951. Survey of marine fisheries of North Carolina. Chapel Hill, Univ. North Carolina Press, xii, 555 p., illus.

Tressler, Donald K., M. C. James, W. Lemon, et al. 1951. Marine products of commerce. New York, Reinhold, xiii, 782 p., many illus.

U. S. Bureau of Fisheries. 1937. Our aquatic food animals. The fishes of the Great Lakes. Memo. I-134 D, 30 p.

U. S. Fish and Wildlife Service. 1945. Fishery resources of the United States. Senate Document No. 51, 79th Congress, 1st Session, 135 p.

Van Oosten, John. 1940. Fishing industry of the Great Lakes. U. S. Bur. Fish. Memo. I-63, 15 p.

Chapter XXV

Freshwater Recreational Fisheries

It has been said, and rightly, that a good manager of sport fisheries is better if he is also a fisherman at heart. Obviously, a fishery biologist can cultivate the best public relations only if he understands the language of anglers. Furthermore, some of the most valuable slants that he may get on his own work will come to him while he is afield with rod in hand.

METHODS

Still Fishing

Still fishing from boat, shore, or bank is the most common angling method in America. Almost every kind and combination of rod, line, hook, and sinker is used. Baits are most often natural and, in decreasing order of importance, are earthworms, minnows, insects, and grubs. In typical pursuit, the angler baits his hook, lowers it to the depth at which he thinks the fish are most likely to be, and waits for them to swallow it. Sometimes a float or bobber is used to regulate the depth to which the bait will sink and to act as a signal when a fish bites. Most of the common sport fishes may be taken by this method.

Trolling

Trolling is pulling a selected lure through the water (Figs. 128 and 129) in such a way that a fish will be tempted to strike at it when he sees it. The lure may be artificial such as a wet fly, spoon, or plug, or it may be natural such as the baits used in still fishing. There are two basic kinds of trolling. In one kind, ordinary light baitcasting tackle

Fig. 128. TROLLING WITH LIGHT TACKLE.   Fig. 129. TROLLING WITH HEAVY TA

is used and relatively shallow waters are fished (Fig. 128); this is the type commonly practiced for walleyes, black bass, and pike. In the second kind, heavier tackle including a wire line is used and deeper waters are fished (Fig. 129). This is the type employed in the deepwater pursuit of lake trout, for example, and is not greatly different from oceanic "deep sea" fishing. One form of this kind of trolling is called chugging or bottom bumping because of the way in which the sinker is chugged or bumped along the bottom as the vessel moves slowly along.

Baitcasting

Baitcasting (Fig. 130) is a very popular form of catching predacious game fish (pike [Fig. 136], black basses, walleyes, etc.). Rods (Fig. 131) are made of tubular or solid metal, split bamboo, or plastic, and are mostly from five to six feet long. With such a rod, a casting reel (Fig. 131) is used which, in good quality, is a precision instrument built to withstand wear of many high speed revolutions during casts. Almost all such reels are quadruple multiplying and are equipped with a level-winding device which distributes the line evenly over the spool as it is wound in. The prevalent line is relatively light in weight and is not more than 15-pound test. Lines are made of braided cotton, linen, silk, or nylon.

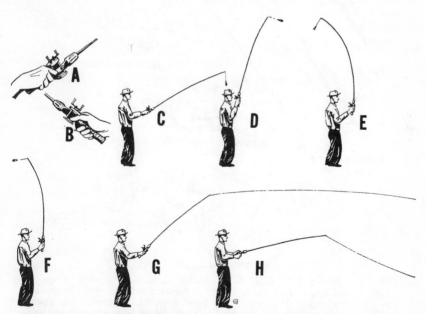

Fig. 130. BAITCASTING. A. Proper grip. B. Reel handles up; thumb on edge of spool. C. Aim; thumb reel. D. Back fast. E. Stop slightly beyond perpendicular. F. Forward twice as fast as back; release thumb slightly as rod tip approaches target. G. Thumb reel to stop when plug hits target. H. Change hands to retrieve.

Both natural and artificial lures are used in baitcasting, but the latter are more popular because they entail less fussing and because soft-bodied baits tend to tear off the hooks when they are thrown. Artificials

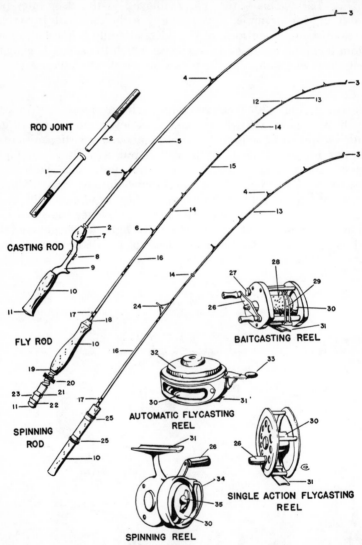

Fig. 131. RODS AND REELS. 1. ferrule; 2. slide; 3. tip top; 4. guide (ring); 5. rod tip; 6. butt guide (ring); 7. forward grip; 8. reel clamp and screw; 9. reel seat (offset type); 10. hand grip; 11. butt cap; 12. guide (snake); 13. tip section; 14. rod joint; 15. middle section; 16. butt section; 17. keeper ring; 18. winding check; 19. reel seat washer; 20. screw locking nut; 21. sliding hood; 22. rear hood; 23. reel seat; 24. large butt or gathering guide; 25. sliding rings; 26. crank; 27. brake; 28. arbor; 29. level-wind; 30. spool; 31. reel clip; 32. re-wind mechanism; 33. finger release; 34. pick-up finger; 35. friction clutch.

are made to resemble everything from nothing through fish to mermaids! There are three basic kinds of artificial lures (Fig. 132): (1) surface floating; (2) shallow running, which by weight or by depressing lip are made to swim from one to a few feet down; (3) deep running, which again by weight, lip angle, or speed of recovery are made to operate at deeper levels. A spoon, for example, when reeled in rapidly may run shallow but when recovered slowly, may run deep. The average lure weighs from 3/8 to 5/8 of an ounce. The weight of the lure carries out the line in baitcasting.

Spinning

Spinning is fundamentally intermediate between baitcasting and flycasting. The rods (Fig. 131) are like fly rods, described in the next paragraph, but are 6 1/2 to 7 feet in length and have a larger guide on the butt section. The weight of the line is the approximate equivalent of the leader in fly fishing and depends on the weight of the lure to carry it out. The lures (Fig. 132) are principally smaller versions of baitcasting plugs and spoons. The reel (Fig. 131), however, for spinning differs from that used for baitcasting or flycasting. The spool of the spinning reel is stationary and the line is wound on it by an arm or bail which moves around it as the crank is turned. This manner of winding does away with the hazard of the back lash which is present in the use of a baitcasting reel. Another safety feature characterizes the spinning reel; it has an adjustable friction clutch on the spool which may be set to pay out line whenever tension on it nears its breaking strength. Both predacious game fish and pan fish are taken by spinning.

Flycasting

Rods for flycasting (Fig. 133) are made of split bamboo, glass or other plastic, or light-weight tubular metal, and range generally from 7 to 9 feet in length (Fig. 131). Most rods sold are 8 to 8½ feet long and weigh 5 or 6 ounces. Reels (Fig. 131) are either single action (crank type) or automatic (spring wind type). An enameled or oiled silk or nylon fly line is used with such a combination of rod and reel. Care is taken in the selection of the line to secure one heavy enough to bring out the action of the rod. The usual weight recommended is "D"; for most rods a level D line will be sufficiently heavy to carry out the lure with ease, which it must do, since a fly is essentially weightless. For particular kinds of fishing, experts use variously tapered lines. A single tapered line runs from a heavier weight, say C, at one end to a lighter weight, say E, at the other. Still other tapers operate to make both ends of a line lighter than the middle (double tapered) or to bring the weight forward ("torpedo head"). Tubular lines are also manufactured and are the tackle industry's most recent development to make lines float. A very light leader is knotted to the forward end of the line (Fig. 134) and is made of gut or some synthetic substance such as nylon. The average leader used is a little shorter than the rod for ease in handling. A fly is attached to the tip of the leader.

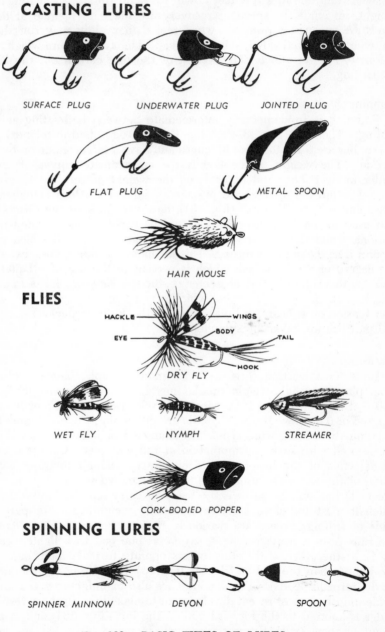

CASTING LURES

SURFACE PLUG   UNDERWATER PLUG   JOINTED PLUG

FLAT PLUG   METAL SPOON

HAIR MOUSE

FLIES

HACKLE — WINGS

EYE — BODY — TAIL

HOOK

DRY FLY

WET FLY   NYMPH   STREAMER

CORK-BODIED POPPER

SPINNING LURES

SPINNER MINNOW   DEVON   SPOON

Fig. 132. BASIC TYPES OF LURES.

Flies used in fishing are of two principal kinds, dry and wet (Fig. 132). Dry flies float on the surface and are sometimes doped to help them resist wetting. Wet flies, including nymphs and streamers, are fished under water and are often soaped or dipped in a detergent to make them sink. In addition, there are fundamental structural differences between the two types. Sometimes small metal spoons or spinners are used with wet flies. Many standard baitcasting lures also have diminutive flycasting editions.

Fly fishing is most popular for the stream trouts (Fig. 135) and for pan fishes such as bluegills and crappies, and game fishes such as the black basses.

Ice Fishing

We will consider here only the most common methods of catching fish through holes chopped in the ice: rod and line; tip-up; and spearing.

Most rod and line fishing through ice is for bluegills, yellow perch, and crappies. The rods commonly used are short and light, being roughly the equivalent of the tip section of a fly rod (from which many of them are made). Natural baits are small minnows and insect nymphs or larvae; a favorite nymph is the burrowing aquatic stage of some mayfly such as *Hexagenia* and a favored larva is that of the corn borer. Successful artificial lures are small spoons or ice flies. Ice flies are wet flies to which a split shot has been added at the shank of the hook near the eye.

Fig. 133. FLYCASTING.

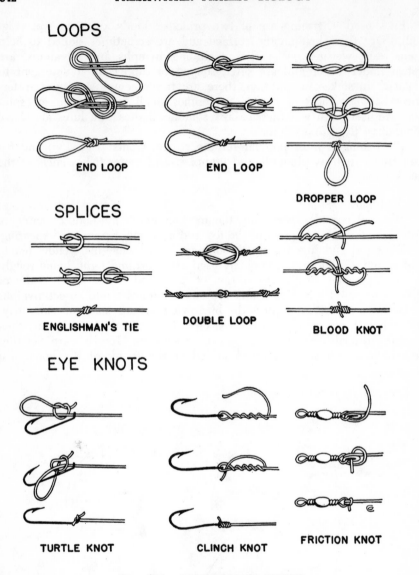

Fig. 134. FISHERMAN'S KNOTS.

Tip-ups of various kinds are used to signal the operator when a fish has been caught. Baited hook, sinker, and line are attached to a spring or hinged device on the surface of the ice which will flash a small flag or marker when a fish has struck. Smelt, pike, and other fishes are taken on tip-ups.

Spearing from a shanty or other shelter pitched over a hole in the ice is a winter sport with many devotees. Such fish as pike are decoyed into range of the spear by live minnows, or minnow models attached to a string, and are then speared with a quick thrust. The usual spear is six-tyned, has a steel shaft, and is secured by a rope to the side of the shelter so that it can be recovered after it has been thrown at a fish.

Other Methods

There are many other methods used in the sport fisheries, both legal and illegal. Among them are spearing from a boat or while swimming under water; snagging with a hook drawn over the body of the fish; dipping with dip nets; skittering with baits on a short line attached to a long pole; lassoing by guiding a loop over the fish's tail or snout; grabbing by running the bare hand along a fish and then grasping it.

Fig. 135.   CUTTHROAT TROUT FROM THE YELLOWSTONE RIVER.

LICENSES

Licenses for sport fishing are required in all states and provinces. Fees are relatively small for residents, greater for non-residents. In some states, an extra tax must be paid if one wishes to fish for trout. The revenue from licenses is used for such things as administration, law enforcement, artificial propagation, lake and stream improvement, creation of fishing waters, acquisition and maintenance of public fishing sites, research, and the creation of an informed public.

CONSERVATION

Perpetuation and enhancement of sport fishing are sought through legal restriction, stocking, environmental improvement, the creation of new fishing waters, and public education. Much of this book has been devoted to a description of routine methods by which the biological basis for management is secured by fishery workers. It is only on such a basis that intelligent management of individual waters can proceed; there are no pat methods or nostrums by which fishing can suddenly be improved in a body of water even when many facts regarding the productivity of that water have been learned. Known general methods of improving fishing must always be modified in practice to fit particular local conditions.

Fig. 136. FUN FOR ALL OF THE FAMILY. Limit catch of pike from northern Michigan on the Seney National Wildlife Refuge.

Most states publish conservation magazines in which recent trends and developments in the art of fish management are explained. Radio, television, motion pictures, news releases, and lectures are also used to bring about public appreciation of what constitutes the proper use and management of the sport fishery resource.

There are several non-professional organizations which act in the interest of the sport fisheries. Outstanding among these at the national and international levels are the Sport Fishing Institute of Washington, D. C., and the Izaak Walton League of America with headquarters in Chicago, Illinois. Local and regional sportsmen's groups also exist in great numbers and are important points of contact between public and technician.

STUDY PROGRAM

Master the techniques of baitcasting, spinning, and flycasting well enough to be able to give elementary instruction in these arts. Know the principle items of gear and pertinent information on characteristics, selection, care, and use to catch fish. Try to catch as many different species as possible.

Prepare a brief report on the administrative, research, and management agencies concerned with the sport fisheries in a state or province. Consider organization, budget, program, and integration with the work of national units and others concerned with the same subjects in the region. Prepare terse critiques of as many aspects as possible and offer practical suggestions of a constructive nature.

Report, at least in outline form, on the work in conservation education in the political entity used above. Evaluate the program and organize constructive criticism.

REFERENCES

There are very many books, pamphlets, and magazines devoted to sport fishing. The following list of books is an arbitrary selection of representative works.

Caine, Lou S. 1949. North American fresh water sport fish. New York, Barnes, xii, 212 p., illus. incl. 8 col. pl. (Contains biological notes by Karl F. Lagler).

Crowe, John. 1947. The book of trout lore. New York, Barnes, xii, 233 p., illus.

Dalrymple, Byron W. 1947. Panfish, the art and enjoyment of light-tackle fishing for the common fishes of the United States. New York, McGraw-Hill, 398 p., illus.

Gabrielson, Ira N., and Francesca Lamonte [Editors]. 1950. The Fisherman's Encyclopedia. New York, Stackpole and Heck, xxix, 698 p., many illus.

Gordon, Seth. 1950. California's fish and game program. California State Senate, 246 p., illus.

Lagler, Karl F. 1949. Fish and fishing in Michigan. Ann Arbor, Folletts, 91 p., 51 text-figs.

Robb, James. 1946. Notable angling literature. London, Robert Jenkins, Ltd., 229 p.

Robinson, Ben C. 1941. Pond, lake and stream fishing. A book of general advice on fresh-water fishing. Philadelphia, McKay, xiv, 370 p., illus.

Schrenkeisen, Ray. [Editor]. 1946. Fishing lake and stream bass, muskellunge, pike, pan fishes, salmon, and trout. Garden City, Doubleday, 185 p., illus.

Shoemaker, Myron E. 1945. Fresh water fishing a fisherman's manual. Garden City, Doubleday, Doran, xiv, 218 p., illus., incl. 9 col. pl.

Stilwell, Hart. 1948. Fishing in Mexico. New York, Knopf, xii, 296 p., illus.

APPENDIX A

SCALES OF COMMON AND REPRESENTATIVE FAMILIES OF AMERICAN FRESHWATER FISHES

Technical names of families and species corresponding to the common names used in the figure captions of this appendix are given in Appendix F, unless otherwise indicated. All of the following scale figures are magnified, some more than others; posterior margin of each is at the right. Further information on the scale characters of these species is given in Lagler, 1947, Transactions of the American Microscopical Society, Vol. 66, No. 2, pp. 149-171.

Fig. 137. GAR FAMILY. Long-nose gar.

Fig. 138. BOWFIN FAMILY. Bowfin.

Fig. 139. MOONEYE FAMILY. Mooneye.

Fig. 140. HERRING FAMILY. American shad.

Fig. 142. SALMON FAMILY. Brook trout.

Fig. 141. HERRING FAMILY. Gizzard shad.

Fig. 143. WHITEFISH FAMILY. Ives Lake cisco, *Coregonus hubbsi* (Koelz).

Fig. 144. WHITEFISH FAMILY. Lake whitefish.

Fig. 145. WHITEFISH FAMILY. Round whitefish.

Fig. 146. SMELT FAMILY. American smelt.

Fig. 147. FRESHWATER EEL FAM-
ILY. American eel.

Fig. 148. SUCKER FAMILY. White
sucker.

Fig. 149. SUCKER FAM-
ILY. Longnose sucker.

Fig. 150. SUCKER FAMILY.
Lake chubsucker.

Fig. 151. CARP FAMILY.
Golden shiner.

Fig. 152. CARP FAMILY.
Mimic shiner.

Fig. 153. CARP FAMILY.
Hornyhead chub.

Fig. 154. CARP FAMILY.
Blacknose dace.

Fig. 155. CARP FAMILY.
Bluntnose minnow.

Fig. 156. CARP FAMILY. Goldfish.

Fig. 158. PIKE FAMILY. Grass
pickerel.

Fig. 157. CARP FAMILY. Carp.

Fig. 159. MUDMINNOW FAMILY.
Central mudminnow.

Fig. 160. KILLIFISH FAMILY.
Banded killifish.

Fig. 161. COD FAMILY. Burbot.

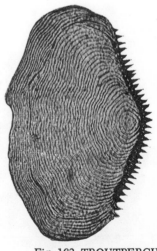

Fig. 162. TROUTPERCH
FAMILY. Troutperch.

Fig. 163. PIRATEPERCH FAMILY.
Pirateperch.

Fig. 164. SILVERSIDE FAM-
ILY. Brook silverside.

Fig. 165. PERCH FAMILY.
Yellow perch.

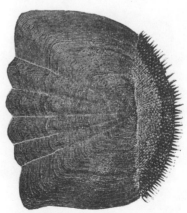

Fig. 166. PERCH FAMILY.
Sauger.

Fig. 167. PERCH FAMILY.
Johnny darter.

Fig. 168. SUNFISH FAMILY. Smallmouth bass.

Fig. 169. SUNFISH FAMILY.
Largemouth bass.

Fig. 170. SUNFISH
FAMILY. Green sunfish.

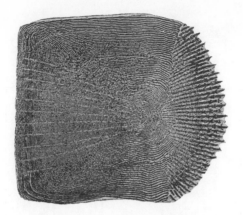

Fig. 171. BASS FAMILY. White bass.

Fig. 172. DRUM FAMILY.
Freshwater drum.

BLANK FORMS FOR RECORDING DATA ON FISHERY SURVEYS

Lake and Stream Survey

Water Analysis

INSTITUTE FOR FISHERIES RESEARCH

DIVISION OF FISHERIES

MICHIGAN DEPARTMENT OF CONSERVATION

COOPERATING WITH THE

UNIVERSITY OF MICHIGAN

County: ....

Lake or stream: ....

T.............R.............Sec.............

Township.............

(Locate station on map and describe on reverse of this form)

Station No.	Date	Time A.M.–P.M.	Temp. Air °F.	Sky	Wind		Preceding Weather	Water Color	Secchi Disk Ft.
					Dir.	Vel.			

Depth Ft.	Temperature		Bottle No.	Oxygen			Carbon Dioxide ppm		PH
	Ther.	Water		c.c. Thio.	Factor	O₂ppm	CO₂	ph-th	MO

Station No.	Date	Time A.M.–P.M.	Temp. Air °F.	Sky	Wind		Preceding Weather	Water Color	Secchi Disk Ft.
					Dir.	Vel.			

Depth Ft.	Temperature		Bottle No.	Oxygen			Carbon Dioxide ppm		PH
	Ther.	Water		c.c. Thio.	Factor	O₂ppm	CO₂	ph-th	MO

Enter other Analyses or Remarks on Reverse Side

Form 5752   3-48   4M

....
Analyzer

Fig. 173. Water analysis record.

356

LAKE AND STREAM SURVEY

INSTITUTE FOR FISHERIES RESEARCH
DIVISION OF FISHERIES
MICHIGAN DEPARTMENT OF CONSERVATION
COOPERATING WITH THE
UNIVERSITY OF MICHIGAN

Bottom Food Summary

County ....
Lake or stream ....
Type of Dredge ....

T .... R .... Sec ....
Township ....
Investigator ....

Station Number											
Date											
Depth: Feet											
Area of bottom sampled											
Type of bottom											
Vegetation											
Vol. of sample c.c.											
ORGANISMS in sample											
Turbellaria											
Nematoda											
Oligochaeta											
Hirudinea											
Gastropoda											
Pelecypoda											
Amphipoda											
Hydracarina											
Ephemeroptera											
Anisoptera											
Zygoptera											
Neuroptera											
Hemiptera											
Coleoptera											
Trichoptera											
Chaoborus											
Chironomidae											
Other Diptera											
Total numbers											

(Continued over)

Fig. 174. Bottom food record.

Station Number															
Date															
Depth: Feet															
Area of bottom sampled															
Type of bottom															
Vegetation															
Vol. of sample c.c.															
ORGANISMS in sample															
Turbellaria															
Nematoda															
Oligochaeta															
Hirudinea															
Gastropoda															
Pelecypoda															
Amphipoda															
Hydracarina															
Ephemeroptera															
Anisoptera															
Zygoptera															
Neuroptera															
Hemiptera															
Coleoptera															
Trichoptera															
Chaoborus															
Chironomidae															
Other Diptera															
Total numbers															

Fig. 174. Bottom food record (continued).

INSTITUTE FOR FISHERIES RESEARCH

DIVISION OF FISHERIES

MICHIGAN DEPARTMENT OF CONSERVATION

COOPERATING WITH THE

UNIVERSITY OF MICHIGAN

PLANKTON RECORD

Lake Survey

County:

Lake:

T................... R............... Sec.................

Type of net:

Diameter at mouth:

Station No.										
Date										
Time										
Weather										
Wind—Velocity										
Wind—Direction										
Length of Haul										
Limits of Haul										
Horizontal? Vertical?										
Depth at Station										
Vol. of Sample										
Vol. cubic meter										
Dominant organism										

Investigator...................................

Form 5153 6-38 1M

Fig. 175. Plankton record.

LAKE AND STREAM SURVEY

AQUATIC VEGETATION ANALYSIS RECORD

INSTITUTE FOR FISHERIES RESEARCH
DIVISION OF FISHERIES
MICHIGAN DEPARTMENT OF CONSERVATION
COOPERATING WITH THE
UNIVERSITY OF MICHIGAN

County:

Collector:

Lake or stream:

Date:

T.......... R.......... Sec...........

AQUATIC SEED PLANTS	Coll. No.	Sta. & Abundance	Depth	Remarks	AQUATIC SEED PLANTS	Coll. No.	Sta. & Abundance	Depth	Remarks
Anacharis canadensis					Lemna trisulca				
					L. minor				
Bidens Beckii									
Brasenia Schreberi					Myriophyllum				
					Naias flexilis				
Callitriche					Nymphaea odorata				
Carex					Nuphar advenum				
					Peltandra virginica				
					Polygonum amphibium				
Ceratophyllum demersum					Pontederia cordata				
Decodon verticillatus					Potamogeton amplifolius				
Dulichium arundinaceum					P. angustifolius				
					P. epihydrus				
					P. filiformis				
Eleocharis					P. foliosus				
Equisetum					P. Friesii				
Eriocaulon septangulare					P. gramineus				
					P. natans				
Heteranthera dubia					P. nodosus				
Hippuris vulgaris					P. pectinatus				
					P. perfoliatus				
Isoetes					P. praelongus				
Juncus					P. pusillus				
					P. zosteriformis				

Form 5295 3-49—1000

AQUATIC SEED PLANTS	Coll. No.	Sta. & Abundance	Depth	Remarks
Ranunculus				
R.				
Rorippa				
Sagittaria				
Scirpus acutus				
S. americanus				
S. subterminalis				
S. validus				
S.				
Sparganium				
Spirodela polyrhiza				
Typha latifolia				
Utricularia purpurea				
U. vulgaris var. amer.				
Vallisneria spiralis				

Note: Under remarks enter fl = flowering stage: fr = fruiting stage: B = winter bud stage: C = covered with marl. Abundance: S = sparse; M = medium; D = dense.

AQUATIC SEED PLANTS	Coll. No.	Sta. & Abundance	Depth	Remarks
MOSSES				
Calliergon				
Campylium				
Drepanocladus				
Fontinalis				
Hygroamblystegium				
Leptodictyum riparium				
Ricria fluitans				
Scorpidium scorpioides				
Sphagnum				
ALGAE				
Chara				
C.				
Nitella				

Seed plants identified by_____
Mosses identified by_____
Algae identified by_____

Fig. 176. Aquatic vegetation analysis record.

FISH MORTALITY

LAKE AND STREAM SURVEY

INSTITUTE FOR FISHERIES RESEARCH
DIVISION OF FISHERIES
MICHIGAN DEPARTMENT OF CONSERVATION
COOPERATING WITH THE
UNIVERSITY OF MICHIGAN

Township .... T .... R .... Sec. ....

County: ....

Lake or stream: ....

Probable extent of mortality ....

Mortality reported ☐ or observed ☐ (check one) by ....

Address .... date ....

Cause of mortality determined by .... date ....

as follows: ....

For correspondence see "Mortality" file, letter dated .... from ....

to .... or refer to I. F. R. Report No. .... or Memo. No. ....

Character and date of mortality, or excerpts from correspondence: ....

....

....

....

....

....

....

....

....

....

....

....

....

....

....

....

....

....

Form completed by .... Date ....

Form 2760 7-9-45 2M

FISH LIST ON REVERSE SIDE

LIST OF FISH IN MORTALITY (IF FIELD CHECK MADE BY INSTITUTE STAFF)

SPECIES	Total number (if counts made), or relative abundance (if estimated)	Total length in inches	
		Range	Average
Largemouth bass			
Bluegill			
Perch			
Northern pike			
Bullhead			
Black crappie			
Pumpkinseed			

Fig. 177. Fish mortality record.

LAKE SURVEY

INSTITUTE FOR FISHERIES RESEARCH
DIVISION OF FISHERIES
MICHIGAN DEPARTMENT OF CONSERVATION
COOPERATING WITH THE
UNIVERSITY OF MICHIGAN

FISH COLLECTION

County: _____ T_____ R_____ S_____

Lake: _____ Township _____

Point of examination _____

Gear used—kind _____ Length _____ Mesh _____

Area covered _____

Immediate shore _____

Temperature—Air _____ Water: surface _____ bottom _____

Weather (present and preceding) _____

Water (color, siltiness, etc.) _____

Depth of collection _____

Bottom _____

Cover _____

Vegetation _____

Natural food _____

Remarks _____

_____

Date _____ Time _____ Field No. _____

Collector _____

(Fish list on reverse)

LIST OF FISH CAUGHT (For data see reverse)

No.	GAME FISHES	Size range	Remarks	No.	OBNOXIOUS FISHES	Size range	Remarks
	Brook trout				Spotted gar		
	Brown trout				Longnose gar		
	Rainbow trout				Bowfin		
	Lake trout				Carp		
	Mud pickerel						
	Northern pike				FORAGE FISHES		
	Muskellunge				Pearl dace		
	White bass				Finescale dace		
	Yellow perch				N. redbelly dace		
	Sauger				Blacknose shiner		
	Yellow pikeperch				Blackchin shiner		
	Smallmouth bass				Mimic shiner		
	Largemouth bass				Sand shiner		
	Warmouth bass				Spottail shiner		
	Green sunfish				Common shiner		
	Bluegill				Golden shiner		
	Longear sunfish				Bluntnose minnow		
	Pumpkinseed				Fathead minnow		
	Rock bass				Tadpole madtom		
	Black crappie				Mudminnow		
	Cisco				Banded killifish		
					Blackstripe topminnow		
	COARSE FISHES				Logperch		
	White sucker				Johnny darter		
	Lake chubsucker				Iowa darter		
	Redhorse (M.				Least darter		
	Black bullhead				Brook silverside		
	Brown bullhead				N. muddler (C. b. bairdii)		
	Yellow bullhead				Brook stickleback		

Fish identifications by

(Fish names follow Hubbs and Lagler, 1941)

Fig. 178. Fish collection record for lake, pond, and impoundment surveys.

LAKE SURVEY

INSTITUTE FOR FISHERIES RESEARCH

DIVISION OF FISHERIES
MICHIGAN DEPARTMENT OF CONSERVATION
COOPERATING WITH THE
UNIVERSITY OF MICHIGAN

FISH COLLECTION SUMMARY

County:

Lake:

T.............. R.............. Sec..............

Township..............

STATION	1	2	3	4	5	6	7	8
LOCATION DESCRIPTION								
TYPE OF GEAR								
Depth—Ft.								
Temp. water °F.								
REMARKS								
DATE								
TIME								
COLLECTOR								

FISH LIST ON REVERSE

LIST OF FISH CAUGHT (For data see reverse)

No.	GAME FISHES	Size Range in.	Young of Year	No. Scale Samples	Order of Abund.	Station	Disposal
	Brook trout						
	Brown trout						
	Rainbow trout						
	Lake trout						
	Mud pickerel						
	Northern pike						
	Muskellunge						
	White bass						
	Yellow perch						
	Sauger						
	Yellow pikeperch						
	Smallmouth bass						
	Largemouth bass						
	Warmouth bass						
	Green sunfish						
	Bluegill						
	Longear sunfish						
	Pumpkinseed						
	Rock bass						
	Black crappie						
	Cisco						
	COARSE FISHES						
	White sucker						
	Lake chubsucker						
	Redhorse (M.)						
	Black bullhead						
	Brown bullhead						
	Yellow bullhead						

No.	OBNOXIOUS FISHES	Size Range in.	Young of Year	Order of Abund.	Station	Disposal
	Spotted gar					
	Longnose gar					
	Bowfin					
	Carp					
	FORAGE FISHES					
	Pearl dace					
	Finescale dace					
	N. redbelly dace					
	Blacknose shiner					
	Blackchin shiner					
	Mimic shiner					
	Sand shiner					
	Spottail shiner					
	Common shiner					
	Golden shiner					
	Bluntnose minnow					
	Fathead minnow					
	Tadpole madtom					
	Mudminnow					
	Banded killifish					
	Blackstripe topminnow					
	Logperch					
	Johnny darter					
	Iowa darter					
	Least darter					
	Brook silverside					
	Northern muddler					
	Brook stickleback					

Fish identifications by.............

(Fish names follow Hubbs and Lagler, 1941)

"REPORTED" After all species reported but not actually seen.
Disposal: D—Discarded, P—Preserved, P.P.—Part preserved.

Fig. 179. Summary of fish collection records.

LAKE SURVEY

INSTITUTE FOR FISHERIES RESEARCH

DIVISION OF FISHERIES

MICHIGAN DEPARTMENT OF CONSERVATION

COOPERATING WITH THE

UNIVERSITY OF MICHIGAN

LAKE SUMMARY

County ....

Lake ....

T............. R............. Sec.............

Township ....

1. Other names of lake

2. Accessibility (how reached, condition of roads)

3. Outlet (immediate and main drainage)

    Permanency   Size

4. Dam in outlet   Distance from lake   Height

    Effect on level   Owner   Use

    Effect on fish movements

5. Inlets (name, size)   Drainage area

6. Pollution (kind, source, severity)

7. Immediate shore (topography, soil, cover)

8. Surrounding country (topography, soil, cover)

9. Use (private, public, semi-private)

10. Approximate number Cottages   Hotels   Resorts   Boat Liveries

11. Intensity of fishing (heavy, medium, light)   Summer   Winter

12. Other uses   Public fishing site

13. Area   Shore Development   Maximum depth

14. Area of Vegetation (acres)   Per cent shoal (less than 15 ft.)

15. Slope at drop-off (gradual, steep)

16. Bottom soil: Shoal   Deep water

17. Color   Secchi disk (range)

18. Temperature (range):   Surface   Bottom

19. Thermocline   Location   Temperature (range)

20. Dissolved oxygen (range):   Above thermocline (in upper 20 feet if absent)   Below thermocline (below 20 feet if absent)

    In Thermocline

    Depth range where temperature is below 70° F. and O_2 above 4 ppm.

21. pH (range) CO_2 Methyl Orange Alk. (range)

22. Cover (kind, abundance)

23. Vegetation (type, abundance)

24. Food (abundance, dominant organisms): Plankton

Bottom: Shoal   Depths

Vegetation

25. Spawning grounds (summarize observations and reports)

26. Predators (kind and abundance)

27. Fish parasites

Severe infestations

Heavy fish losses observed or reported

28. Fishing: general reputation

History   Reported by

29. Previous 4 year stocking (total numbers of each species)

	Abundance	Dominant size in catch	Growth rate
30. Game fish			
Forage fish			
Coarse fish			
Obnoxious fish			

Continuations (use item numbers):

Prepared by   Date of survey

Fig. 180. Summary of records on lake, pond, and impoundment surveys.

Fig. 181. Record of management recommendations, practices, and results.

STREAM SURVEY

INSTITUTE FOR FISHERIES RESEARCH
DIVISION OF FISHERIES
MICHIGAN DEPARTMENT OF CONSERVATION
COOPERATING WITH THE
UNIVERSITY OF MICHIGAN

1. MAIN DRAINAGE   Name of Stream   Trib. to
2. STREAM SECTION: No.   From
   To   Township   T.   R.   Sec.
3. County   Length
4. Dredged   How Recent?
5. Tributaries—Name Streams and prevailing Fish

6. WATER SUPPLY   Present level
   Degree of flooding
7. POLLUTION

8. DAM—Location   Owner   Use
   Head   Effect on level   Passable for fish?
9. IMMEDIATE SHORE
10. SURROUNDING COUNTRY
11. USE OF WATER: Ownership   Recreation?
12. FISHING: Public fishing   Easily fished?
13. General reputation
14. History
15. Use as minnow stream
16. Previous stocking
17. SPECIES OF FISH: Game fish
18. Coarse fish
19. Obnoxious fish
20. Forage fish

21. SPAWNING GROUNDS
22. PREDATORS   BEAVER
23. REMARKS

Form 6014 10-42 1M

Fig. 182. Stream survey record.

24. STATION	Lower	Middle	Upper
Location			
25. AVERAGE WIDTH AND DEPTH			
26. VOLUME			
27. VELOCITY			
28. COLOR AND TURBIDITY			
29. AIR TEMPERATURE—Hr. and sky			
30. WATER TEMPERATURE			
31. POOLS—Size, Type, Frequency			
32. BOTTOM TYPES: Pools			
Riffles			
33. SHADE—COVER			
34. pH			
35. O_2 ppm.			
36. CO_2 ppm.			
37. M. O. Alkalinity			
38. AQUATIC VEGETATION			
39. Plankton			
40. FISH FOODS PER SQ. FT.			
Mayflies			
Stoneflies			
Beetles			
Caddisflies			
Midges			
Other Diptera			
Miscellaneous			
Others			
Vol. in cc. per sq. ft.			

Prepared by .... Date ....

Fig. 182. Stream survey record (continued).

STREAM SURVEY

INSTITUTE FOR FISHERIES RESEARCH

FISH COLLECTION

DIVISION OF FISHERIES

MICHIGAN DEPARTMENT OF CONSERVATION

COOPERATING WITH THE

UNIVERSITY OF MICHIGAN

County:

Lake

T .... R .... Sec ....

Township ....

Point of examination   Section No.   Description

GEAR USED—kind   Length   Mesh

Area covered

Immediate SHORE

TEMPERATURE—Air   Water

Weather (present and preceding)

WATER (Color, siltiness, etc.)

DEPTH   Current velocity

BOTTOM

COVER

VEGETATION

NATURAL FOOD

REMARKS

DATE   Time   Field No.

COLLECTOR

FISH LIST ON REVERSE

Fig. 183. Fish collection record for stream surveys.

No.	GAME FISHES	Size Range	Remarks	No.	FORAGE FISHES	Size Range	Remarks
	Brook Trout				Creek Chub		
	Brown Trout				............Chub		
	Rainbow Trout				Black-nose Dace		
	Northern pike				............Dace		
	Perch				............Dace		
	Small-Mouth Bass				Common Shiner		
	............Bass				............Shiner		
	............Sunfish				............Shiner		
	Rock Bass				Blunt-nosed Minnow		
					............Minnow		
					Mudminnow		
					Johnny Darter		
					............Darter		
					............Darter		
					............Darter		
					Muddler (bairdii)		
					Muddler (cognatus)		
					Brook stickleback		
	COARSE FISHES						
	Common Sucker						
	Hog Sucker						
	Mullet (M............)						
	OBNOXIOUS FISHES						
	Dogfish						
	Carp						

Fig. 183. Fish collection record for stream surveys (continued).

Record of fish planted   MICHIGAN DEPARTMENT OF CONSERVATION   Division of Fisheries

Name of lake or stream

County   Township   Drainage   Town   Range   Section Number

	TROUT			BLACK BASS		Wall-eye pike	Perch	Bluegills
	Lake	Brook	Rainbow	Brown	Small mouth	Large mouth			
1947									
1948									
1949									
1950									
1951									
1952									
1953									
1954									
1955									
1956									
1957									
1958									
1959									

(Record continued on reverse side)

Fig. 184. Fish planting record.

APPENDIX C

ABBREVIATIONS FOR WORDS USED IN THE NAMES OF TECHNICAL JOURNALS AND PERIODIC PUBLICATIONS[1]

General procedures for abbreviations and omissions in citing names of journals or periodicals are as follows:

1. Omit unimportant words such as articles, prepositions, and conjunctions where their omission does not alter or obscure meaning.

2. Do not abbreviate names of publications having only one word unless there is special reason for doing so.

3. Abbreviate only those words which are of common usage. If uncommon words are shortened, you may make it impossible for another worker to decipher the citation.

Practical abbreviations follow for words occurring commonly in the names of domestic publications. Plurals and singulars are essentially the same. Accepted practice in different fields has made the form of abbreviations inconsistent.

Acad., academy
Agric., agriculture, agricultural
Amer., American
Anat., anatomical, anatomy
Ann., annal, annual
App., appendix
Appl., applied
Assoc., association
Atl., Atlantic

Bd., board
Bibliog., bibliographical, bibliography
Biochem., biochemical, biochemistry
Biol., biological, biology
Bot., botanical, botany
Bull., bulletin
Bur., bureau

Canad., Canadian
Chem., chemical, chemistry
Circ., circular
Climatol., climatological, climatology

Coll., college
Com., commerce, commercial
Comm., commission, committee
Comp., comparative
Conf., conference
Cong., congress
Cons., conservation
Contr., contributions
Cult., culture, culturist

Dept., department
Dev., development
Div., division
Doc., document

Ecol., ecological, ecology
Econ., economics
Educ., education, educational
Emb., embryological, embryology
Endocrin., endocrinological, endocrinology
Eng. or engin., engine, engineering
Ent., entomological, entomology
Exp., experiment, experimental

[1]Adapted from: Crabb, E. D., 1941. Abbreviation of names of biological publications. Univ. Colo. Studies, Ser. D, 1 (3): 177-191.

Fish., fisheries, fishery
Forest., forestry

Geol., geological, geology

Helminthol., helminthology
Hematol., hematology
Hered., hereditary, heredity
Hist., historical, history
Hort., horticultural, horticulture
Hyg., hygiene

Ichthyol., ichthyological, ichthyology

Immunol., immunology
Indust., industrial, industry
Inst., institute, institution
Internat., international
Invest., investigation

Jour., journal

Lab., laboratory
Leaf., leaflet
Lett., letters

Mag., magazine
Malacol., malacological, malacology
Mgt., management
Math., mathematical, mathematics
Med., medical, medicine
Mem., memoir
Meteorol., meteorological, meteorology
Micr. or Microscop., microscopical
Misc., miscellaneous
Monog., monographs
Morph., morphological, morphology
Mus., museum
Mycol., mycological, mycology

Nation., national
Nat., natural, naturalist

Occ., occasional
Oceanog., oceanographic, oceanography

Orig., original
Ornithol., ornithological, ornithology

Pac., Pacific
Paleontol., paleontological, paleontology
Pamp., pamphlet
Pap., papers
Parasit., parasitological, parasitology
Pharm., pharmaceutical, pharmacy
Phys., physical, physics
Physiol., physiological, physiology
Polytech., polytechnic(al)
Proc., proceedings
Prof., professional
Prog., progressive
Prov., province, provincial
Psych., psychological, psychology
Publ., publication

Qual., qualitative
Quant., quantitative
Quart., quarterly

Rec., record
Rept., report
Res., research, resources
Rev., review
Roy., royal

Sci., science, scientific
Ser., series
Soc., society
St., state
Sta., station
Suppl., supplement
Surv., survey

Tech., technical, technology
Trans., transactions
Trop., tropical

Univ., university

Vet., veterinary

Zool., zoological, zoology

CLINICAL ASPECTS OF CERTAIN FISH DISEASES WITH SPECIAL REFERENCE TO THOSE ENCOUNTERED IN TROUT CULTURE[1]

EXTERNAL DISEASE	MAJOR SYMPTOMS	ETIOLOGY	THERAPY	PROPHYLAXIS
Gyro or Worm Itch	Scraping sides on bottom of pond. Loss among trout up to 3 in. long can be heavy. **Diagnosis:** Microscopic examination of skin scrapings under low power.	Gyrodactylus elegans (like Fig. 58). (Trematoda). A small worm easily seen with low power dissecting microscope. Posterior end of worm with haptor bearing small hooks on margin; 1 pair of large hooks (anchors) in center of haptor. Large hooks leave lesions through which bacteria or fungus spores may gain foothold. Give birth to precocious live young which immediately attach to fish. Unless controlled, great numbers may build up on fish causing high loss among fish up to 3 in. in length.	Formalin[2] 1:4,000 for 1 hr. Acetic acid 1:500 for 1 min.	Formalin[2] 1:4,000 for 1 hr. every 2 weeks.
Ichthy	Scraping sides on bottom of pond. White spots on skin. Gray film on skin. **Diagnosis:** Microscopic examination of white pustules under low power.	Protozoan. Ichthyophthirius multifilis. Adult on fish may be 1 mm. in diameter. Spherical or oval in shape, ciliated, moves slowly; large crescent-shaped nucleus near center of body. Young, cone-shaped and free swimming. Bores into deeper layers of epidermis of fish. Grows to adult, leaves fish, falls to bottom and forms cyst. In cyst, multiplies by	Formalin[2] 1:4,000 for 1 hr. or acetic acid 1:500 for 1 min. Treatments should be given for 3 or 4 consecutive days until imbedded forms are gone, or, hold fish in swiftly running water until no more white spots evident. Salt (NaCl) in 3% solution is also effective for treatments given daily until the imbedded organisms are gone. Aquarium fishes can be treated with quin-	Where water supply is contaminated, build sand filter to remove infective stages of parasite.

EXTERNAL DISEASE	MAJOR SYMPTOMS	ETIOLOGY	THERAPY	PROPHYLAXIS
		division; cyst breaks releasing hundreds of young which seek another fish host.	ine salts, 1:50,000 to 1:100,-000 for several days. Acriflavine 1:100,000 is also effective.	
Protozoan Itch	Grayish film on skin and fins. Loss of appetite. Debility. **Diagnosis:** Microscopic examination of mucus film.	Protozoans. *Costia necatrix* and *C. pyriformis.* Live on skin and gills of fish, destroying epithelial cells. May form resistant spores. Multiply on fish by division. Under microscope appear as small, rapidly-moving oval bodies. Poor diet may predispose for disease.	Formalin² 1:4,000 for 1 hr. or acetic acid 1:500 for 1 min., and change of diet.	Formalin² 1:6,000 for 1 hr. in weekly treatments. Feeding well balanced diet.
Blue Slime	Bluish film on skin and fins. **Diagnosis:** Coloration of mucus film is bluish; *Costia* not predominating as above.	In trout, can be caused by absence of biotin in diet.	Addition of biotin-rich yeasts to the diet.	Feeding well-balanced diet, including, of course, biotin
Copepod Infestations ("Lice")	Observed on gills and body of fish. Behavior of infested fish same as clean fish. **Diagnosis:** Macro-examination of gills. Many copepods parasitize fish; as example is given *Salmincola edwardsii,* on brook trout. *Adult* attached to gills of brook trout, yellowish white color, several mm. long, attached to gills by bulb-shaped enlargement of modified mouth parts buried in gill	tissue; pair of long egg sacs posteriorly. Young hatch, swim freely for about 2 days and die unless a brook trout is found. *Young* attach to gills of brook trout, become sexually mature in about 3 weeks and mate. After mating, males leave fish and die. *Females* remain on fish for several weeks, usually producing 2 batches of eggs, then die. Life cycle usually requires about 10 weeks. Can do great	Until recently, these parasites, once attached to fish, could not be removed by treatment. Promising results have been obtained with gamma isomer of hexa-chlorocyclo-hexane (trade names: Gammexane, Lindane, etc.); copepods yield to 0.1:1,000,000 in pond water. Caution required because of toxicity to fish and fish food organisms.	Where water supply is contaminated, build sand filter and eliminate all parasitized fish, or treat water daily for 3 months with strong salt (NaCl) solution. Where water supply is clean, treat as above but sand filter is not necessary. Daily treatment of water with chlorine in amounts sub-lethal to fish may have merit, but not proven.

EXTERNAL DISEASE	MAJOR SYMPTOMS	ETIOLOGY	THERAPY	PROPHYLAXIS
		harm to young fish in hatcheries by sucking blood and damaging tissues.		
Gill Disease	Loss of appetite and sluggishness. Gills swollen, congested in early stages. Later, filaments become fused, enlarged and pale at tips. Excessive secretion of mucus. Fungus may develop. **Diagnosis:** Low power microscope shows clubbed or fused gill filaments.	Many types of gill disorder exist. Long, slender bacteria that form mat over gills have been associated with some cases of gill trouble. No bacteria are present in other cases. May sometimes be caused by irritation from minute sharp sestons or eroding chemicals. May also be caused by insufficient pantothenic acid in diet.	One-hour treatments with Pyridylmercuric Acetate (PMA) 1:500,000[2] for fry up to 2 in. long, and 1:350,000 for 3- to 6-in. have been effective in all cases of gill trouble in Michigan. PMA is toxic to rainbow trout and should be used with caution on this species. A dilution of 1:600,000 can be used on fry up to 2 in. long. Do not use PMA where it can contaminate food for fish. For example, do not treat fish in upper pond of a series and feed fish in lower pond at same time. Wait until all PMA has been dispersed. "Roccal," a quaternary ammonia	PMA[2] 1:500,000 for 1 hr. once each week for brook and brown trouts. Use with caution on other species. "Roccal" (10% solution), 1:50,000 used as 1 hour treatment weekly gives good prophylaxis. Not toxic to rainbow trout but margin of safety to trout narrower than PMA. Efficiency of quaternary ammonia disinfectants is lowered by hard water. disinfectant, effective when 10% stock solution supplied is used 1:50,000 in 1 hour treatment repeated for 3 days. Care required; see adjacent statement on prophylaxis.
Fungus	Tufts of gray filaments on surface of body. **Diagnosis:** Easily observed by unaided eye.	*Saprolegnia parasitica* and *S. invaderis* are principal species involved. May develop on any part of fish where lesions permit entrance of spores. General debility of fish increases susceptibility. Small root-like filaments penetrate the skin, may invade muscle tissue causing necrosis. If necrotic areas progress, eventual	Malachite green; Oxalate crystals, zinc free. 1:10,000 for 2 min. for trout, and 2 to 4 sec. for minnows. May also be used as pond treatment for 1 hr. in much diluted concentration. One pound is necessary for a pond 200 ft. long, 10 ft. wide and water depth of 15 in. Copper sulphate 1:2,000 for	One pond treatment per week with malachite green and formalin (1:4,000). Formalin will control gyrodactylid worms which provide lesions for fungus spores. For eggs: Treat daily with malachite green. Make stock solution using 2 grams malachite green to 1 gal. of water. Pour 2 oz. of stock into

EXTERNAL DISEASE	MAJOR SYMPTOMS	ETIOLOGY	THERAPY	PROPHYLAXIS
		death of the fish may result. Reproduction is either by biciliate zoospores or by resting cells (chlamydospores). Fungus may occur on fish eggs and will spread from one egg to another causing them to die in large numbers. Proper precautions, such as picking dead eggs from the trays daily, or daily prophylaxis, will keep fungus at a minimum.	about 2 min., depending upon effect on fish.	the head of hatching trough and 1 oz. midway down the trough, permitting the normal flow of water to continue. Depending upon the flow of water and size of trough, it may be necessary to vary slightly the amount of chemicals to suit the conditions. Accordingly, a basic treatment using several dilutions should be tried on a few eggs first.
Fin Rot or Tail Rot	Disintegration of tissue between fin rays and, later, of fin rays themselves. Begins as distinct white line at outer border of fin and progresses towards base. Fin rot is also one of the symptoms of furunculosis or ulcer disease.	**Diagnosis:** Appearance as described. High power microscope shows large numbers of rod-shaped bacteria. Believed to be caused by a bacterium. Overcrowding fish in pond and *Gyrodactylus* may cause lesions to permit entrance of bacteria which invade tissues. Advanced cases difficult to cure because bacteria become deeply imbedded in tissue and out of reach of chemicals.	Copper sulphate, 1:2,000, for 1 to 2 min. Several treatments at intervals of 24 hrs. usually necessary to check spread of disease. Also recommended: formalin 1:4,000 followed by a flush treatment of malachite green as under Fungus, above.	Copper sulphate 1:2,000, for 1 to 2 min. once each week.
Whirling Disease or Pinhead Condition (Octomitiasis)	Affects trout up to 3 in. long. Loss of appetite; slim body making head look large ("pinhead" condition); lassitude. Fish may dart and whirl in corkscrew pattern. Outbreaks often spotty. Note: whirling may also indicate infectious pancreatic necrosis.	Protozoan. *Octomitus salmonis* (Fig. 57). Minute, pearshaped, rapidly moving flagellate. Intestine, usually free but sometimes in intestinal lining in very small fingerlings. **Diagnosis:** Abundance of *Octomitus* in whitish intestinal mucus.	Carbarsone, 1 gram per pound of food in all food for 4 consecutive days. Calomel, same proportions as above. Carbarsone is preferred in Michigan because it is less toxic than calomel.	Treatment with carbarsone for 4 consecutive days immediately before fish are transferred, and for 4 consecutive days one week after transfer.

INTERNAL DISEASE	MAJOR SYMPTOMS	ETIOLOGY	THERAPY	PROPHYLAXIS
Furunculosis	Blisters and ulcers extending deep into tissue. Sudden high mortality with high water temperatures. Hemorrhages on swim bladder, large intestine and peritoneum. **Diagnosis:** Presence of one or more of above symptoms. Confirmation made on culture media. Material for culture taken from kidney.	*Bacterium salmonicida.* Small, rod-shaped bacterium. May enter blood stream of fish through intestinal tract or lesions in skin. Causes generalized septicemia when bacteria collect in capillaries; destroys walls of blood vessels causing hemorrhage. Bacteria show predilection for spleen, liver, and kidneys, and can destroy these organs.	As soon as symptoms and mortalities occur, start treatment with sulfonamides and make every effort to have diagnosis confirmed by bacteriological analysis. Best results obtained with sulfamerazine, sulfamethazine, and a mixture of two parts of sulfamerazine with one part of sulfaguanidine (latter recommended for brown trout). Dosage is 8 to 12 grams of drug to 100 pounds of fish per day. Treat for 2 to 3 days after time when mortalities return to low, normal rate. If furunculosis is not confirmed bacteriologically and deaths do not decline, discontinue treatment as hopeless. If the strain of trout (in brook trout especially) is very susceptible to furunculosis or bacteria become drug resistant, there is little hope in treatment. In such cases, chloramphenicol or terramycin at rate of 2.5 to 3.0 grams of *pure antibiotic activity* in food per 100 pounds of fish daily may be effective.	The best prophylaxes are to prevent entrance of the pathogen into the hatchery and to raise disease-resistant strains of fish. At a site of infection it may be best to eliminate the source of infection and sacrifice the infected fish. Prolonged use of drugs may cause appearance of drug-resistant strains of the pathogen.

INTERNAL DISEASE	MAJOR SYMPTOMS	ETIOLOGY	THERAPY	PROPHYLAXIS
Kidney Disease	Swelling of kidney with presence of grey pustules followed by necrosis (in brook trout and some salmons); kidney pustules may be absent and lesions present on other organs or in the form of skin blisters (brown and rainbow trouts).	Small gram positive diplobacilli in large numbers in pustules, lesions, or blisters; systematic position of pathogen unknown.	In brook trout and salmon, sulfonamides arrest progress of disease with sulfamerazine, sulfisoxazole (Gantrisin R), and sulfadiazine best. Dosage same as for furunculosis. None of the antibiotics tested are effective.	If a seasonal affliction, treat with sulfonamides just before and during critical period. Continuous use of sulfas may cause appearance of drug-resistant strain of pathogen. Best is to free water supply of carriers and to observe strict sanitary routines.
Infectious Pancreatic Necrosis. (Until recently "Acute Catarrhal Enteritis")	Heavy losses among fingerling brook trout soon after they begin to take food. Violent whirling and corkscrewing followed by rapid breathing and sinking. Stomach and anterior intestine distended, with colorless, opaque mucus indicating stoppage of bile flow. This is chief differential from Octomitiasis, which has yellow fluid in intestine. Octomitus may also be present in necrosis cases.	Possible virus, highly infectious with fingerling trout losses to 80%.	Unknown	Strict sanitation may help in localizing the disease.
Mycosis-like Granuloma	Hard, white, diffused tumor about pyloric caeca. Other foci widespread. Known from fingerling brook trout in the East.	Unknown. Unidentified fungus-like organism may be implicated. Its cells are in disease foci. Pathological condition has accompanied furunculosis and kidney disease.	Unknown	Unknown

[1]This summary was originally prepared for the first edition of this book by Dr. Leonard N. Allison, Institute for Fisheries Research, Michigan Department of Conservation. For the current edition, additions and emendations were provided by Dr. S. F. Snieszko, Microbiological Laboratory, U. S. Fish and Wildlife Service.

[2]These solutions are colorless. Small amount of malachite green, oxalate crystals, zinc free, added to treatment aids in observing distribution of chemical in pond.

APPENDIX E. CONVERSION TABLES

Temperatures—Centigrade to Fahrenheit*
(to nearest 0.1° F.)

°C	.0	.1	.2	.3	.4	.5	.6	.7	.8	.9
0.	32.0	32.2	32.4	32.5	32.7	32.9	33.1	33.3	33.4	33.6
1.	33.8	34.0	34.2	34.3	34.5	34.7	34.9	35.1	35.2	35.4
2.	35.6	35.8	36.0	36.1	36.3	36.5	36.7	36.9	37.0	37.2
3.	37.4	37.6	37.8	37.9	38.1	38.3	38.5	38.7	38.8	39.0
4.	39.2	39.4	39.6	39.7	39.9	40.1	40.3	40.5	40.6	40.8
5.	41.0	41.2	41.4	41.5	41.7	41.9	42.1	42.3	42.4	42.6
6.	42.8	43.0	43.2	43.3	43.5	43.7	43.9	44.1	44.2	44.4
7.	44.6	44.8	45.0	45.1	45.3	45.5	45.7	45.9	46.0	46.2
8.	46.4	46.6	46.8	46.9	47.1	47.3	47.5	47.7	47.8	48.0
9.	48.2	48.4	48.6	48.7	48.9	49.1	49.3	49.5	49.6	49.8
10.	50.0	50.2	50.4	50.5	50.7	50.9	51.1	51.3	51.4	51.6
11.	51.8	52.0	52.2	52.3	52.5	52.7	52.9	53.1	53.2	53.4
12.	53.6	53.8	54.0	54.1	54.3	54.5	54.7	54.9	55.0	55.2
13.	55.4	55.6	55.8	55.9	56.1	56.3	56.5	56.7	56.8	57.0
14.	57.2	57.4	57.6	57.7	57.9	58.1	58.3	58.5	58.6	58.8
15.	59.0	59.2	59.4	59.5	59.7	59.9	60.1	60.3	60.4	60.6
16.	60.8	61.0	61.2	61.3	61.5	61.7	61.9	62.1	62.2	62.4
17.	62.6	62.8	63.0	63.1	63.3	63.5	63.7	63.9	64.0	64.2
18.	64.4	64.6	64.8	64.9	65.1	65.3	65.5	65.7	65.8	66.0
19.	66.2	66.4	66.6	66.7	66.9	67.1	67.3	67.5	67.6	67.8
20.	68.0	68.2	68.4	68.5	68.7	68.9	69.1	69.3	69.4	69.6
21.	69.8	70.0	70.2	70.3	70.5	70.7	70.9	71.1	71.2	71.4
22.	71.6	71.8	72.0	72.1	72.3	72.5	72.7	72.9	73.0	73.2
23.	73.4	73.6	73.8	73.9	74.1	74.3	74.5	74.7	74.8	75.0
24.	75.2	75.4	75.6	75.7	75.9	76.1	76.3	76.5	76.6	76.8
25.	77.0	77.2	77.4	77.5	77.7	77.9	78.1	78.3	78.4	78.6
26.	78.8	79.0	79.2	79.3	79.5	79.7	79.9	80.1	80.2	80.4
27.	80.6	80.8	81.0	81.1	81.3	81.5	81.7	81.9	82.0	82.2
28.	82.4	82.6	82.8	82.9	83.1	83.3	83.5	83.7	83.8	84.0
29.	84.2	84.4	84.6	84.7	84.9	85.1	85.3	85.5	85.6	85.8
30.	86.0	86.2	86.4	86.5	86.7	86.9	87.1	87.3	87.4	87.6
31.	87.8	88.0	88.2	88.3	88.5	88.7	88.9	89.1	89.2	89.4
32.	89.6	89.8	90.0	90.1	90.3	90.5	90.7	90.9	91.0	91.2
33.	91.4	91.6	91.8	91.9	92.1	92.3	92.5	92.7	92.8	93.0
34.	93.2	93.4	93.6	93.7	93.9	94.1	94.3	94.5	94.6	94.8
35.	95.0	95.2	95.4	95.5	95.7	95.9	96.1	96.3	96.4	96.6
36.	96.8	97.0	97.2	97.3	97.5	97.7	97.9	98.1	98.2	98.4
37.	98.6	98.8	99.0	99.1	99.3	99.5	99.7	99.9	100.0	100.2
38.	100.4	100.6	100.8	100.9	101.1	101.3	101.5	101.7	101.8	102.0
39.	102.2	102.4	102.6	102.7	102.9	103.1	103.3	103.5	103.6	103.8
40.	104.0	104.2	104.4	104.5	104.7	104.9	105.1	105.3	105.4	105.6

Tables bearing an asterisk are reproduced through the courtesy of the Institute for Fisheries Research, Michigan Department of Conservation.

Inches (nearest 0.1) to Millimeters (by groups)*

Factor = 0.0393700

In.	.0	.1	.2	.3	.4	.5	.6	.7	.8	.9
0.	0-1	2-3	4-6	7-8	9-11	12-13	14-16	17-19	20-21	22-24
1.	25-26	27-29	30-31	32-34	35-36	37-39	40-41	42-44	45-46	47-49
2.	50-52	53-54	55-57	58-59	60-62	63-64	65-67	68-69	70-72	73-74
3.	75-77	78-80	81-82	83-85	86-87	88-90	91-92	93-95	96-97	98-100
4.	101-102	103-105	106-107	108-110	111-113	114-115	116-118	119-120	121-123	124-125
5.	126-128	129-130	131-133	134-135	136-138	139-140	141-143	144-146	147-148	149-151
6.	152-153	154-156	157-158	159-161	162-163	164-166	167-168	169-171	172-173	174-176
7.	177-179	180-181	182-184	185-186	187-189	190-191	192-194	195-196	197-199	200-201
8.	202-204	205-207	208-209	210-212	213-214	215-217	218-219	220-222	223-224	225-227
9.	228-229	230-232	233-234	235-237	238-240	241-242	243-245	246-247	248-250	251-252
10.	253-255	256-257	258-260	261-262	263-265	266-267	268-270	271-273	274-275	276-278
11.	279-280	281-283	284-285	286-288	289-290	291-293	294-295	296-298	299-300	301-303
12.	304-306	307-308	309-311	312-313	314-316	317-318	319-321	322-323	324-326	327-328
13.	329-331	332-334	335-336	337-339	340-341	342-344	345-346	347-349	350-351	352-354
14.	355-356	357-359	360-361	362-364	365-367	368-369	370-372	373-374	375-377	378-379
15.	380-382	383-384	385-387	388-389	390-392	393-394	395-397	398-400	401-402	403-405
16.	406-407	408-410	411-412	413-415	416-417	418-420	421-422	423-425	426-427	428-430
17.	431-433	434-435	436-438	439-440	441-443	444-445	446-448	449-450	451-453	454-455
18.	456-458	459-461	462-463	464-466	467-468	469-471	472-473	474-476	477-478	479-481
19.	482-483	484-486	487-488	489-491	492-494	495-496	497-499	500-501	502-504	505-506
20.	507-509	510-511	512-514	515-516	517-519	520-521	522-524	525-527	528-529	530-532
21.	533-534	535-537	538-539	540-542	543-544	545-547	548-549	550-552	553-554	555-557
22.	558-560	561-562	563-565	566-567	568-570	571-572	573-575	576-577	578-580	581-582
23.	583-585	586-588	589-590	591-593	594-595	596-598	599-600	601-603	604-605	606-608
24.	609-610	611-613	614-615	616-618	619-621	622-623	624-626	627-628	629-631	632-633
25.	634-636	637-638	639-641	642-643	644-646	647-648	649-651	652-654	655-656	657-659
26.	660-661	662-664	665-666	667-669	670-671	672-674	675-676	677-679	680-681	682-684
27.	685-687	688-689	690-692	693-694	695-697	698-699	700-702	703-704	705-707	708-709
28.	710-712	713-715	716-717	718-720	721-722	723-725	726-727	728-730	731-732	733-735
29.	736-737	738-740	741-742	743-745	746-748	749-750	751-753	754-755	756-758	759-760
30.	761-763	764-765	766-768	769-770	771-773	774-775	776-778	779-781	782-783	784-786

Eighths of an Inch to Millimeters*

1/8-inches	mm.	1/8-inches	mm.	1/8-inches	mm.	1/8-inches	mm.	1/8-inches	mm.
0.125	3.18	6.125	155.58	12.125	307.98	18.125	460.38	24.125	612.8
0.250	6.35	6.250	158.75	12.250	311.15	18.250	463.55	24.250	616.0
0.375	9.53	6.375	161.93	12.375	314.33	18.375	466.73	24.375	619.1
0.500	12.70	6.500	165.10	12.500	317.50	18.500	469.90	24.500	622.3
0.625	15.88	6.625	168.28	12.625	320.68	18.625	473.08	24.625	625.5
0.750	19.05	6.750	171.45	12.750	323.85	18.750	476.25	24.750	628.7
0.875	22.23	6.875	174.63	12.875	327.03	18.875	479.43	24.875	631.8
1.000	25.40	7.000	177.80	13.000	330.20	19.000	482.60	25.000	633.4
1.125	28.58	7.125	180.98	13.125	333.38	19.125	485.78	25.125	638.2
1.250	31.75	7.250	184.15	13.250	336.55	19.250	488.95	25.250	641.4
1.375	34.93	7.375	187.33	13.375	339.73	19.375	492.13	25.375	644.5
1.500	38.10	7.500	190.50	13.500	342.90	19.500	495.30	25.500	647.7
1.625	41.28	7.625	193.68	13.625	346.08	19.625	498.48	25.625	650.9
1.750	44.45	7.750	196.85	13.750	349.25	19.750	501.65	25.750	654.1
1.875	47.63	7.875	200.03	13.875	352.43	19.875	504.83	25.875	657.2
2.000	50.80	8.000	203.20	14.000	355.60	20.000	508.00	26.000	660.4
2.125	53.98	8.125	206.38	14.125	358.78	20.125	511.18	26.125	663.6
2.250	57.15	8.250	209.55	14.250	361.95	20.250	514.35	26.250	666.8
2.375	60.33	8.375	212.73	14.375	365.13	20.375	517.53	26.375	669.9
2.500	63.50	8.500	215.90	14.500	368.30	20.500	520.70	26.500	673.1
2.625	66.68	8.625	219.08	14.625	371.48	20.625	523.88	26.625	676.3
2.750	69.85	8.750	222.25	14.750	374.65	20.750	527.05	26.750	679.5
2.875	73.03	8.875	226.43	14.875	377.83	20.875	530.23	26.875	682.6
3.000	76.20	9.000	228.60	15.000	381.00	21.000	533.40	27.000	685.8
3.125	79.38	9.125	231.78	15.125	384.18	21.125	536.58	27.125	689.0
3.250	82.55	9.250	234.95	15.250	387.35	21.250	539.75	27.250	692.2
3.375	85.73	9.375	238.13	15.375	390.53	21.375	542.93	27.375	695.3
3.500	88.90	9.500	241.30	15.500	393.70	21.500	546.10	27.500	698.5
3.625	92.08	9.625	244.48	15.625	396.88	21.625	549.28	27.625	701.7
3.750	95.25	9.750	247.65	15.750	400.05	21.750	552.45	27.750	704.9
3.875	98.43	9.875	250.83	15.875	403.23	21.875	555.63	27.875	708.0
4.000	101.60	10.000	254.00	16.000	406.40	22.000	558.80	28.000	711.2
4.125	104.78	10.125	257.18	16.125	409.58	22.125	561.98	28.125	714.4
4.250	107.95	10.250	260.35	16.250	412.75	22.250	565.15	28.250	717.6
4.375	111.13	10.375	263.53	16.375	415.93	22.375	568.33	28.375	720.7
4.500	114.30	10.500	266.70	16.500	419.10	22.500	571.50	28.500	723.9
4.625	117.48	10.625	269.88	16.625	422.28	22.625	574.68	28.625	727.1
4.750	120.65	10.750	273.05	16.750	425.45	22.750	577.85	28.750	730.3
4.875	123.83	10.875	276.23	16.875	428.63	22.875	581.03	28.875	733.4
5.000	127.00	11.000	279.40	17.000	431.80	23.000	584.20	29.000	736.6
5.125	130.18	11.125	282.58	17.125	434.98	23.125	587.38	29.125	739.8
5.250	133.35	11.250	285.75	17.250	438.15	23.250	590.55	29.250	743.0
5.375	136.53	11.375	288.93	17.375	441.33	23.375	593.73	29.375	746.1
5.500	139.70	11.500	292.10	17.500	444.50	23.500	596.90	29.500	749.3
5.625	142.88	11.625	295.23	17.625	447.68	23.625	600.08	29.625	752.5
5.750	146.05	11.750	298.45	17.750	450.85	23.750	603.25	29.750	755.7
5.875	149.23	11.875	301.63	17.875	454.03	23.875	606.43	29.875	758.8
6.000	152.40	12.000	304.80	18.000	457.20	24.000	609.60	30.000	762.0

Decimal Equivalents of Fractions Expressed in Sixteenths
useful for converting sixteenths of inches or ounces into decimal fractions.

Fraction	Decimal Equiv.	Fraction	Decimal Equiv.	Fraction	Decimal Equiv.	Fraction	Decimal Equiv.	Fraction	Decimal Equiv.
1/16	.0625	4/16	.2500	7/16	.4375	10/16	.6250	13/16	.8125
2/16	.1250	5/16	.3125	8/16	.5000	11/16	.6875	14/16	.8750
3/16	.1875	6/16	.3750	9/16	.5625	12/16	.7500	15/16	.9375

*Extended from an original table by Dr. David S. Shetter, Institute for Fisheries Research, Michigan Conservation Department.

Ounces to Grams (with range in grams for each 1/10 of an ounce
using the factor 0.03527399)

Ounces	.0	.1	.2	.3	.4	.5	.6	.7	.8	.9
0.	0-1	2-4	5-7	8-9	10-12	13-15	16-18	19-21	22-24	25-26
1.	27-29	30-32	33-35	36-38	39-41	42-43	44-46	47-49	50-52	53-55
2.	56-58	59-60	61-63	64-66	67-69	70-72	73-75	76-77	78-80	81-83
3.	84-86	87-89	90-92	93-94	95-97	98-100	101-103	104-106	107-109	110-111
4.	112-114	115-117	118-120	121-123	124-126	127-128	129-131	132-134	135-137	138-140
5.	141-143	144-145	146-148	149-151	152-154	155-157	158-160	161-163	164-165	166-168
6.	169-171	172-174	175-177	178-180	181-182	183-185	186-188	189-191	192-194	195-197
7.	198-199	200-202	203-205	206-208	209-211	212-214	215-216	217-219	220-222	223-225
8.	226-228	229-231	232-233	234-236	237-239	240-242	243-245	246-248	249-250	251-253
9.	254-256	257-259	260-262	263-265	266-267	268-270	271-273	274-276	277-279	280-282
10.	283-284	285-287	288-290	291-293	294-296	297-299	300-301	302-304	305-307	308-310
11.	311-313	314-316	317-318	319-321	322-324	325-327	328-330	331-333	334-335	336-338
12.	339-341	342-344	345-347	348-350	351-352	353-355	356-358	359-361	362-364	365-367
13.	368-369	370-372	373-375	376-378	379-381	382-384	385-386	387-389	390-392	393-395
14.	396-398	399-401	402-403	404-406	407-409	410-412	413-415	416-418	419-420	421-423
15.	424-426	427-429	430-432	433-435	436-437	438-440	441-443	444-446	447-449	450-452
16.	453-455	456-457	458-460	461-463	464-466	467-469	470-472	473-474	475-477	478-480
17.	481-483	484-486	487-489	490-491	492-494	495-497	498-500	501-503	504-506	507-508
18.	509-511	512-514	515-517	518-520	521-523	524-525	526-528	529-531	532-534	535-537
19.	538-540	541-542	543-545	546-548	549-551	552-554	555-557	558-559	560-562	563-565
20.	566-568	569-571	572-574	575-576	577-579	580-582	583-585	586-588	589-591	592-593
21.	594-596	597-599	600-602	603-605	606-608	609-610	611-613	614-616	617-619	620-622
22.	623-625	626-627	628-630	631-633	634-636	637-639	640-642	643-644	645-647	648-650
23.	651-653	654-656	657-659	660-661	662-664	665-667	668-670	671-673	674-676	677-678
24.	679-681	682-684	685-687	688-690	691-693	694-695	696-698	699-701	702-704	705-707
25.	708-710	711-712	713-715	716-718	719-721	722-724	725-727	728-729	730-732	733-735
26.	736-738	739-741	742-744	745-747	748-749	750-752	753-755	756-758	759-761	762-764
27.	765-766	767-769	770-772	773-775	776-778	779-781	782-783	784-786	787-789	790-792
28.	793-795	796-798	799-800	801-803	804-806	807-809	810-812	813-815	816-817	818-820
29.	821-823	824-826	827-829	830-832	833-834	835-837	838-840	041-843	844-846	847-849
30.	850-851	852-854	855-857	858-860	861-863	864-866	867-868	869-871	872-874	875-877
31.	878-880	881-883	884-885	886-888	889-891	892-894	895-897	898-900	901-902	903-905
32.	906-908	909-911	912-914	915-917	918-919	920-922	923-925	926-928	929-931	932-934

1 lb. = 453.5924277 grams
1 oz. = 28.349527 grams

CHECKLIST AND ECONOMIC CLASSIFICATION OF COMMON AND REPRESENTATIVE FRESHWATER FISHES OF NORTH AMERICA, NORTH OF MEXICO

Common and Scientific Names	Economic Classification					
	Sport	Commercial	Fine food	Coarse food	Forage	Other
LAMPREY FAMILY Petromyzontidae						
Sea lamprey *Petromyzon marinus* Linnaeus						X
Silver lamprey *Ichthyomyzon unicuspis* Hubbs and Trautman						X
Chestnut lamprey *Ichthyomyzon castaneus* Girard						X
Pacific lamprey *Lampetra (= Entosphenus) tridentata* (Gairdner)	X					
American brook lamprey *Lampetra (= Entosphenus) lamottei* (LeSueur)					X	
Western brook lamprey *Lampetra planeri* (Bloch)					X	
STURGEON FAMILY Acipenseridae						
White sturgeon *Acipenser transmontanus* Richardson	X					
Atlantic sturgeon *Acipenser oxyrhynchus* Mitchill	X	X				
Shortnose sturgeon *Acipenser brevirostris* LeSueur	X	X				
Green sturgeon *Acipenser acutirostris* Ayres	X					
Lake sturgeon *Acipenser fulvescens* Rafinesque	X	X	X			

Common and Scientific Names	Economic Classification					
	Sport	Commercial	Fine food	Coarse food	Forage	Other
Shovelnose sturgeon . . . . *Scaphirhynchus platorynchus* (Rafinesque)	X	X				

PADDLEFISH FAMILY
Polyodontidae

Paddlefish . . . . *Polydon spathula* (Walbaum)		X				

BOWFIN FAMILY
Amiidae

Bowfin . . . . *Amia calva* Linnaeus	X					X

GAR FAMILY
Lepisosteidae

Longnose gar . . . . *Lepisosteus osseus* (Linnaeus)						X
Spotted gar . . . . *Lepisosteus productus* Cope						X
Shortnose gar . . . . *Lepisosteus platostomus* Rafinesque						X
Alligator gar . . . . *Lepisosteus spatula* (Lacépède)						X

HERRING FAMILY
Clupeidae

Alewife . . . . *Pomolobus (= Alosa) pseudoharengus* (Wilson)					X	
Skipjack herring . . . . *Pomolobus (= Alosa) chrysochloris* Rafinesque					X	

Common and Scientific Names	Economic Classification					
	Sport	Commercial	Fine food	Coarse food	Forage	Other
American shad . . . . *Alosa sapidissima* (Wilson)		X	X			
Gizzard shad . . . . *Dorosoma cepedianum* (LeSueur)						X
SMELT FAMILY Osmeridae						
American smelt . . . . *Osmerus mordax* (Mitchill)		X	X			
GRAYLING FAMILY Thymallidae						
Arctic grayling . . . . *Thymallus arcticus* (Pallas)	X		X			
SALMON FAMILY Salmonidae						
Pink salmon . . . . *Oncorhynchus gorbuscha* (Walbaum)		X	X			
Chum salmon . . . . *Oncorhynchus keta* (Walbaum)		X	X			
Coho salmon . . . . *Oncorhynchus kisutch* (Walbaum)		X	X			
Sockeye salmon . . . . *Oncorhynchus nerka nerka* (Walbaum)		X	X			
Kokanee . . . . *Oncorhynchus nerka kennerlyi* (Suckley)		X	X			
Chinook salmon . . . . *Oncorhynchus tshawytscha* (Walbaum)		X	X			

Common and Scientific Names	Economic Classification					
	Sport	Commercial	Fine food	Coarse food	Forage	Other
Atlantic salmon (sea run form) . . . . *Salmo salar* Linnaeus	X	X	X	.	.	.
Lake Atlantic salmon . . . . *Salmo salar* Linnaeus	X	.	X	.	.	.
Cutthroat trout . . . . *Salmo clarki* Richardson	X	.	X	.	.	.
Rainbow (steelhead) trout . . . . *Salmo gairdneri* Richardson	X	.	X	.	.	.
Golden trout . . . . *Salmo aguabonita* Jordan	X	.	X	.	.	.
Brown trout . . . . *Salmo trutta* Linnaeus	X	.	X	.	.	.
Lake trout . . . . *Salvelinus namaycush* (Walbaum)	X	X	X	.	.	.
Brook trout . . . . *Salvelinus fontinalis* (Mitchill)	X	.	X	.	.	.
Sunapee trout . . . . *Salvelinus aureolus* Bean	X	.	X	.	.	.
Arctic char . . . . *Salvelinus alpinus* (Linnaeus)	X	.	X	.	.	.
Dolly Varden . . . . *Salvelinus malma* (Walbaum)	X	.	X	.	.	.

WHITEFISH FAMILY
Coregonidae

Common and Scientific Names	Sport	Commercial	Fine food	Coarse food	Forage	Other
Inconnu . . . . *Stenodus leucichthys* (Güldenstädt)	.	X	X	.	.	.
Shallowwater cisco . . . . *Coregonus artedii* LeSueur	.	X	X	.	.	.

Common and Scientific Names	Sport	Economic Classification				
		Commercial	Fine food	Coarse food	Forage	Other
Deepwater cisco . . . . *Coregonus johannae* (Wagner)		X	X	.	.	.
Longjaw Cisco . . . . *Coregonus alpenae* (Koelz)		X	X	.	.	.
Shortjaw cisco . . . . *Coregonus zenithicus* (Jordan and Evermann)		X	X	.	.	.
Shortnose cisco . . . . *Coregonus reighardi* (Koelz)		X	X	.	.	.
Blackfin cisco . . . . *Coregonus nigripinnis* (Gill)		X	X	.	.	.
Kiyi . . . . *Coregonus kiyi* (Koelz)		X	X	.	.	.
Bloater . . . . *Coregonus hoyi* (Gill)		X	.	X	.	.
Lake whitefish . . . . *Coregonus clupeaformis* (Mitchill)		X	X	.	.	.
Round whitefish . . . . *Coregonus* (= *Prosopium*) *cylindraceus* (Pallas)		X	.	X	.	.
Mountain whitefish . . . . *Coregonus* (= *Prosopium*) *williamsoni* Girard	X	.	X	.	.	.

MOONEYE FAMILY
Hiodontidae

Mooneye . . . . *Hiodon tergisus* LeSueur					X	.
Goldeye . . . . *Hiodon alosoides* (Rafinesque)		X	.	X	.	.

Common and Scientific Names	Economic Classification					
	Sport	Commercial	Fine food	Coarse food	Forage	Other

MUDMINNOW FAMILY
Umbridae

Central mudminnow . . . . X .
Umbra limi (Kirtland)

Eastern mudminnow . . . . X .
Umbra pygmaea (DeKay)

PIKE FAMILY
Esocidae

Muskellunge . . . . X . . X . .
Esox masquinongy Mitchill

Northern pike . . . . X X . X . .
Esox lucius Linnaeus

Chain pickerel . . . . X . . X . .
Esox niger LeSueur

Redfin pickerel . . . . X . . X . .
Esox americanus americanus Gmelin

Grass pickerel X
Esox americanus vermiculatus LeSueur

BLACKFISH FAMILY
Dalliidae

Alaska blackfish . . . . X . .
Dallia pectoralis Bean

CHARACIN FAMILY
Characidae

Banded tetra . . . . X . . . .
Astyanax fasciatus (Cuvier)

Common and Scientific Names	Economic Classification					
	Sport	Commercial	Fine food	Coarse food	Forage	Other

SUCKER FAMILY
Catostomidae

	Sport	Commercial	Fine food	Coarse food	Forage	Other
Blue sucker — *Cycleptus elongatus* (LeSueur)		X		X		
Bigmouth buffalo — *Ictiobus (= Megastomatobus) cyprinellus* (Valenciennes)		X		X		
Black buffalo — *Ictiobus niger* (Rafinesque)		X		X		
Smallmouth buffalo — *Ictiobus bubalus* (Rafinesque)		X		X		
Quillback carpsucker — *Carpiodes cyprinus* (LeSueur)		X		X		
River carpsucker — *Carpiodes carpio* (Rafinesque)		X		X		
Highfin carpsucker — *Carpiodes velifer* (Rafinesque)		X		X		
White sucker — *Catostomus commersoni* (Lacépède)		X		X		
Utah sucker — *Catostomus ardens* Jordan and Gilbert		X		X		
Sacramento sucker — *Catostomus occidentalis* Ayres				X		
Columbia largescaled sucker — *Catostomus macrocheilus* Girard				X		
Columbia smallscaled sucker — *Catostomus columbianus* (Eigenmann and Eigenmann)				X		
Longnose sucker — *Catostomus catostomus* (Forster)		X		X		

Common and Scientific Names	Economic Classification					
	Sport	Commercial	Fine food	Coarse food	Forage	Other
Hog sucker *Hypentelium nigricans* (LeSueur)					X	
Humpback sucker *Xyrauchen texanus* (Abbott)		X		X		
Lake chubsucker *Erimyzon sucetta* (Lacépède)					X	
Creek chubsucker *Erimyzon oblongus* (Mitchill)					X	
Spotted sucker *Minytrema melanops* (Rafinesque)					X	
Silver redhorse *Moxostoma anisurum* (Rafinesque)		X		X		
Northern redhorse *Moxostoma aureolum* (LeSueur)		X		X		
Eastern redhorse *Moxostoma macrolepidotum* (LeSueur)				X		
Greater redhorse *Moxostoma valenciennesi* Jordan		X		X		
Golden redhorse *Moxostoma erythrurum* (Rafinesque)		X		X		
Black redhorse *Moxostoma duquesnei* (LeSueur)		X		X		
River redhorse *Moxostoma carinatum* (Cope)				X		

CARP FAMILY
Cyprinidae

Sacramento blackfish *Orthodon microlepidotus* (Ayres)				X	X	

Common and Scientific Names	Economic Classification					
	Sport	Commercial	Fine food	Coarse food	Forage	Other
Chiselmouth . . . . *Acrocheilus alutaceum* Agassiz and Pickering					X	
Hardhead . . . . *Mylopharodon conocephalus* (Baird and Girard)			X	X		
Hitch . . . . *Lavinia exilicauda* Baird and Girard			X	X		
Sacramento squawfish . . . . *Ptychocheilus grande* (Ayres)			X	X		
Colorado squawfish . . . . *Ptychocheilus lucius* Girard				X		
Columbia squawfish . . . . *Ptychocheilus oregonense* (Richardson)						X
Bonytail . . . . *Gila robusta elegans* Baird and Girard				X		
Redside shiner . . . . *Gila* (= *Richardsonius*) *balteata* (Richardson)					X	
Golden shiner . . . . *Notemigonus crysoleucas* (Mitchill)					X	
Splittail . . . . *Pogonichthys macrolepidotus* (Ayres)			X	X		
Fallfish . . . . *Semotilus corporalis* (Mitchill)					X	
Creek chub . . . . *Semotilus atromaculatus* (Mitchill)					X	
Emerald shiner . . . . *Notropis atherinoides* Rafinesque					X	
Redfin shiner . . . . *Notropis umbratilis* (Girard)					X	

Common and Scientific Names	Economic Classification					
	Sport	Commercial	Fine food	Coarse food	Forage	Other
Common shiner . . . . *Notropis cornutus* (Mitchill)					X	.
Spottail shiner . . . . *Notropis hudsonius* (Clinton)					X	.
Mimic shiner . . . . *Notropis volucellus* (Cope)					X	.
Sand shiner . . . . *Notropis deliciosus* (Girard)					X	.
Flathead chub . . . . *Hybopsis* (= *Platygobio*) *gracilis* (Richardson)					X	.
Lake chub . . . . *Hybopsis plumbea* (Agassiz)					X	.
River chub . . . . *Hybopsis micropogon* (Cope)					X	.
Hornyhead chub . . . . *Hybopsis biguttata* (Kirtland)					X	.
Blacknose dace . . . . *Rhinichthys atratulus* (Hermann)					X	.
Longnose dace . . . . *Rhinichthys cataractae* (Valenciennes)					X	.
Silvery minnow . . . . *Hybognathus nuchalis* Agassiz					X	.
Bluntnose minnow . . . . *Pimephales notatus* (Rafinesque)					X	.
Fathead minnow . . . . *Pimephales promelas* Rafinesque					X	.
Stoneroller . . . . *Campostoma anomalum* (Rafinesque)					X	.

Common and Scientific Names	Economic Classification					
	Sport	Commercial	Fine food	Coarse food	Forage	Other
Goldfish . . . . *Carassius auratus* (Linnaeus)					X	X
Carp . . . . *Cyprinus carpio* Linnaeus		X		X		
Tench . . . . *Tinca tinca* (Linnaeus)					X	

NORTH AMERICAN FRESHWATER CATFISH FAMILY

Ictaluridae (= Ameiuridae)

Channel catfish . . . . *Ictalurus punctatus* (Rafinesque)	X	X	X			
Blue catfish . . . . *Ictalurus furcatus* (LeSueur)			X			
White catfish . . . . *Ictalurus catus* (Linnaeus)			X			
Yellow bullhead . . . . *Ictalurus (= Ameiurus) natalis* (LeSueur)	X		X			
Brown bullhead . . . . *Ictalurus (= Ameiurus) nebulosus* (LeSueur)	X		X			
Flat bullhead . . . . *Ictalurus (=Ameiurus) platycephalus* Girard	X		X			
Black bullhead . . . . *Ictalurus (= Ameiurus) melas* (Rafinesque)	X		X			
Flathead catfish . . . . *Pylodictis olivaris* (Rafinesque)		X	X			
Stonecat . . . . *Noturus flavus* Rafinesque	X		X			

Common and Scientific Names	Economic Classification					
	Sport	Commercial	Fine food	Coarse food	Forage	Other
FRESHWATER EEL FAMILY Anguillidae						
American eel . . . . *Anguilla rostrata* (LeSueur)	X	X				
KILLIFISH FAMILY Cyprinodontidae						
Mummichog . . . . *Fundulus heteroclitus* (Linnaeus)					X	
Banded killifish . . . . *Fundulus diaphanus* (LeSueur)					X	
California killifish . . . . *Fundulus parvipinnis* (Girard)					X	
Blackstripe topminnow . . . . *Fundulus notatus* (Rafinesque)					X	
Variegated cyprinodon . . . . *Cyprinodon variegatus* (Lacépède)					X	
Desert cyprinodon . . . . *Cyprinodon macularius* Baird and Girard						X
LIVEBEARER FAMILY Poeciliidae						
Gambusia (= Mosquitofish) . . . . *Gambusia affinis* (Baird and Girard)					X	X
Sailfin molly . . . . *Mollienisia latipinna* LeSueur						X
COD FAMILY Gadidae						
Burbot . . . . *Lota lota* (Linnaeus)	X		X			

Common and Scientific Names	Economic Classification					
	Sport	Commercial	Fine food	Coarse food	Forage	Other
TROUTPERCH FAMILY Percopsidae						
Troutperch . . . . *Percopsis omiscomaycus* (Walbaum)					X	
PIRATEPERCH FAMILY Aphredoderidae						
Pirateperch . . . . *Aphredoderus sayanus* (Gilliams)					X	
SILVERSIDE FAMILY Atherinidae						
Brook silverside . . . . *Labidesthes sicculus* (Cope)					X	
BASS FAMILY Serranidae						
White bass . . . . *Roccus (= Lepibema) chrysops* (Rafinesque)	X	X	X			
Yellow bass . . . . *Roccus mississippiensis* (Jordan and Eigenmann)(= *Morone interrupta* Gill)	X					
White perch . . . . *Roccus (= Morone) americanus* (Gmelin)	X		X			
SUNFISH FAMILY Centrarchidae						
Smallmouth bass . . . . *Micropterus dolomieui* Lacépède	X		X			
Spotted bass . . . . *Micropterus punctulatus* (Rafinesque)	X		X			

Common and Scientific Names	Sport	Commercial	Fine food	Coarse food	Forage	Other
Redeye bass . . . . *Micropterus coosae* Hubbs and Bailey	X	.	X	.	.	.
Largemouth bass . . . . *Micropterus salmoides* (Lacépède)	X	.	X	.	.	.
Green sunfish . . . . *Lepomis cyanellus* Rafinesque	X	.	.	.	.	.
Spotted sunfish . . . . *Lepomis punctatus* (Valenciennes)	X	.	.	.	.	.
Yellowbelly sunfish . . . . *Lepomis auritus* (Linnaeus)	X	.	X	.	.	.
Orangespotted sunfish . . . . *Lepomis humilis* (Girard)	.	.	.	.	.	X
Longear sunfish . . . . *Lepomis megalotis* (Rafinesque)	.	.	.	.	.	X
Bluegill . . . . *Lepomis macrochirus* Rafinesque	X	.	X	.	.	.
Redear sunfish . . . . *Lepomis microlophus* (Günther)	X	.	X	.	.	.
Pumpkinseed . . . . *Lepomis gibbosus* (Linnaeus)	X	.	X	.	.	.
Blackbanded sunfish . . . . *Enneacanthus* (= *Mesogonistius*) *chaetodon* (Baird)	X	.	.	.	.	.
Sacramento perch . . . . *Archoplites interruptus* (Girard)	X	.	X	.	.	.
Warmouth . . . . *Chaenobryttus gulosus* (Cuvier) [=*coronarius* (Bartram)]	X	.	X	.	.	.
Rock bass . . . . *Ambloplites rupestris* (Rafinesque)	X	.	X	.	.	.

Common and Scientific Names	Economic Classification					
	Sport	Commercial	Fine food	Coarse food	Forage	Other
Flier . . . . *Centrarchus macropterus* (Lacépède)	X		X			
White crappie . . . . *Pomoxis annularis* Rafinesque	X		X			
Black crappie . . . . *Pomoxis nigromaculatus* (LeSueur)	X		X			
PERCH FAMILY Percidae						
Yellow perch . . . . *Perca flavescens* (Mitchill)	X	X	X			
Yellow walleye . . . . *Stizostedion vitreum vitreum* (Mitchill)	X	X	X			
Blue walleye (= Blue pike) . . . . *Stizostedion vitreum glaucum* Hubbs	X	X				
Sauger . . . . *Stizostedion canadense* (Smith)	X	X				
Logperch . . . . *Percina caprodes* (Rafinesque)					X	
Rainbow darter . . . . *Etheostoma caeruleum* Storer					X	
Johnny darter . . . . *Etheostoma nigrum* Rafinesque					X	
DRUM FAMILY Sciaenidae						
Freshwater drum . . . . *Aplodinotus grunniens* Rafinesque	X		X			

Common and Scientific Names	Economic Classification					
	Sport	Commercial	Fine food	Coarse food	Forage	Other
SEAPERCH FAMILY Embiotocidae						
Freshwater viviparous perch . . . . *Hysterocarpus traski* Gibbons						X
CICHLID FAMILY Cichlidae						
Rio Grande perch . . . . *Cichlasoma* (= *Herichthys*) *cyanoguttatum* (Baird and Girard)	X			X		
SCULPIN FAMILY Cottidae						
Mottled sculpin . . . . *Cottus bairdi* Girard					X	
Spoonhead sculpin . . . . *Cottus ricei* Nelson					X	
Slimy sculpin . . . . *Cottus cognatus* Richardson					X	
STICKLEBACK FAMILY Gasterosteidae						
Threespine stickleback . . . . *Gasterosteus aculeatus* Linnaeus					X	
Brook stickleback . . . . *Eucalia inconstans* (Kirtland)					X	
Ninespine stickleback . . . . *Pungitius pungitius* (Linnaeus)					X	
Fourspine stickleback . . . . *Apeltes quadracus* (Mitchill)					X	

Index

This index is primarily an analysis of the principal and general references in the text. The many fish names, for example, are indexed only to families, genera, and broad categories of common names.

Page numbers of illustrations are given in parentheses.